English
Barometers
1680–1860

PLATE 1
D. Adams, Fleet Street, London.

Collection of His Grace
the Duke of Bedford
Woburn Abbey

ENGLISH BAROMETERS 1680–1860

A HISTORY OF
DOMESTIC BAROMETERS
AND THEIR MAKERS

Nicholas Goodison

Clarkson N. Potter, Inc./Publisher   NEW YORK

DISTRIBUTED BY CROWN PUBLISHERS, INC.

CONTENTS

THE PLATES

ONE HUNDRED and thirty of the 158 photographs were taken specifically for this book. Most of them are the work of Mr. Raymond Fortt,
to whose care and imagination I am deeply indebted. Some of the
exceptions portray barometers which were not readily accessible and
others barometers of which adequate photographs already existed. I
must thank all those owners, private and corporate, who allowed me
to commission photographs of their possessions and who gladly put
up with the disturbance involved: their names will in most cases be
found beneath the Plates. I must also thank the following for supplying me with the remaining photographs which I wanted and for
allowing me to use them.

Norman Adams Ltd PLATE 97
E.T. Biggs and Sons Ltd PLATES 116, 117
Trustees of the British Museum PLATE 86
M. Harris and Sons PLATE 98
Hotspur Ltd PLATE 151
Ronald A. Lee PLATES 68, 70, 156
Mallett and Son (Antiques) Ltd PLATES 14, 42, 43
Metropolitan Museum of Art New York PLATES 10, 108
Phillips of Hitchin Ltd PLATE 76
Randolph PLATE 158
Director of the Science Museum London PLATES 15, 133, 135, 149
Arthur S. Vernay Inc PLATES 107, 134
Director of the Victoria and Albert Museum London PLATES 62, 74, 75, 112
Department of Collections, Colonial Williamsburg PLATES 82, 153

LIST OF PLATES

LIST OF DRAWINGS

PREFACE

Dr. JOHNSON once observed that when two Englishmen meet their first talk is of the weather. Our weather does not compare with the sumptuous variety in New England where Mark Twain counted 136 different kinds within twenty-four hours but it is notoriously fickle; and Englishmen pass valuable hours discussing its moods, its promises and its betrayals. The advance of the science of meteorology has done little to diminish their interest. The BBC weather forecast commands avid attention and the barometer, which hangs in the hall of each Englishman's castle, is daily consulted with a rude tap. The predictions of neither are believed: they are used rather as a basis for further discussion.

The commercial manufacture of domestic mercurial barometers began in this country about thirty years before Dr. Johnson's birth in 1709. During the early years of his life it was becoming fashionable among upper-class households to own one of these useful instruments. By the time of his death in 1784 the barometer was becoming a widely owned piece of furniture and during the next hundred years vast numbers were made, sold, hung and tapped.

The purposes of this study are to present a history of the domestic mercurial barometer in this country, to describe a representative selection of extant examples, and to provide information for reference on a large number of makers. No comprehensive, accurate or logically arranged work on the subject has ever been published. The study is divided into three parts. Part I, after a brief chapter of technical introduction, is the heart of the book and traces the development of domestic barometers and their makers over the chosen period: it ends at 1860 because by then industrial manufacturing techniques and a poverty of invention had reduced the aesthetic appeal of cabinet-work and because soon after this date the improvement of the aneroid mechanism caused a decline in the use of the mercurial tube. Part II gives biographical details and describes extant barometers of about fifty important makers. Part III lists the names of about 1,700 other makers together with addresses, dates, occupations and examples of their work. The makers of Part II are chosen either because of their contemporary reputation or because one or more barometers of exceptional quality by them survive. The selection is regrettably subjective and the chief difficulty has been to restrict the number: this has involved relegating many of the great scientific instrument-makers of the eighteenth century and many of the prolific barometer makers of the nineteenth century to Part III. In both Part II and Part III the terminal date 1860 is arbitrary and many of the firms listed flourished long afterwards. One day perhaps the vast work of collating information from commercial directories will be carried to the end of the century.

I cannot hope to have avoided all inaccuracies and am certainly guilty of many sins of omission. I can only plead as an excuse the difficulties of an explorer who tries to map uncharted territory. This book is based almost entirely on material found in primary sources, reference to which is made in the footnotes, and on a study of over 3,000 barometers in museums, private furniture collections, household halls and antique shops up and down the country. Even so I am conscious that my map is far from complete and that some of its features are perhaps wrongly plotted. I hope that readers will tell me of evidence which I appear to have overlooked or of errors which I have made. I intend this work, like F.J.Britten's pioneer work on horological history, to stimulate further research into an interesting subject and to raise the standard in future editions of the inadequate and misleading descriptions of the barometer which are found in almost all the standard reference books about furniture.

I have avoided as far as possible using information derived from secondary sources. Occasionally however when a previous author has quoted an original document which I have been unable to trace I have re-quoted it and acknowledgement will be found in the footnotes. I have gratefully made use in Part II of a few biographical facts about various makers which are derived from Professor E.G.R.Taylor's *Mathematical Practitioners of Hanoverian England:* I am indebted to Professor Taylor for inviting me to read parts of this unpublished work. I have also culled some biographical details about eighteenth-century makers from the late Sir Ambrose Heal's papers in the British Museum.

Many others have been of great assistance. Mr. W.Marney, of Messrs Garner and Marney Ltd, has been subjected for some years to a series of lengthy and educative visits to his workshop and his patience has been admirable Dr. W.E.K.Middleton has made many useful suggestions and helped me to trace barometers which I might not otherwise have seen. Several private collectors and dealers have allowed me to dismantle, study and photograph their barometers and some of their names will be found beneath the illustrations: many others remain anonymous because I have not illustrated their possessions but I remain no less grateful to them. The Directors and staff of the many museums which I have visited, all of which are mentioned in the text, have invariably treated me with the utmost courtesy and patience; and I am most indebted to them for the facilities I have been given when studying their collections. Various librarians have also suffered from me and I would like to thank them for their patience: the assistance which I have received from librarians all over the country in the compilation of Part III has been of the greatest value. Several furniture dealers have helped me to study particular barometers by introducing me to their clients and by supplying me with facts and photographs from their records, and I must especially thank Mr. Ronald A. Lee and Mr. Stephen J. Jussel for their warm interest. Finally, countless correspondents all over the world, who must perforce remain nameless, have supplied me with information about barometers in their possession.

The eight diagrammatic drawings were kindly executed for me by Mr. Heywood Hill. I must also thank Mrs. E. Bunting who most carefully typed my manuscript.

I have received nothing but encouragement from my publishers and for their persistent help and patience I am very grateful.

N.G.

CHAPTER **1**

1 *General Introduction*

THE BAROMETER is an instrument for the measurement of the weight of the air. Most people think of it as a weather-glass because its only domestic application is to give guidance about the weather. This application is however a secondary use of the instrument and arose because in the seventeenth century it was noticed that a connection existed between the alterations of the weight of the air and the alterations of the weather. Since the scope of this book is to study the evolution of the mercurial barometer as a domestic instrument, I do not propose to describe in detail either its early development by the scientists of the seventeenth century or its subsequent scientific evolution except in so far as they affect the subject in hand: but a description of the principles on which the instrument depends will help many readers to follow later chapters with greater ease.

(a) AIR   Air is composed principally of the gases oxygen and nitrogen: it has weight and responds to the gravitation of the earth. It is impenetrable and is subject only to displacement or compression. The air at the earth's surface is compressed by the air above it; i.e. the air (or atmospheric) pressure, which at sea level is about 14–15 lb. per square inch, is a direct consequence of the air's weight. This physical property of weight was first observed in the seventeenth century: and the reduction of the pressure with height was the subject of countless observations and experiments. Air also has the other properties of a fluid; and it is important to understand that its pressure is transmitted equally in all directions—whether the surface on which it presses is horizontal, vertical or overhanging.

The simple barometer consists of a glass tube of circular section under 3 ft. in length, sealed at its upper end, which stands in a cistern of mercury in such a way that its lower end is well immersed (Fig. i). The commonest alternative to this cistern-tube arrangement is the use of a bent or 'siphon' tube (Fig. ii) in which the air pressure acts on the surface of the mercury in the short limb. The tube is usually of lead glass and should be of uniform bore: in domestic barometers the diameter of the bore is often less than a quarter of an inch and only rarely larger, a bore of an eighth of an inch being common. The top of the tube contains a vacuum and the weight of the air on the surface of the mercury in the cistern or in the short limb of the siphon tube balances the mercury in the tube. Since a vacuum gives no resistance any change of air pressure causes the mercury to move in the tube. In England the mean pressure of the atmosphere is balanced by a column of mercury of about 29·5″: at sea level, where the maximum range of variation is from about 27·5″ to just over 31″, the column seldom drops below 28·5″ and seldom exceeds 30·5″. Most domestic barometers therefore were, and are, made with scales measuring 28″–31″. In modern times meteorology has become a science and barometric measurements are subject to scientific definitions of the standards of length and of gravity: but such exact definitions were unknown to the makers of the barometers to be discussed in this book and should be disregarded.

It is important to remember that the weight of the atmosphere is assessed by measuring not the absolute height of the mercury column but its height above the surface of the mercury in the cistern or the short limb of the siphon tube. As the column rises the level in the cistern or short limb drops and the constructor of the instrument must take this into account if he is to achieve accuracy. In the case of the siphon tube of consistent bore the formula is simple—a 0·5″ drop in the column means a rise of 0·5″ in the short limb and therefore a total change between the two levels of 1″. In the case of the cistern it is not so simple: if the area of the cistern is a hundred times the area of the bore of the tube a fall of 1″ in the column will cause a rise of ·01″ in the cistern and the scale of the instrument should be adjusted to account for this before an accurate reading can be taken. In fact, although early makers were aware of the problem, few as will be seen did more than make the relation of the cistern area to the bore of the tube large enough for the inaccuracy to be reduced: towards the end of the eighteenth century however many efforts were made to solve the problem by both scientists and scientific instrument-makers. Some of these attempts to 'zero' the scale will be mentioned later.

(b) THE MERCURIAL BAROMETER (i) INSTRUMENT

FIG. i. Cistern tube

(ii) SCALES
AND
WEATHER
INDICATIONS

FIG. ii.
Siphon
or bent
tube

(c) MERCURY

Domestic barometers usually have a scale representing the inches 28–31 although this is not universal: sometimes the scale is marked down to 27″ or 26″. For the sake of more accurate measurement these inches are usually but not invariably subdivided into decimals, and a vernier scale, making possible readings to ·01″, is a common feature on straight-tube or 'stick' barometers. The vernier will be described later in this chapter.

In addition to these scales, domestic instruments are engraved with the familiar weather indications 'Very Dry, Settled Fair, Fair, Changeable, Rain, Much Rain, Stormy', or a variation of these. These weather indications are not reliable guides to the weather: it is the movement of the mercury, not its absolute height, which presages alterations of the weather. Thus if the mercury stands at 31″ ('Very Dry') and begins to move down, it could mean that rain is coming: and rain will frequently occur when the mercury stands as high as 30″ ('Fair'). For the instrument to have any value at all, frequent observations of its station should be made: and for this reason instruments are usually fitted with a pointer which can be set to correspond with the height of the mercury so that at the next reading any change can be readily detected.

Weather indications are not completely useless: they are at least engraved in the correct order and at the correct extremes of the scale. Instrument-makers continued, even though they knew at an early date that their use was limited, to engrave them on their scales because tradition dictated it. It still does today: a purchaser would probably think the instrument imperfect if it carried no weather indications. I recently watched a young couple complaining to a sympathetic shopkeeper that their new barometer was working imperfectly: it read 'Fair' when it was raining. The shopkeeper said he would return it to the manufacturer.

Mercury has been known since about 300 B.C. and was used for medicinal purposes by alchemists from the fifteenth century onwards. It occurs mainly in cinnabar, a red sulphide, and is found, seldom in large concentrations, in various parts of the world. The main European sources in the seventeenth century were Spain and Illyria and it was also mined in Tuscany.

It is extracted by heat in the form of vapour and then condensed: after purification it is a free flowing liquid and does not wet things which it touches.

Mercury came to be used in the barometric experiment because its weight (its specific gravity is 13·5951 at 0°C but early scientists and makers did not define this accurately) made it possible to use a reasonably short tube. The almost total absence of vapour pressure at ordinary temperatures is its other chief advantage. It has disadvantages however. Firstly it is liable to contamination, not only absorbing air moisture but also having the facility to dissolve baser metals of lower specific gravities such as tin, lead and zinc; this contamination can be avoided to a great extent by boiling and the mercury can be purified of other metallic traces by a mixture of acids. Secondly it expands with heat, which can thus cause an independent rise in the barometric column (heat also of course expands the glass of the tube and the metal of the scales but only in the most exact scientific observations are these changes important). Thirdly it suffers from the capillary attraction of the glass tube; the centre of the mercury column usually preceding the circumference in any movement, especially in tubes of narrow bore. Finally it is less sensitive than lighter fluids to alterations of pressure: but this disadvantage is outweighed by the fact that it needs a very much smaller and more manageable tube. In spite of these disadvantages mercury was almost exclusively used as the barometric fluid from the middle of the seventeenth century until the beginning of the twentieth when aneroid mechanisms of sufficient accuracy had been evolved.

Owing to contamination the mercury in an old barometer needs to be cleaned or renewed at frequent intervals: and since the tube, especially if it is made of old coarse glass, is usually fouled and extremely difficult to clean, it is not surprising that practically no early barometers still possess their original tubes.

2 *Types of Barometer*

A SUMMARY of the chief types of barometer is convenient at this stage if only because it will establish the meanings of certain terms which will occur often in later pages. Many different types were proposed by scientists late in the seventeenth century with the aim of improving the accuracy of the barometer as a scientific instrument. In the ordinary cistern-tube instrument the mercury rose and fell only over some 2·5″–3″ in northern Europe and it was thought that more accurate readings could be achieved if in some way this limited movement could be extended. It is interesting that the various attempts to extend the scale proved scientifically so inadequate that throughout the eighteenth and nineteenth centuries scientists still preferred a straight cistern or siphon tube instrument and concentrated more on refining the materials and components in order to achieve the required accuracy. In 1794 a maker of considerable ability and experience felt obliged to say that 'the barometer with a straight tube . . . is preferable to all the subsequent variations in its form': and he observed that the inventors who intended to make the variations of the mercury more sensible by augmenting the scale of the barometer 'only multiplied errors, and rendered it less capable of answering the purposes for which it was designed'.[1] The proposed extensions to the scale mostly failed because they were too complicated: they involved other liquids which were unsuitable or mechanical links which themselves suffered from deterioration or atmospheric effects. The straight tube was preferable because the mercury was observed directly. But although the seventeenth-century scientists' proposals failed they had an important influence on later domestic instrument-makers and several of their ideas became embodied in makers' designs.

In this chapter I propose to describe only the types of tube which found widespread expression in domestic barometers. The more abstruse designs which were given rarer physical expression at the hands of commercial makers will be described in context later in the book. Nor do I intend to discuss in detail the origins of these various ideas. Dr. W. E. K. Middleton has recently discussed them and many more in his extensive and readable history of the barometer as a scientific instrument.[2] Repetition in this study would absorb an unjustifiable amount of space.

(a) CISTERN-TUBE
(i) STRAIGHT-TUBE
('STICK')
BAROMETER

This is the simple, and indeed original, barometer which I have already described (p. 2 Fig. i). It consists of a sealed tube, its open lower end immersed in a cistern of mercury. Initially in the seventeenth century the cisterns were made of glass and were open to the air: later, as will be seen, sealed wooden cisterns came into use which were 'fixed', i.e. cemented to the tube and immovable. These will be described in detail later.

In practically every book on the subject Evangelista Torricelli (1609–47) is said to have invented this original barometer in 1643. That this is a naïve simplification of the deliberations and experiments which resulted in the evolution of the barometer has been ably demonstrated by C. de Waard[3] and Dr. Middleton,[4] who also argues convincingly that 1644 is the correct date for the crucial experiment.

[1] George Adams
Lectures on Natural and Experimental Philosophy
(1794) p. 479.
[2] *The History of the Barometer* (1964):
see also J. A. de Luc's classic work
Recherches sur les Modifications de l'Atmosphère (1772) Part 1 p. 13 *et seq.*

[3] *Expérience barométrique, ses antécédents et ses explications* (1936)
[4] *History of the Barometer*
Chapters 1–2:
also in an article
The Place of Torricelli in the History of the Barometer
('Isis' Vol. 54 Part 1 No. 175, 1963).

In a straight tube the mercury moves only a very short distance. If the tube is bent just below the lowest point to which the mercury can fall (i.e. at about 27·5″ above the cistern level) and then extended at an angle the mercury will move over a far greater distance (Fig. iii). The extent of the movement will depend on the obtuseness of the angle: in theory it should be possible to achieve enormous magnifications of the movement by choosing an angle of little over 90° (and some early makers claimed to have achieved such instruments), but in practice it was not possible to draw the tube long enough. Even in tubes of accepted length the mercury column, owing to capillary action, tended to break if the movement was at all sudden: and it was impossible to read the instrument accurately since the meniscus could never be at right angles to the tube.

Initially cisterns were of glass as with the straight-tube instrument of which the angle tube was a modification: and their subsequent development was closely connected.

The invention of the angle tube is wrapped in obscurity. Traditionally[1] it was the invention of Charles II's 'Master Mechanic' Sir Samuel Morland (1625–96) but so far no trustworthy written evidence has been discovered to support the tradition. Dr. Middleton[2] has discussed the subject recently and in the absence of contradictory evidence concluded that the tradition should be accepted. He pointed out that the apparently independent invention of the angle barometer by Bernardus Ramazzini, Professor of Medicine at Modena, in 1695 should not be allowed to confuse the issue; this was ante-dated by the publication of John Smith's book in 1688 in which Morland is named as the inventor.[3]

The earliest apparent literary reference to an angle barometer occurs in the *Transactions* of the Philosophical Society of Oxford for 24 June 1684.[4]

'Mr. Walker mention'd a barometer he has, ye tube of which, at about 27 inches from ye open end, turnes in an obtuse angle, for ye better observing ye ascent of ye mercury'.

(ii) ANGLE-TUBE BAROMETER

FIG. iii. Angle tube

---

[1] Practically all writers have subscribed to the tradition from John Smith's *A Compleat Discourse of the Nature, Use, and Right Managing of that Wonderful Instrument the Baroscope or Quick-Silver Weather-Glass* (1688) onwards.
[2] *History of the Barometer* p. 110 *et seq.*: also in an article *Sir Samuel Morland's Barometers* (Archives Internationales d'Histoire des Sciences, December 1962).

[3] *A Compleat Discourse* p. 1.

[4] Quoted by R. T. Gunther in *Early Science in Oxford* (1925) Vol. 4. pp. 77–8.
'Mr Walker' was Joshua Walker, a Fellow of Brasenose College, who was elected to the Society on 26 March 1684.

This is followed up by an entry of 1 July 1684:

> 'Mr. Walker presented his barometer, mentioned in ye minutes of ye praeceding week, to ye Society; ye tube of it, at ye distance of (about) 27 inches from ye upper end, was bent, in an angle of 108 degrees, for ye better observing ye motion of ye mercury, which, in ye sloaping part of this tube, does rise, and fall, $2\frac{1}{2}$ inches, for one inch in a tube exactly perpendicular'.

FIG. iv.
Bulb-
cistern
tube

Whether or not these interesting records give Walker precedence over Morland is not really of importance. They do demonstrate however that the principle of the angle tube was not well known in 1684 and provide an approximate date for its invention.

(b) SIPHON TUBE

The siphon tube, already mentioned on p. 2 (Fig. ii), was not used commonly as an alternative to the cistern tube in domestic barometers in England until the nineteenth century.

(i) STRAIGHT-TUBE ('STICK') BAROMETER

When a bent up tube of the siphon type was used in straight-tube barometers a simple bulb-shaped cistern was incorporated in the short limb[1] (Fig. iv). This imparted the characteristics of a cistern tube and permitted a more extensive movement of the mercury than the strict siphon tube could achieve. As with the cistern tube the measurement of the barometric height is taken from the difference between the level of the mercury in the tube and the level in the bulb: and since, as can be readily appreciated, no effective way can be successfully devised for zeroing the scale of a bulb tube it can never be made to achieve a scientifically acceptable degree of accuracy.

(ii) ANGLE-TUBE BAROMETER

The bulb-cistern tube was also employed in angle barometers which, as has already been observed, not only evolved from but closely followed the development of the straight-tube instrument.

(iii) WHEEL BAROMETER

The commonest application of the siphon tube was in the wheel barometer. In this no bulb or cistern is incorporated. The tube is of simple siphon shape (Plate 2), the shorter limb which is open to the air being about 6″–8″ long and containing sufficient mercury to ensure that at maximum atmospheric pressure it is never emptied. A weight, usually glass, rests on the surface of the mercury and is suspended by a silk cord which passes round a small brass pulley wheel (one, two or three times, according to the maker's whim) and is attached at the other end to a counterpoising weight which moves freely and is usually, in nineteenth-century instruments, channelled by a section of

[1] According to de Luc *Recherches sur les Modifications de l'Atmosphere* (1772) Part 1, p. 12 this type of tube had become 'le plus commun', i.e. in Europe. Many examples survive. De Luc called such barometers 'baromètres a bouteille' and Middleton *History of the Barometer* p. 133 follows him in calling them 'bottle barometers'.

glass tube. The arbor of the pulley wheel passes through the dial of the barometer and carries the index or hand which demonstrates the barometric height. If the air pressure rises the mercury will fall in the short limb and the hand will move to the right. If the tube is of even bore a rise of 0·5″ in the long limb will be accompanied by a fall of 0·5″ in the short limb, i.e. the difference between the two levels will increase by 1″. The hand must therefore be made to demonstrate this 1″ movement on the dial. In most extant wheel barometers the short limb of the tube is widened in order to give the float sufficient space to move freely: this necessitates an equivalent widening of the tube at the top of the main limb in order to preserve the simple calculation of the rise and fall.

The obvious advantage of the wheel design is that the scale on which readings are observed is very much magnified: it is possible to show movements of ·01″ and not difficult to achieve more minute divisions. Its weakness however is that the mercury cannot be directly observed: and since changes of temperature, let alone capillary attraction or plain dirt, affect the weight, thread and pulley, the wheel barometer never became a scientific instrument.[1]

It was however invented as a scientific instrument, being one of many attempts in the seventeenth century to extend the scale of the common barometer. The idea appears to have occurred to Robert Hooke (1635–1703), the Royal Society's first 'Operator' and subsequently its Curator of Experiments (1664 onwards) and Secretary (1677–92), in about 1662. His proposals were probably put before the Society on 30 December 1663 and were published in detail in 1665.[2] The instrument illustrated in his *Micrographia* (Plate 3), which may not be the earliest version of his barometer,[3] was 'contriv'd to shew all the minute variations in the pressure of the air' and was not basically very different from the wheel barometer which became so common a hundred and fifty years later. The main difference was the large bulb at the top which acted like a conventional cistern and caused 'all the sensible rising and falling of the mercury to be visible in the surface of the mercury' in the short limb. His instrument did not completely solve the problem of the fluctuation of the cistern level but he took care to make the 'bolt-head', as the bulb was called, large, and to make the mercury level rest at the diameter, i.e. the widest part, of the bulb in order to minimize any variation. He also devised his scale em-

[1] These shortcomings were regularly criticized by scientists, e.g. J. T. Desaguliers *A Course of Experimental Philosophy* (1744) p. 264, de Luc *Recherches sur les Modifications de l'Atmosphere* Part 1, p. 21, etc.
[2] *Micrographia* (1665): the account of the wheel barometer occurs in the preface.

[3] The Royal Society has a rough sketch (*Classified Papers* 20 No. 32) showing a wheel barometer viewed from the side: it is similar but has an impractical glass cylinder at the top of the tube instead of a sphere. Middleton *History of the Barometer* p. 94 suggests that it antedates 1665.

PLATE 2
Mechanism
of wheel barometer
mounted on demonstration board

pirically by making several observations of the changing distances between the two levels.

Hooke used steel 'bullets' for his float and counterpoise, and a silk cord: he also proposed a tube of up to half an inch in diameter. His circular scale he divided into 200 parts (his diagram has only ninety-six), but although he was concerned in the construction of his instrument to discover the variation of the mercury level which was equivalent to a movement of 1″ he does not say how many inches his scale represents. The proposed circumference of the pulley wheel however suggests two. As will be seen the earliest domestic wheel barometers used a scale of 3″ divided into hundredths.

Thomas Tompion, with whom Hooke was well acquainted, probably used this type of siphon tube with its 'bolt-head' in his two famous wheel barometers (Plates 143 and 146) but later repairs make it difficult to be categorical. I have only seen two contemporary barometers which without any doubt incorporated such tubes: these are not wheel barometers at all and are illustrated in Plates 113 and 140.

In a later version of his design[1] Hooke extended the tube and used the 'bolt-head' only for diluting any air which inadvertently remained in or entered the alleged vacuum: in this tube the movement in each limb was equal, as in the later common wheel barometers.

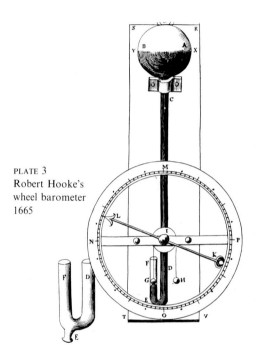

PLATE 3
Robert Hooke's wheel barometer 1665

3 Vernier, Thermometer, Hygrometer

It is appropriate at this stage to describe these three ancillary features which are commonly found on domestic barometers.

From about the middle of the eighteenth century it became common practice to fit a vernier scale to household barometers of the straight-tube type. By 1800 the practice was almost universal.

(a) VERNIER

[1] Royal Society *Philosophical Transactions* Vol. 1. (1666) p. 219.

As I have said in section 1 (b) (ii) of this chapter the scales of domestic straight-tube barometers were usually but not invariably divided in decimals of an inch. A vernier can readily be constructed to suit any division, and a duo-decimal division was not uncommon on nineteenth-century scientific instruments: but for the purpose of this description a decimal division is a justifiable assumption. The vernier (or nonius) is a means of obtaining a reading to a further place of decimals. Whereas for instance on a common barometer the height of the mercury can readily be observed by eye to an accuracy of ·1″, the vernier enables it to be read to an accuracy of ·01″. Plate 23 demonstrates how this is done. The right hand scale represents precise inches divided in decimals: the left hand scale, which slides against it, is the vernier and attached to it is a pointer which is set to the level of the mercury. The vernier is 1·1″ long and is divided into ten equal parts, i.e. each division is ·11″. These divisions are numbered downwards from the zero or pointer line.

Now it stands to reason that if the zero line of the vernier is exactly level with one of the decimal divisions of the main scale, the next line (1) on the vernier must be misplaced from the next division of the main scale by ·01″: and the sixth division must be misplaced from its corresponding division by ·06″, and so on. Therefore if the zero line does not correspond with any decimal line on the main scale the accurate reading can be found by observing which vernier line *does* correspond with a line on the main scale. In Plate 23 for example the reading is 29·27″ and in Plate 99 it is 29·71″.

When using the verniers on old barometers readers will frequently experience two difficulties. Firstly the mercury column will often be either convex or concave owing to the capillary attraction of the glass: the pointer should be set level with the centre of the column and not the edges since it is the centre of the column which leads the movement.[1] Secondly not all eighteenth and nineteenth-century scale dividers were accurate workers: Plate 37 shows the scale of a domestic instrument of *c.* 1810 in which the vernier is useless because the division of it is uneven (note especially the 0–1 division, the brevity of which renders every reading inaccurate).

As will be seen later a thermometer was often affixed to the more expensive eighteenth-century barometers and became a common feature on nineteenth-century instruments. The history of the thermometer is a separate and extensive subject and much has been published

(b) THERMOMETER

[1] Some early barometers survive whose makers undoubtedly meant readings to be taken from the edges; but generally makers' intentions are obscure. Although Desaguliers noted in *Experimental Philosophy* p. 274 that the centre of the meniscus gave the truer measurement the practice of noting it was not commonly accepted until Ramsden introduced his improved pointer (p. 203).

about it:[1] I only propose to mention here the types of thermometer which are most frequently found on English barometers.

On early barometers (until *c.* 1730) sealed alcohol thermometers are often found which employ the so-called Royal Society scale, i.e. 0° at Blood Heat descending to 90° with Hard Frost at 85°. This scale was arbitrary and it is doubtful whether much effort was made to render the performance of different instruments comparable: they gave only a rough indication of temperature. Before castigating the makers of these thermometers we must remember that they were struggling against odds, one of the chief difficulties being to achieve finely drawn tubes of even bore. An example of the Royal Society scale with an alcohol thermometer is illustrated in Plate 13: the tube is missing.

D. G. Fahrenheit (1686–1736), a scientist of Amsterdam, was the first maker to produce tolerably accurate thermometers with a numerical scale which could be reproduced on any number of instruments. He devised three scales:—

(i) *c.* 1709	90°	Mouth temperature of a healthy human being
with		
three	0°	'Temperé'
'fixed		
points'	90°	Freezing point of a mixture of sal ammoniac and snow

In this thermometer Fahrenheit used alcohol which undergoes a more considerable expansion than mercury but is less responsive to temperature changes and not so uniform in its expansion.

(ii) 1717	90°	Mouth temperature of a healthy human being
with		
two	0°	Freezing point of a mixture of sal ammoniac and snow
'fixed		
points'		

In this Fahrenheit employed mercury, finding that only with mercury could he devise thermometers which agreed with each other. Its uniform expansion and the range of temperature over which it remained liquid (-39°C to $+360$°C) made it far the most suitable fluid.

(iii) 1724	96°	Mouth temperature of a healthy human being
with		
three	32°	Freezing point of water
'fixed		
points'	0°	Freezing point of a mixture of sal ammoniac and snow

For this either mercury or alcohol was used but the former preferred, especially for clinical purposes with which Fahrenheit was mostly concerned. This third scale is the Fahrenheit scale as we know it today.

Examples of all three Fahrenheit scales are found on thermometers

[1] Dr W. E. K. Middleton is planning to publish a new history of the thermometer shortly.

attached to barometers although by the middle of the eighteenth
century only his third scale was used.

In 1735 there were some sixteen rival international scales but nearly
all the instruments which a student of English barometers will meet
employ the third Fahrenheit scale. The two other leading scales,
namely those proposed by R. A. F. de Réaumur (1683–1757) and
A. Celsius (1701–44), were widely adopted by European instrument-
makers but the former is occasionally found on English instruments.
Proposed in 1730, this was based on dilute alcohol and had only one
'fixed point', the freezing point of water at 0°. The scale rose to 80°,
at which water boiled. Réaumur's use of alcohol—he had probably
not read Fahrenheit's proposals of 1717—was retrograde: but his scale
is still commonly used today. A thermometer with Fahrenheit and
Réaumur scales can be seen in Plate 129. Celsius' scale which was
proposed in 1742 is found only rarely. It consisted of 100 degrees
between the boiling of water at 0° and the freezing of water at 100°.
This scale was inverted in 1743 by J. P. Christin of Lyons and eventually became commonly known as 'Centigrade', a name which is now
rightly surrendering again to 'Celsius'.

Various equations are used for converting one scale to another; and
the following, which I find the simplest, may be of assistance:

$$\text{To convert} \begin{cases} \text{F}° \text{ to C}°: -32°, \text{ then } \times \frac{5}{9} & \text{C}° \text{ to R}°: \times \frac{4}{5} \\ \text{F}° \text{ to R}°: -32°, \text{ then } \times \frac{4}{9} & \text{R}° \text{ to F}°: \times \frac{9}{4}, \text{ then } +32° \\ \text{C}° \text{ to F}°: \times \frac{9}{5}, \text{ then } +32° & \text{R}° \text{ to C}°: \times \frac{5}{4} \end{cases}$$

(c) HYGROMETER

The hygrometer is meant to demonstrate the humidity of the air.
Only one type of hygrometer is commonly found on English domestic
barometers: nor is it found on instruments before *c.* 1760. It consists
of a dial measuring usually about 2·5″ in diameter and engraved with
the words 'Damp' (or 'Moist') and 'Dry' (Plate 4): there is also
usually a scale, often showing 30 degrees of each state. Through the
centre of the dial passes the beard of a wild oat. This beard grows
from the inner husk which envelops the grain of the wild oat (Plate
5): the husk is of course removed before the beard is used. The main
limb of the beard, which in a dry taut state measures about 0·5″, is of
spiral form and unwinds in relation to the tail when it is moistened. A
lightweight index, usually a piece of straw, is glued to the tail of the
beard and this turns as the spiral limb relaxes or tautens. The scale,
which is alleged to show the degree of humidity, is in no way scientific

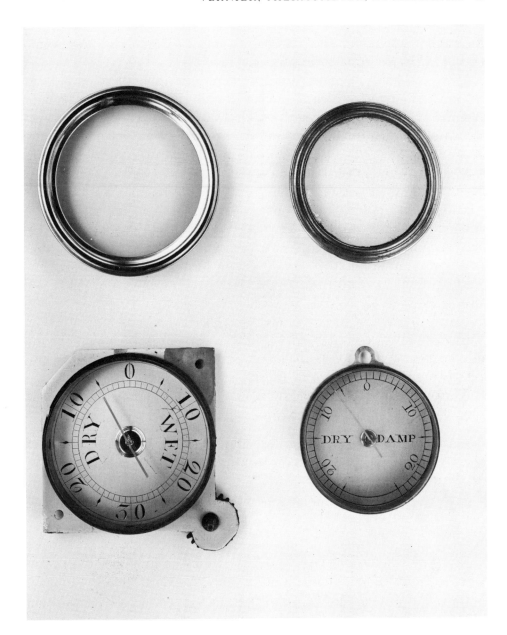

PLATE 4. Typical oatbeard hygrometers

in spite of its specious divisions: but the device does roughly demonstrate whether the air nearby is getting drier or more humid.

The oatbeard is tough but does not always last very long: it often disintegrates after only a few months. Many, or indeed most, of the hygrometers found on domestic barometers therefore have become of decorative value only, the oatbeard having been replaced more often than not by a masquerading straw or pin.

This type of hygrometer was first described in English by Robert Hooke,[1] who was enjoined by the Royal Society to construct an instrument using an oatbeard on 12 October 1663. His instrument measured about 4″ in diameter and incorporated a means of discerning how many revolutions the index had performed, a feature which did not survive when instrument-makers of the late eighteenth century began to produce common hygrometers.

Many other types of hygrometer were evolved in the seventeenth and eighteenth centuries: one writer in about 1700 mentioned hygrometers consisting of 'sheeps' gutts or fiddle-strings, pieces of leather,

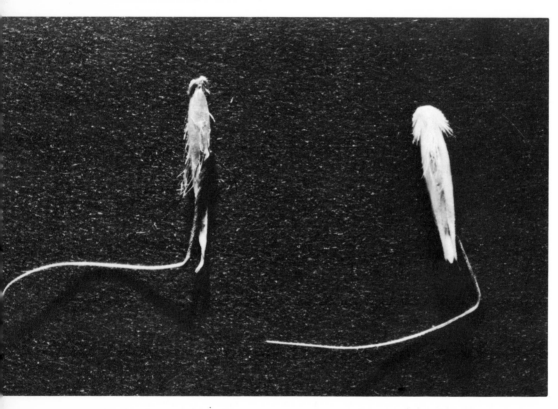

PLATE 5
Oatbeards
(husks still attached)

ropes, cords, sponge, wool, paper or deal-shavings'.[2] But instrument-makers seldom used hygrometers of any other design than that employing an oatbeard in their barometers. Extant examples which use gut are described later (Plates 83, 100).

[1] *Micrographia* Obs. 27: in his *Method for making a History of the Weather*, which is printed in Thomas Sprat's *History of the Royal Society* (4th edition 1734), Hooke attributed the invention to Emanuel Magnan.

[2] Gustavus Parker *An Account of a portable Barometer, with Reasons and Rules for the Use of it* (1700?).

CHAPTER 2

Period 1680–90

(a) THE
FIRST
COMMERCIAL
MAKERS

FOR MANY YEARS after its introduction to England the barometer remained the preserve of the scientists. It was used principally as an instrument for the measurement of heights or in experiments with the air pump, although regular meteorological observations were also made. Barometers were constructed by makers such as Robert Hooke, Richard Shortgrave (fl 1658–d. 1676) and Harry Hunt (1635–1713), successive Operators to the Royal Society, and by commercial instrument-makers such as Thomas Tompion (1638–1713), who supplied barometers to Robert Boyle and to Hooke: but they were not apparently made for domestic use. Perhaps commercial instrument-makers failed to realize that advantage could be taken of the Englishman's interest in the weather: or perhaps they thought that potential customers would not fall for such an expensive novelty. It was not in fact until about 1680 that barometers appeared in the shops. It is impossible to give an accurate date for this event but there is a certain amount of literary evidence which points to the early years of the decade 1680–90.

The instigator of the commercial manufacture of barometers is thought to have been Francis North (1637–85), Baron of Guilford and Lord Chancellor during the last years of Charles I's reign. His claims rest on a passage in his brother Roger North's biography which was published in 1742. It is worth quoting the complete passage:[1]

'His Lordship was much affected by the discoveries, which fell in the consequences of the Torricellian experiment; whereby a new world of air, compressing every thing it touches, is reveal'd. He

[1] Hon. Roger North *The Life of the Right Honourable Francis North, Baron of Guilford* (1742) p. 295. The author died in 1734 and the *Life* was published posthumously.

could not but observe a manifest connection between the alterations of the mercurial station, and the course of the winds and weather: but could not fix in his mind any certain rules of indication, but rather the contrary, viz. that events failed as often as corresponded with the ordinary expectation. But yet he would not give it over for desperate, and hoped that a more general observation might generate a better prognostic of the weather from it, than was yet known. And that must be expected from a more diffused, if not an universal, use of it, which could not then be thought of; because the instruments were rare, and confined to the cabinets of the virtuosi: and one was not to be had but by means of some of them. Therefore his Lordship thought fit to put some ordinary tradesmen upon making and selling them in their shops: and accordingly he sent for Jones, the clock-maker in the Inner-Temple Lane; and, having shewn him the fabrick, and given him proper cautions in the erecting of them, recommended the setting them forth for sale in his shop; and, it being a new thing, he would certainly find customers. He did so, and was the first person that exposed the instrument to sale publickly in London. But his Lordship, perceiving that his business lay in other operations he was more used to and that he began to slight these, sent for Mr. Winn, a famous instrument-maker over-against his house in Chancery Lane, and did the like to him, who pursued the manufactury to great perfection, and his own no small advantage; and then others took it up, and few clockmakers, instrument-makers, cabinet-makers and diverse other trades, were without them always in their shops, ready for sale'.

The validity of this account can be doubted on the grounds that it was written considerably after the event and that the author was not averse to exaggerating the virtues of his brother whose memory he was defending against various detractors. It is possible that some instrument-maker—Wynne perhaps—anticipated demand and displayed barometers in his shop on his own initiative. As far as I know however there is no evidence to contradict North's account: and since he was only sixteen years younger than his brother and was active in his profession from 1675 his evidence demands respect.

Henry Wynne (fl 1654–d.1709) was a well-known instrument-maker, who sold 'any sort of mathematical instruments whether for sea or land'[1] and there is no reason to disbelieve North's account that he was the first tradesman to sell barometers on a fair scale. Unfortunately no barometers survive with his signature but it is likely that he never

1 Quoted by E. G. R. Taylor *The Mathematical Practitioners of Tudor and Stuart England* (1954) p. 242.

signed them: or perhaps they have suffered the fate of many early barometers and been discarded when the tube or cistern has broken or the mercury deteriorated beyond use. He is mentioned as a baro-meter-maker by Robert Hooke who employed him as such in the years 1678–80.[1] That he was well known is beyond question and once Jones had proved fruitless it is not surprising that Lord North turned to him.

No barometers by Henry Jones appear to survive: he cannot have made many if 'his business lay in other operations he was more used to'. He was an eminent clockmaker and examples of his extant work prove the quality of his workmanship. Previous writers on baro-meters however have given him more credit than he deserves.

I have suggested that barometers were first made for commercial sale soon after 1680. It may seem odd that nearly forty years passed between the first application of mercury to the barometric experiment and the acceptance of the mercurial barometer as a household weather-glass; but it was a long time before the correlation between weather changes and the variations of the mercury level was accepted. This could not be proved until many amateur meteorologists had kept lengthy records; and was not apparently proved beyond doubt even in Lord North's mind when he decided to instigate commercial manufacture. If Roger North's account is accepted barometers were first sold commercially before his brother's death in 1685. His account also suggests that both Jones and Wynne must have been well established when his brother approached them. Jones was elected to the Clockmakers' Company in 1663 and Wynne in 1662 although he was working in 1654. They could probably not be described as well known therefore before 1670 at the earliest. But judging from other sources this date seems too early. In 1672 for example a Scottish mathematician, George Sinclair, discussed the barometer in a dis-course on hydrostatics:[2] his discussion concentrates on the mercurial barometer as an instrument for the measurement of heights and the only weather-glasses he mentions contain water. The references to the manufacture of barometers in Hooke's *Diary* suggest instruments which were specially commissioned (from Wynne, Tompion, Short-grave and Hunt) either for members of the Royal Society or for amateur scientists: the *Diary* covers the years 1672–80 and only the last relevant entry—'Bid Win send Lord Ranalaugh weather-glasses' (6 October 1680)—mentions instruments in the plural. A letter from

[1] *Diary of Robert Hooke* 1672–80 (edited by H. W. Robinson and W. Adams 1935). The MSS are in the Guildhall Library. Wynne is mentioned in connection with barometers in entries for 2 February 1678 and 6 October 1680.

[2] *The Hydrostatics . . . Together with a short History of Coal* (1672).

Richard Legh to his wife at Lyme Hall dated 1675 also suggests that barometers were not readily available:

> 'The carrier will bring a long deale box with a bottle that hath quicksilver in itt. Prithee command there be great care of itt, that neither of them—the box nor bottle—be stirred till I come home. 'Tis a device I had of Jonas Moore to know the weather by'.[1]

This letter suggests that in 1675 barometers were still 'confined to the cabinets of the virtuosi' among whom Jonas Moore, who knew Hooke well and who was elected a Fellow of the Royal Society in 1674, was certainly numbered. Legh was interested in the latest developments in London and bought a clock from Joseph Knibb in the same year, which suggests that he took the trouble to find the best. It is unlikely that he would have failed to buy a barometer from one of the clock or instrument-makers if barometers had been easy to buy. Finally, a letter writer could say as late as 1683: 'I was up and down Fleet Street to inquire of the wether-glass you bought . . . near Serjeants Inn, but I can hear no tidings of it'.[2] This does not suggest that barometer makers were easily found.

After 1680 the industry soon flourished. As North says, makers other than Wynne assumed the manufacture of barometers and 'few clockmakers, instrument-makers, cabinet-makers and diverse other trades, were without them always in their shops, ready for sale'. The connection between clockmakers and cabinet-makers was understandably close and it is logical that they should both have sold products which were probably the fruits of mutual co-operation. It is difficult to distinguish clockmakers from instrument-makers. Early clockmakers tend to be remembered only for their clocks, horologists nowadays seldom giving them credit for their other work: but most of the eminent clockmakers, including Quare, Tompion and Graham, were equally well known in their day for their astronomical and other 'mechanick' instruments. Furthermore it is often forgotten that a number of instrument-makers were admitted to the Clockmakers' Company in 1667 since there was no other Guild which could protect their interests (several members of the Company probably never made a clock in their lives): their admission four years before the admission of Quare and Tompion demonstrates the close association between the two trades in the classic age of English clockmaking.

Among the other 'diverse' tradesmen who displayed barometers in their shops were opticians like John Yarwell (1648–1712) and John Marshall (1663–1725), both members of the Spectaclemakers'

---

[1] Raines Collection: quoted by Evelyn Legh *The House of Lyme from its foundation to the end of the eighteenth century* (1917) p. 282.

[2] William Hayhurst to R. Kenyon, July 1683, quoted by R. T. Gunther *Early Science in Cambridge* (1937) p. 216.

Company and both with shops in St Paul's Churchyard. As will become evident throughout this work, it is not possible to say who actually made every instrument and the late seventeenth century is no exception. It is notable that North only says that the various classes of tradesmen 'sold' barometers and Yarwell and Marshall probably both sold barometers made by John Patrick. So, according to Clay and Court, did Quare.[1]

Be that as it may, the fact is that by 1690 barometers were easily obtainable and many notable examples are extant which were made before the turn of the century. By 1688 there were enough makers, which also means enough customers, for John Smith to find it worth while to publish his brief guide to the manufacture and setting up of the barometer.[2] By 1694 he could say that it was 'easy to be furnished in London' with a quicksilver weather-glass.[3]

(b) THE EARLY BAROMETERS

I have not yet seen a decorative barometer which was made, in my opinion, before about 1690. The early barometers made and sold by Henry Wynne and the 'clockmakers, instrument-makers and cabinet-makers' who followed suit must have been of a fairly simple sort and this may be one reason for their failure to survive. A newly invented product almost always appears crude a few years later when more imaginative designers and craftsmen have applied their ideas. Makers moreover probably refrained from elaborate construction in order to keep the cost within the pockets of potential buyers: the mercury alone—and a good straight-tube barometer was said by John Smith to need between two and four pounds of mercury[4]—was expensive enough, and an elegant frame would add greatly to the cost. It would also be natural for makers to continue making the type of instrument, until public taste refined their workmanship, which they had been making for the scientists during the previous two decades.

Description of the earliest commercial barometers must rely largely on contemporary writing. Fortunately there are a number of books which give a satisfactory picture. Most of them derive from the

[1] R. S. Clay and T. H. Court *The History of the Microscope* (1932) p. 251. I do not know these authors' source.

[2] *A Compleat Discourse of the Nature, Use, and Right Managing of that Wonderful Instrument, the Baroscope or Quick-Silver Weather-Glass* (1688).

[3] John Smith *Horological Disquisitions* (1694) p. 61.

[4] *A Compleat Discourse* pp. 30–1.

A Compleat

DISCOURSE

OF THE

Nature, Use, and Right Managing

Of that Wonderful

INSTRUMENT,

THE

BAROSCOPE,

OR

Quick-Silver Weather-Glass.

In IV. PARTS.

By *JOHN SMITH*, C.M.

To which is added, The true Equation of Natural Days; drawn up for the use of the Gentry, in order to their more true Adjusting, and Right Managing of Pendulum Clocks and Watches.

LONDON,

Printed for Joseph Watts, at the *Angel* in *S. Paul's Church-Yard.* MDCLXXXVIII.

earliest which is John Smith's *A Compleat Discourse of the Nature, Use, and Right Managing of that Wonderful Instrument, the Baroscope or Quick-Silver Weather-Glass* (Plate 6) published in 1688. Smith, who was elected to the Clockmakers' Company in 1674, is chiefly known for having written two of the earliest English books on horology: no barometers by him survive although it is fair to infer from his two works on the barometer (his *Horological Disquisitions* of 1694 contains twenty-three pages on the barometer which add little to the *Compleat Discourse*) that he made them like many contemporary clockmakers. Whether he did or not is of only academic interest.

In *A Compleat Discourse* Smith says that barometers, which he still calls baroscopes, had been made so far after 'divers manners but chiefly three ways'.[1] First, there was the straight-tube type which he ascribes 'chiefly' to Robert Boyle:[2] second, the type with a tube 'whose top inclines', i.e. the angle barometer, which he says was devised by Sir Samuel Morland: third, the wheel barometer invented by Hooke. Of these the angle barometer did 'not admit of any regular figure' and the wheel was 'very dear and costly'. Besides these disadvantages he was not convinced that the nicer movements of the mercury which they revealed were any better at forecasting the weather than the movements in the ordinary straight tube. For these reasons the more refined types were not often made or used and Smith comes down solidly in favour of the straight cistern-tube barometer himself since it is a sufficient indicator of weather changes, is 'most regular, of smallest price, and most easy to be made and managed'. His *A Compleat Discourse* is in fact entirely concerned with it, and may thus seem wrongly titled.

The angle and wheel types have been explained in Chapter One. There do not appear to be any angle barometers extant earlier than those discussed in the next chapter: and although wheel barometers were made for Hooke by Hunt and Shortgrave and perhaps Tompion none survives of an early date except the magnificent instruments made by Tompion for William III (Plates 143, 146) and these too belong to the next chapter.

Smith's description of the ordinary barometer in 1688 is reminiscent of the instrument which Richard Legh sent home with a proper fear for its fragility: but it is not as primitive. One concession to taste is that if ornament is required, the choicest woods—walnut, ebony or olive, although any sort could be used—are recommended for the

---

[1] *A Compleat Discourse* p. 1 *et seq.*

[2] The Hon. Robert Boyle (1627–91) an eminent scientist and one of the founder members of the Royal Society. He was one of the first to carry out barometric experiments in this country. For his place in the history of the barometer see Middleton *History of the Barometer, passim.*

wooden frame. It is also admitted that the maker and owner may not
be satisfied with a plain wooden frame, the shape and decoration of
the case being left to their individual fancies. In other ways too the
recommended barometer is an advance on the simple instruments
used earlier. A deeply bevelled groove is recommended for the
protection of the tube from breakage: or better still, following the
practice of some contemporary makers, a wooden cover could be
fitted up the whole length of the tube below the plates. The register
plates have become more detailed than their simple predecessors.
They are made of brass, each measuring about six by one and a
quarter inches: the inside edge of each is engraved with graduated
divisions of three complete inches with decimal subdivisions. On one
of the plates (not specifically the right-hand one although this in
practice was normally used) the inches 28-31 were engraved at the
four main divisions, reading upwards, and a sliding index was fitted,
in a groove rather longer than the scale, to denote the previous station
of the mercury. The other plate was also engraved with the scale but
not numbered. Instead it was engraved with words to denote 'those
usual states of weather, which learned and ingenious men have
observed for the most part' to follow the movement of the mercury
past each graduation. The words which Smith suggests are—

$$
\text{At} \left\{
\begin{array}{ll}
28 & \text{Great Storms} \\
28\frac{1}{2} & \text{Much Rain} \\
29 & \text{Rain} \\
29\frac{1}{2} & \text{Uncertain or Changeable} \\
30 & \text{Fair} \\
30\frac{1}{2} & \text{Setled Fair} \\
31 & \text{Very Dry}
\end{array}
\right.
$$

Whether he was following or instituting common practice it is not
possible to say but, as will be seen, this list, with the substitution of
'Changeable' for 'Uncertain' and of 'Stormy' for 'Great Storms',
became the commonest selection of weather indications throughout
the history of the mercurial barometer. It is interesting to compare
these with George Sinclair's list, also published in 1688.[1] The mercurial
barometer was only part of Sinclair's studies. He was concerned
originally with the barometer, like many scientists, because of its
relevance in the vacuum controversy and because of its use in the
measurement of heights—and in particular of the depths of coal

---

[1] *A Discovery of the Secrets of Nature, which are found in the Mercurial-Weather-Glass*, appended to his
Principles of Astronomy and Navigation (1688) p. 42.

mines. He wrote this tract because he considered the correlation between weather changes and the movements of the mercury 'a subject not hitherto treated of'. He did not specify the inches 28–31 but his proposed half-inch graduations were—

Long Fair
Fair
Changeable
Rain
Much Rain
Stormy
Tempests

That 'Changeable' should be above the mean and that there should be four degrees of bad weather to only two good ones is perhaps a reflection of the traditional weather in Scotland.

Sinclair's weather-glass was mounted on a frame of oak[1] which he thought would last for 'many years'. He also took an optimistic view of the staying powers of the glass and mercury which he considered 'incorruptible by nature' and mentioned as an alternative to engraved brass plates 'a piece of Lombard-paper wrought in the Taliduse-press'.[2] Paper was often used, the scales and weather indications being printed or written: not many early examples survive for obvious reasons.

The rest of John Smith's description shows no advance over the straight-tube barometers alluded to in the writings of the seventeenth-century scientists. The cistern is a round glass vessel about 0·75″ deep and 3″ to 3·5″ in diameter with a flat bottom: the tube is 'at least' three feet long, with a bore of between 0·2″ and 0·25″, made of strong even-blown and clear glass: it is filed 'very true and even' at the lower end in order to avoid the entry of air when the finger is put over the end while erecting the instrument, but the end is cut 'somewhat asloop' so that not all the circumference of the tube should rest on the bottom of the cistern and restrict the movement of the mercury. The cistern is placed in a wooden cistern box which is attached to the frame.

Very few glass cisterns survive: some have doubtless been broken but more have been replaced, for the sake of convenience and modernity, by closed boxwood cisterns of later date. Except by measuring the cistern box therefore it is not possible to check whether the original maker took any care over his proportions: and since the tube has almost invariably been renewed the excercise is usually

[1] *Ibid.* p. 49.   [2] *Ibid.* p. 42.

pointless. I can see no reason to doubt however that glass cisterns were used commonly in the cheaper barometers until well into the eighteenth century. I doubt if boxwood was used much before 1690, if then: in his *Horological Disquisitions* of 1694 Smith does not mention it. That glass bowls were still used commonly in the early eighteenth century is suggested by the second volume of the *Lexicon Technicum* of 1710, in which the cistern is assumed to be either of glass or close-grained wood. Several eighteenth-century examples survive.

In summary the instrument described by Smith is still primitive even though considerable care is advised in the preparation and selection of materials. The cistern is still of glass and fragile: there is not a hint of any more efficient means of excluding dust (such as a cover of pigskin) than the wooden cistern box: the instrument is cumbersome and has to be dismantled if taken any distance. In reality moreover it seems that makers failed to conform even to the meagre recommendations made by the author. He had discovered by trial and error that a tube of 0·2″ bore needed a cistern of at least 3″ diameter and that one of 0·25″ bore needed a cistern of 3·5″ diameter if the instrument was to minimize the effect of the change of the cistern level on the reading and preserve any degree of accuracy. Smith complained 'I know there be few yet made of this size' because mercury was a 'dear commodity' and observed 'how defective most baroscopes, already made, are in this point of perfection'.[1]

No effective answer was found to this problem until about 1760. John Smith's large cistern was used by good eighteenth-century craftsmen such as Bennett, Ramsden, Sisson, Springer and Watkins but it was never a solution: it only minimized the fault. Most makers disregarded the problem altogether as presumably did their customers.

[1] Smith *A Compleat Discourse* pp. 15 and 27.

CHAPTER 3

Period 1690–1720

THE DESIGN of barometers showed a rapid advance at the beginning of the eighteenth century. Demand for domestic use grew apace soon after they were first generally offered for sale: so much so that Richard Neve was able to say in 1708 that few gentlemen were 'without one of them'[1] and Edward Saul a few years later could write that they were in common use in 'most houses of figure and distinction'.[2] Demand tends to encourage inventiveness on the part of makers who wish to compete effectively with their rivals. The combination of some of the scientific ideas mentioned in Chapter One and the manufacturing techniques of the great clock and instrument-makers of the day brought the barometer in its various forms to a pitch of refinement which was not really improved upon for fifty years; and not substantially until a hundred and fifty years later when materials were better analysed and understood.

The high quality of the better cases also is consistent with the technical and artistic competence of contemporary clockmakers: wealthy patrons commissioned instruments of the highest quality from the leading makers of the day and were not disappointed. The instruments at Hampton Court are among the finest examples of contemporary craftsmanship. It would be misleading however to mention only the work of these makers as previous writers have done. Undoubtedly a wide range of instruments was manufactured: and although it is

---

[1] *Baroscopologia* (1708). Neve was a polymath and this book is largely derived from Smith's *Horological Disquisitions* which was itself a revised version of Smith's *A Compleat Discourse*.

[2] *An Historical and Philosophical Account of the Barometer, or Weather-Glass* (1735) p. 11: the book was substantially written in about 1710 when Saul was tutor to the Earl of Rutland.

easy to be misled by surviving instruments into believing that the products of this period were of a high minimum quality, it is not a true picture. I do not need to repeat that the barometer is a fragile instrument: and it is unlikely that a broken barometer of simple and outmoded design would have been retained by its owner in say 1820 when so many of the cheap and fashionable 'stick' and 'banjo' instruments were available.

(a)
MAKERS
1690-1720

There was no real change in the structure of the industry. Barometers continued to be assembled and sold by the cabinet-makers, clock-makers, instrument-makers and opticians: there is little doubt that, as with clocks, 'makers' employed one craftsman to supply the case and another to engrave the register plates, contracting the work to an outside cabinet-maker or diallist more often than not. Among eminent clock and mathematical instrument-makers who included barometers among their wares at this time were Henry Wynne's former apprentice Thomas Tuttell (fl 1688 –d.1702), John Brown (fl 1648–95), Daniel Quare (1649–1724), Thomas Tompion (1638–1713), Clement Forster (fl 1670–94) and James Markwick (fl 1692 –d.1730); an early barometer by John Shaw (fl 1672–1752) is also extant.[1] Spectaclemakers like Marshall and Yarwell, already mentioned, continued to sell barometers as did numbers of cabinet-makers. The most interesting maker of the time was John Patrick (fl 1686–1712) who appears to have been apprenticed to a member of the Joiners' Company in 1686 but whose workshop was devoted mainly to the manufacture of barometers and thermometers. His instruments, as already mentioned, were sold by other workshops and such was his reputation that he was labelled the 'Torricellian Operator' in the first volume of the *Lexicon Technicum* of 1704.[2] Another specialist in barometers was John Warner (fl 1684–1722). The existence of specialist producers at this early date is strong evidence for a steady demand: and as was the case with clocks, demand was not confined to London or even England. Patrick and Quare particularly, once the barometer had been made more easily transportable, made instruments for export: barometers by them both survive with weather indications in French and by Quare with German indications.

There were also several makers who continued to produce barometers for scientific experiments and observations. Less relevant to

[1] Illustrated in the *Dictionary of English Furniture* (edited by P. MacQuoid and R. Edwards, 2nd edition 1954), *s.v.* 'Barometer' Fig. 1.

[2] Edited by John Harris, *s.v.* 'Barometer': the phrase is repeated by Desaguliers in his *Experimental Philosophy* p. 269.

the present study are those makers who probably worked exclusively for philosophical clients, such as Harry Hunt (1635–1713) who was Hooke's assistant until 1676 and then operator to the Royal Society in succession to Richard Shortgrave. He made meteorological instruments, including barometers of various types, for members of the Society, and was one of the earliest makers to be commended for his portable barometers (see p. 301). Francis Hauksbee the elder (fl 1700–d. 1713), himself a Fellow of the Royal Society from 1705, was another prominent maker of air-pumps and barometers for philosophical users. Unlike Hunt however he had his own workshop, and although there is no positive evidence that he sold his barometers to members of the public it is almost certain that he did so. He is worth attention here because, like Patrick, he knew the value of advertisement. From 1704 he organized a series of 'physico-mechanical' lectures at his house (see p. 150). These were not only a source of profit but were also a means of publicising his instruments, which were needed for the lecturers' demonstrations. He was the forerunner of other instrument-makers whose claim to patronage can often be found in the printed summaries of lecture courses throughout the century. He lived at a time moreover when a man could be both a craftsman and a natural philosopher. As will become clear in later pages several instrument-makers in the eighteenth century were Fellows of the Royal Society. Their workshops produced barometers both for scientific and for domestic use and there was often little distinction between the two.

The most significant fact about these thirty years is that the mercurial barometer was beginning to be widely accepted as a domestic weather-glass in preference to the common water weather-glasses. Consequently large numbers of indifferent quality were made and sold by opportunists who, like the sellers of cheap and inefficient electrical appliances of today, took advantage of the sudden demand in order to make a quick profit. Saul mentions 'needy foreigners' and 'peddling philosophers' who had lately been hawking inferior weather-glasses about the country.[1]

(b)
BAROMETERS
1690–1720

Although the structure of the industry, with the exception of freaks like John Patrick, changed little during this period the same cannot be said of its products. John Smith's two books had emphasized two limitations of the common barometer. Firstly the extent of the scale was unsatisfactorily short and secondly the instrument could not be

[1] Saul *An Historical and Philosophical Account* p. 107.

moved without a great deal of trouble. By 1710, while barometers were not in general much more accurate than they had been in 1690, a purchaser could choose between a wide variety of types, several of them based on seventeenth-century proposals for the extension of the scale, and could buy a barometer which was fully portable. The careful dismantling of the instrument, which Smith recommended before it was moved further than the next room, and the exaggerated fear of breakage entertained by Legh were both things of the past.

In spite of its relative inaccuracy the straight-tube instrument continued to be the most in demand. Expense was undoubtedly one reason. John Smith had described the wheel barometer as costly: and in 1710, whereas Patrick's cheapest portable straight-tube barometers cost two guineas, his angle barometers, admittedly with a mirror in the middle, cost fifteen. Patrick however was a well-known maker patronized by the rich: and a better guide to current prices is probably the range offered by Clement Forster in about 1694—from twelve to fifty shillings. Only straight-tube instruments could have been offered at these prices. Tompion charged as much as £4. 6. 0. for a portable barometer in 1701.

Portable barometers were required not only by the domestic user who found the manoeuvres recommended by John Smith irksome. Scientists, amateur and professional, who wished to compare the level of the mercury at different heights, surveyors who used the barometer for computing the heights of hills, and mariners who were beginning to appreciate the advantages of being able to forecast changes of the weather, especially storms, all needed an instrument which could be carried about with ease.[1]

In the second volume of the *Lexicon Technicum*, which was published in 1710, there are three recognized ways of making a barometer portable. Firstly, in order to prevent the mercury from spilling over the edge of the cistern and to stop the air from entering the bottom of the tube, the author recommends the maker to tie a piece of 'gentle leather' over the brim of the glass or wooden cistern. Secondly, to stop the mercury from breaking the top of the tube when it surges, the mercury should be screwed or squeezed into the tube so that it is always full: or thirdly, to stop the same contingency, the bore of the top inch or so of the tube should be constricted.

The first method was probably sufficient for a householder who was only interested in occasionally moving his instrument from one room to another: but it did not make the barometer really portable and it

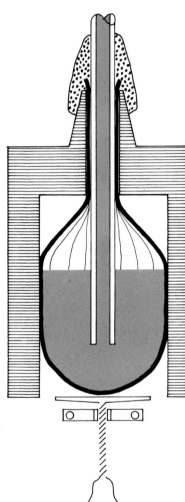

FIG. V.
Portable cistern
(a) leather bag

---

[1] For a succinct summary of the historical search for portability in a scientific context see Middleton *History of the Barometer* p. 143 *et seq.*

did not obviate the risk of breaking the top of the tube with the surging of the mercury. The comments of a garrulous inventor named Gustavus Parker in about 1700 are just:

> 'The business of a portable barometer have been the endeavours of several men above thirty years last past: to find out some way or other to put the quick-silver glass into a secure travelling posture: at last they got a way to tye a piece of leather over the cistern and round the tube, and such they called their portable barometers, which the Philosophical Transactions saies, are no way to be trusted to, by reason of their intolerable errors, and besides are in no ways portable'.[1]

The method was probably widely used for cheaper instruments at the beginning of the eighteenth century.

The third method, the constriction of the bore of the tube, was used commonly in marine barometers to diminish the effect on the mercury column of the rolling of the ship. It was still being used for this purpose in the nineteenth century. But constricting the bore did not make the barometer fully portable: it only reduced the risk of breakage.

The second method, the screwing of the mercury into the tube during travel, was the most efficient and eventually became commonly used. In its earliest form this was done by cementing a leather bag to the lower end of the tube to contain the mercury (Fig. v): the bag rested inside the usual cistern box and a screw, to which was attached a flat disc of metal, was fitted at the bottom so that when the tube was inverted the mercury could be securely constrained from movement by application of the screw. Later a closed cistern was used, usually of box or some other very fine grain wood, its base consisting of leather: the same type of screw was used (Fig. vi). This second variety has been used, with minor variations, in domestic instruments ever since. It was in use by 1710 although the fact that it is given no particular prominence in the second volume of the *Lexicon Technicum* suggests that it was by no means commonly applied then. Unfortunately most early cisterns have been destroyed with their tubes, and categorical assertions are impossible.

The principle of the closed cistern probably came from the Continent. The *Transactions* of the Philosophical Society of Oxford for 22 April 1684 report that

> 'A joyner at Roven in Normandy, has made barometers entirely closd, without any communication of externall air, (unless it can be

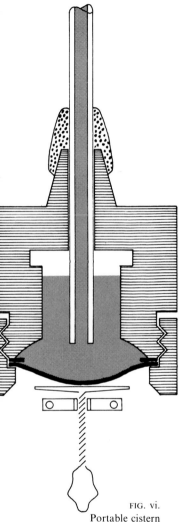

FIG. vi.
Portable cistern
(b) leather-based
wooden cistern

---

[1] Gustavus Parker *An Account of a Portable Barometer, with Reasons and Rules for the Use of it.* (1700?—the date is printed MDCXCX.)

suppos'd to pass thro ye pores of ye woode) which exactly observe ye motions of ye other sort. They have this convenience that ye mercury cannot get out, because all is very closely glew'd. They may be carried in a coach, or otherwise, without prejudice'.[1]

Christian Huygens, in a letter to his brother dated 4 March 1695 and written at The Hague, mentions a similar design effected by the son of the architect James Roman; but comments that the passage of the air through the boxwood is a disadvantage, the boxwood in his view presumably restricting the air's force.[2]

A similar form of portable barometer was described by Joachim d'Alencé in a book published in Amsterdam in 1688.[3] This consisted of a straight tube cemented to a boxwood cistern, the interior of which was spherical, in such a way that the open end of the tube was in the centre of the sphere. The cistern was rather over half-filled with mercury, so that in whatever position the instrument was held the open end of the tube would always be immersed in the mercury. Later in the same treatise d'Alencé suggested a cylindrical cistern.

Such instruments were based on the same principle as the later English ones—i.e. a closed cistern in which the open lower end of the tube can never be exposed to the air—but were inferior in that they incorporated no device to prevent movement of the mercury during transport. Agitation of the instrument would almost certainly have led to the infiltration of air into the tube.

It is not clear when or by whom the idea of squeezing the mercury into the tube was first applied. The idea is not mentioned in either of John Smith's relevant books, written in 1688 and 1694, which suggests that it was not known then. Nor is it mentioned in the *Lexicon Technicum* of 1704. On 2 August 1695 Daniel Quare was granted a patent[4] for a term of fourteen years which reads:

'Whereas our trusty and welbeloved subiect Daniel Quare hath humbly rep'sented unto us that with much study and industry, and at his great expence hee hath invented and brought to pfec̃con "a portable weather glass or barometer, which may be removed and carried to any place though turned upside downe without spilling one drop of the quicksilver or letting any air into the tube, and that neverthelesse the air shall have the same liberty to operate upon it as on those comõn ones now in use with respect to the weight of the atmosphere"; which invencõn will be of great use to our subjects in

[1] Quoted by Gunther *Early Science in Oxford* (1925) Vol. 4, p. 61.

[2] *Oeuvres Complètes* (compiled under the auspices of the Societé Hollandaise des Sciences 1905) Vol. 10, pp. 709–10.

[3] *Traittez des Baromètres et Notiomètres ou Hygromètres* (1688) p. 32 *et seq.*: the book was published under the nom de plume of 'Mr. D . . .'.

[4] No. 342.

gen'all both by sea and land, and hath never yet been knowne or made use of in this our Kingdome, and haveing therefore prayed our Letters Patente for the sole use and benefitt of the same . . .'.

Quare had previously shown his barometer to the Royal Society on 16 January 1695: and the Society's *Journal Book*[1] reported that it was

'so contrived as to be portable, and even inverted without spilling the quick silver, or letting in any air, or excluding the pressure of the atmosphere, which the Society were well satisfied with, and were pleased to declare, that it was the first of that sort they had seen. Mr. Quaire desired to be excused for discovering the secret thereof.'

Neither this passage nor the Patent says very much about Quare's invention: the only details which are given are that the barometer could be inverted without spilling the mercury and without letting air into the tube. There are no grounds for the assertion, which has been unanimously made by previous writers, that the device patented by Quare consisted of a leather-based cistern and screw. There is indeed overwhelming literary evidence against such claims on Quare's behalf.

Firstly, in 1698, two years after the patent was granted, William Derham wrote an account of some experiments which he had carried out at the Monument in 1696–7:[2] he appended some interesting instructions on how to make a 'portable barometer':

'Provide a strong glass tube, let the head of it be pinched at about an inch from the top, so as to make a narrow neck, whose orifice shall be as big almost as a straw. This (which is Mr. Quare's way) will much bridle the blow of the mercury against the top, as it danceth up and down, which endangers breaking off the top of the tube. The bottom of the tube I would have ground aslant near half an inch, that the bottom of the tube touching the bottom of the cistern, the orifice thereof may lie about the middle of the mercury in the cistern; which will prevent the air getting into the tube, by reason the mercury is always about the mouth of the tube. The cistern must be made wide, either of glass, or close grained wood round the brim of which, on the out-side, must be a notch to tye on the leather that is to cover it. When the tube is filled, cleared of air, and plunged into the cistern near full of mercury, enclose the mercury with gentle leather tied very fast round the tube near the bottom, which being spread over the cistern, tye it round that also: the tube and cistern, thus conjoined with leather, must be lodged in the case, made very

[1] I am grateful to the Royal Society for permission to quote extracts from their archives.
[2] *Philosophical Transactions* Vol. 20 (1698) p. 2 *et seq.*

fit to receive both, where they must lie very fast. Through the case let 3 or 4 holes be bored, to let the air in freely to the leather that covers the cistern, which lying close against the holes, will firmly enough keep the mercury from running out at them'.

It is clear from this that Derham, a Fellow of the Royal Society and closely in touch with the latest developments, considered Quare's 'portable' device to consist of pinching the top of the tube.

Secondly, the strictures of Gustavus Parker already quoted (p. 29) and probably written in 1700, specifically mention only the tying of a piece of leather over the cistern. Thirdly, the first volume of the *Lexicon Technicum* of 1704, the compilation of which was begun in 1702, mentions only Derham's method of making a portable barometer. It is almost inconceivable that if the screw device had been known mention of it would have been omitted. Fourthly, Christian Huygens, writing to his brother Constantin who had met Quare in Kensington, said on 4 March 1695: 'Les baromètres du Quaker sont du livre de d'Alancè, mais peut estre il les aura perfectionnez.'[1] This certainly suggests that Quare's device was some sort of closed cistern: but it would be very odd if either Huygens or his brother had observed the use of a revolutionary screw device and not commented specifically on it. Finally there are extant barometers by Quare which do not incorporate the screw device so commonly attributed to him. These were presumably before *c.* 1702 and could either have incorporated a tube and cistern answering to Derham's description or a leather bag of the type illustrated in Fig. v, but without the screw.[2]

The second alternative is supported by an entry in the Royal Society's *Journal Book* for 31 January 1695 which reads: 'Doctor Hook mentioned that he had been told that a barometer was made by Mr. Tompion about a year since, which did the same thing with that of Mr. Quaire, and Doctor Sloan say'd that he had discoursed Mr. Tompion about it, who say'd it was to be done by help of a bladder, without further explaining himself'. A 'bladder' sounds like a leather bag: and the record suggests that Quare's precedence in applying the device is in doubt.

Quare's patent did not meet with the approval of the Clockmakers' Company: the Court of the Company was traditionally opposed to

[1] Huygens *Oeuvres Complètes* Vol. 10, pp. 709–10.
[2] See p. 186 *et seq.*: I am obliged to say 'could have incorporated' because I have so far not seen a barometer of this type which was still fitted with its original tube and cistern. In some cases later repairers have even gone to the length of fitting such barometers with a screw; in most cases however it is usual to find a modern tube with a leather-based cistern but neither screw nor pinched head. Repairers should not be castigated unduly for fitting portable cisterns of the screw type to early barometers. It was usually done with the aim of increasing efficiency and it has an interesting parallel in the substitution of anchor escapements for the original verges in early clocks. It is quite likely that some of Quare's early barometers were converted soon after they were made and possibly in Quare's own workshop.

patents on the grounds that by means of them a maker could acquire a monopoly of improvements in design which were not novelties.[1] The *Minutes* of the Company reveal that an attempt was made to prevent the granting of the patent: and, when it was granted, it was resolved that the Company would defend any of its members or their servants and John Patrick, who had assisted the Company in the affair no doubt for sound commercial reasons, in any lawsuits which they might incur through making and selling portable barometers.[2] These *Minutes* suggest that other members of the Company were already making portable barometers in 1695. They were also being made before 1700 by craftsmen other than clockmakers. John Patrick is the most eminent example, and Edmund Halley mentioned the accuracy of Harry Hunt's portable barometers in a letter in 1697.[3]

The screw device was presumably first used *c.* 1701. The barometer advertised by Thomas Tuttell at about this date (Plate 149) looks as if it has a portable screw and perhaps this device was used by Tompion in the portable barometer which he supplied to the Hon. Robert Harley in 1701. It is not clear however who invented it or which maker first applied it but it is interesting that the 1788 edition of Chambers' *Cyclopaedia*[4] attributed it to Patrick and that Charles Hutton, writing in 1795, said 'it seems Mr. Patrick first made a contrivance of this kind'.[5] I have not yet discovered any sources on which these writers could have based this assumption. The device, together with the leather-based cistern which soon developed from it, has already been described (p. 29).

I have dwelt at some length on the early development of portable barometers because it was an important development. The use of a screw and a leather-based cistern gained speedy acceptance and by 1800 they were the rule rather than the exception.

It is possible to form a fairly lucid picture of the variety of instruments available at the beginning of the eighteenth century. Most of the literary evidence is concerned with John Patrick. This is regrettable but it is a measure of his contemporary reputation: and since he was known in his day to be the leading specialist maker of barometers, the 'Torricellian Operator', the variety of instruments which he offered can be taken as representative if not quite comprehensive. A reasonable number of instruments also survive, by various makers, although they are mostly those of better quality.

[1] See S. E. Atkins and W. H. Overall *Some Account of the Worshipful Company of Clockmakers of the City of London* (1881) p. 242 *et seq.* for a discussion of the Company's attitude to patents.

[2] *Clockmakers' Company Journal.*

[3] June and 30 September 1695.

[3] *Philosophical Transactions* Vol. 19 (1697) p. 582.

[4] Revised by Abraham Rees, *s.v.* 'Barometer'.

[5] *Mathematical and Philosophical Dictionary* (1795), *s.v.* 'Barometer'.

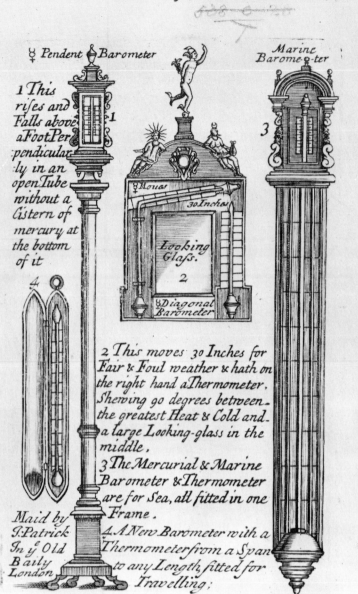

of the Quickſilver Barometer,
in Ship-Court in the Old-Baily, London:

⊹ Pendent ⚥ Barometer

Marine
Barome⚥ter

1 *This riſes and Falls above a Foot Perpendicularly in an open Tube without a Ciſtern of mercury at the bottom of it*

§ Hours
30 Inches

Looking Glaſs.
2

§ *Diagonal Barometer*

2 *This moves 30 Inches for Fair & Foul weather & hath on the right hand a Thermometer, Shewing 90 degrees between the greateſt Heat & Cold and a large Looking-glaſs in the middle.*

3 *The Mercurial & Marine Barometer & Thermometer are for Sea, all fitted in one Frame.*

4 *A New Barometer with a Thermometer from a Span to any Length, fitted for Travelling;*

Maid by J. Patrick In ye Old Baily London

In a pamphlet of about 1700[1] Patrick was offering

1. The common barometer
2. The portable
3. Ditto, with a thermometer
4. Ditto, with a marine barometer
5. The pendant, moving a foot
6. The diagonal, moving 30 inches
7. A new barometer with a thermometer of a span long, or to any length proper for carriage.

Four of these (Nos. 4, 5, 6 and 7) are illustrated in the pamphlet (Plate 7) where they are numbered in order 3, 1, 2 and 4. Considerably

[1] *A new Improvement of the Quicksilver Barometer, Made by John Patrick, in Ship-Court in the Old Baily, London.* This pamphlet is undated but is extensively quoted in John Harris's *Lexicon Technicum* Vol. 1 (1704), work on which began in 1702.

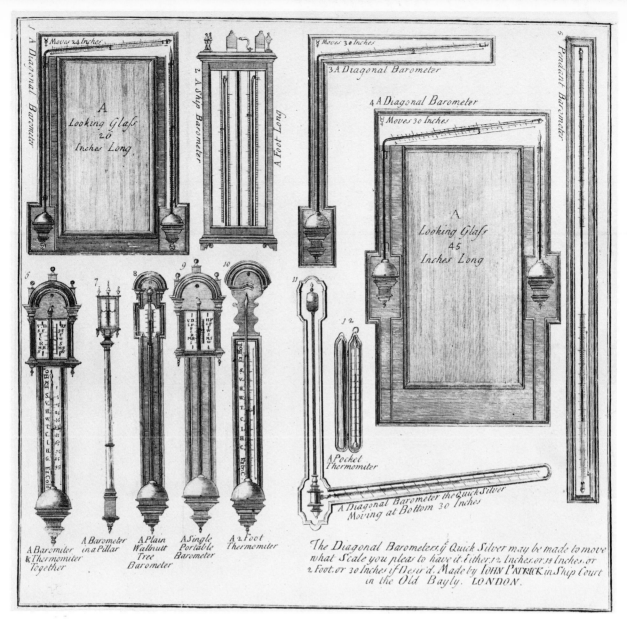

The Diagonal Barometers, if Quick Silver may be made to move what Scale you pleas to have it. Either 12 Inches. or 18 Inches. or 2 Foot. or 30 Inches if Desir'd. Made by IOHN PATRICK in Ship Court in the Old Bayly. LONDON.

more credence should be given to the text of this pamphlet however than to its accompanying illustration. There is no doubt at all for instance that the drawing marked 4 is not 'A new barometer with a thermometer from a span to any length fitted for travelling' but only a thermometer: in a later advertisement of Patrick's meteorological instruments (Plate 8 Fig. 12) it is given its correct title. Fig. 1 furthermore is not a pendant barometer in spite of its title: the principle of this type of barometer is described later (p. 46) and it is sufficient to note here that unless the instrument depicted in Fig. 1 is over eighteen feet high the mercury's rise and fall of 'above a foot perpendicular' cannot be seen. Plate 8 Fig. 5 shows a pendant barometer and Plate 7 Fig. 1 is no more than a cistern-tube barometer 'in a pillar' with a scale of 3″ marked on its register plates: a later and simpler version of it can be seen in Plate 8 Fig. 7. Finally the dimensions of the marine barometer (Plate 7 Fig. 3) are equally improbable and this is an ordinary if decorative cistern-tube barometer. Why this illustration should be so inaccurate and why Patrick should have allowed its distribution is a mystery. Perhaps the extravagant decoration of the angle barometer with its depictions of Hermes, Apollo and Artemis appealed to his sense of showmanship rather in the manner in which extravagant claims on behalf of their products must appeal to the modern manufacturers of domestic appliances.

Patrick's later advertisement (Plate 8) is a more accurate if more prosaic effort. Again it is undated but it cannot have been printed long before or after 1710. The most notable difference between the two advertisements is that all the mercurial barometers of the later version are fitted with a portable screw whereas none in the earlier version is. Otherwise, apart from the inclusion of an unusual type of 'diagonal' barometer (Fig. 11), the later advertisement offers no new barometers: it only offers a greater variety without any apparent attempt to deceive. I shall discuss the particular barometers in this advertisement later. Meanwhile there is one more piece of contemporary evidence about Patrick's output which must be taken into account.

In 1710 the German traveller and connoisseur Zacharias Conrad von Uffenbach visited Patrick's workshop and an account of his visit, which mentions several barometers, appears in his journal:

'. . . . we went to an optico and weather-glass maker, Patrick, to the left of the Old Bailey, and there we saw the following articles: barometers where the mercury can be screwed up, so that they may be conveniently carried about and used on board ship. The cheapest cost two guineas. Halley's ship-barometer with a blue liquor. They resemble thermometers with the degrees on a scale, on which the blue liquor can be used as a thermometer by means of a pointer; but that which the liquor registers above or below is shewn by the change of the barometer. Thus it is that this invention is much better than that with the mercury, since the latter dances about so prodigiously with the movement of the ship that no observation can be made. We saw also a newly invented barometer where the mercury hovered in the middle, above and below being only air. Further, one that was bent and fastened into a mirror-frame. The curve is intended to make the degrees appear larger. This kind costs fifteen guineas. He had another similar one for

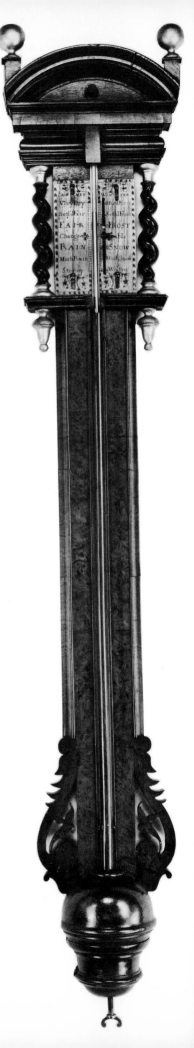

PLATE 9
Anon.
41·5″ × 7·5″
Hampton Court:
*reproduced by gracious permission
of Her Majesty the Queen*

the same price on a metal stand, so that both sides could be seen'.[1]

Uffenbach does not mention a 'common' barometer although Patrick specifies the common barometer first in his earlier advertisement. Such instruments (i.e. open cistern barometers) could still have accounted for much of his stock in 1710: but he seems to have concentrated on portable screw-type cisterns by about this date (Plate 8 Figs. 6, 7, 8, 9) and it is possible that he no longer stocked the less mobile open cistern barometers. The screw-type cistern seems to have achieved widespread acceptance by the second decade of the century and it becomes increasingly difficult to distinguish between it and its simpler predecessor in the work of contemporary authors. Perhaps Uffenbach was not, like any curious visitor, selecting only the most ingenious instruments for mention and neglecting the common ones, but was misled by the novelty of the screw-type cistern into interpreting it specifically as a marine barometer. To Patrick it was probably an ordinary stock instrument, a 'common' barometer.

A number of distinctive features can be discerned in the more refined common barometers of this period. The casework usually consists of veneers of walnut (Plate 9) or other 'choicest woods', as John Smith suggested, on a frame of oak: the edges of the case are often attractively moulded and the application of fretted scrollwork at the side of the base is common (Plates 9, 10, 11). The barometer of Plate 10 demonstrates the contemporary fashion for walnut inlaid with floral marquetry and also the time-honoured reference to Hermes, the messenger of Zeus the Cloud-gatherer, whose Latin name Mercury makes him a doubly appropriate patron of the mercurial weather-glass (cf Plate 7 Fig. 2). While the tube is most frequently left exposed in a groove (Plates 10 and 11) it is often covered with a protective sheath of wood (Plate 9) or, as is exemplified by Patrick's barometer of Plate 109, completely panelled. The cistern cover is usually of rather heavy proportions and turned in solid walnut. The register plates are frequently mounted in a hood reminiscent of contemporary clock designs with plain or twisted wooden pillars, gilt or plain capitals and a curved pediment (Plates 9 and 109): this is often surmounted by gilt wood spherical finials which are equally often lost.

---

[1] W. H. Quarrell and M. Mare *London in 1710* (Faber and Faber 1934): diary entry for 15 October p. 145.

PLATE 10
Anon.
43″ × 8″
Collection of Irwin Untermyer

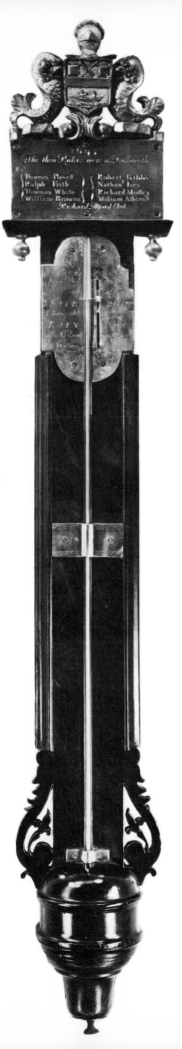

In some cases however a decorative hood is mounted above the plates (Plate 10 and 11), thus elongating the frame. The plates are usually of silvered brass and often decorated with the familiar engraved border (Plates 9 and 10) and acanthus motifs. A protective glazed door at this period is very rare. It will be noticed that scales cover the conventional 3″ and that these are frequently divided in decimals. Weather indications broadly follow the list proposed by John Smith (p. 22) although in all these examples which I have chosen to illustrate weather states are given for both summer and winter. A manual pointer is fixed in a groove on the right hand plate: it is often sickle-shaped as on the barometer of Plate 11.

Each of these three examples deserves a few special comments before leaving: the oak and pine carcase of the barometer of Plate 9, which is at Hampton Court,[1] is veneered with walnut of an attractive pale colour. The edges of its moulded pediment appear to have been shaved off at some juncture but otherwise the case is in good condition. The plates are adjustable and the scale and weather indications accord precisely with the Patrick barometer of Plate 109. The tube and portable cistern are both modern, but this barometer appears to have been fitted with a portable screw from the start and should be dated *c.* 1705.

My study of the barometer of Plate 10 is only second-hand but I am told that its carcase is of oak. Its brass plates are of a typical shape and they carry the weather indications

Summer	Winter
Very Dry	Hard Frost
Settld Fair	Settld Frost
Fair	Frost
Changeable	Uncertain
Rain	Snow
Much Rain	Much Snow
Stormy	Tempest

The modern tube is not fitted with a portable screw in spite of appearances. The original cistern was probably open.

[1] Queen's Gallery.

PLATE 11
Anon.
47″ × 8·2″
Company of Watermen and Lightermen

The barometer of Plates 11 and 12, although it has since been converted, was apparently also originally fitted with an open cistern, a fact which would accord with the date of its acquisition by the Company of Watermen and Lightermen in 1695. Its oak carcase is veneered with well-figured walnut and its carved wooden cresting, which represents a modified version of the Arms of the Company, is gilt. The plates, the commemorative plaque and the clamps which hold the tube in position are all of silver.

Many of the features exemplified by these barometers can be seen in the cistern-tube barometers offered in Patrick's later advertisement (Plate 8 Figs. 6, 8 and 9). All three are closed cistern barometers fitted with a portable screw and all are fitted in frames with moulded edges and heavy turned cistern covers. Only Fig. 8 is explicitly of walnut but this was the commonest wood at this time. Figs. 6 and 9 have pillared hoods with curved pediments and ball finials while Fig. 8 has the curved pediment but no pillars or finials. Patrick, judging both from his extant work and from his advertisements, did not often use the fretted scroll motif. The tube of Fig. 9 is left exposed but is fitted in a groove for partial protection; in Fig. 8 it is protected by a fluted wooden sleeve; in Fig. 6 it is set behind a panel on which a spirit thermometer, which uses the Royal Society scale (p. 11), is mounted. All three have manually adjustable pointers each of which slides in a groove on the right hand register plate: and Figs. 6 and 9 are given the common form of Summer and Winter weather indications, initial letters representing—

Very Dry	Hard Frost
Settled Fair	Settled Frost
Fair	Frost
Changeable	Weather
Rain	Snow
Much Rain	Much Snow
Stormy	Weather

PLATE 12
Detail of Plate 11

Other points worthy of notice are that the register plates of Figs. 6 and 9 are adjustable, as can be seen from the slots in which the screws are fixed, thus allowing them to be set correctly for differing heights above sea level (cf Plate 9), and that in all three illustrations the frame is fixed to the wall by means of a screw which passes through a hole in the hood (cf Plates 9 and 109). This is true too of the barometer of Plate 7 Fig. 3 which, despite its description as a 'Marine barometer', is in fact no more than an earlier version of Plate 8 Fig. 6 although it is of course not fitted with a screw-type cistern.

Returning to Plate 8 Fig. 7 is another closed cistern barometer fitted with a portable screw. Patrick calls it a 'barometer in a pillar'. Students of furniture will recognize this immediately as the type of barometer associated with the name of Quare. With some slight differences it was indeed Quare's favourite design and out of nearly forty cistern-tube barometers carrying Quare's signature which I have studied either in person or in photographs only one is not a pillar barometer (Plate 113): many of these are, like Patrick's pillar barometer, made to be hung on the wall but more than half of them are also fitted with hinged or sprung feet (Plates 116 and 118); Patrick's earlier version of a pillar barometer (Plate 7 Fig. 1) also had feet. Practically all previous writers who have discussed these pillar barometers have treated them as the prevalent type of portable barometer at the beginning of the eighteenth century: they have been induced to do this by the abundance of extant pillar barometers by Quare. Their view is entirely wrong. As I have indicated on p. 32 by no means all of Quare's pillar barometers were fitted with screw-type portable cisterns: nor was Patrick's pillar barometer in his earlier advertisement (Plate 7 Fig. 1). Furthermore countless contemporary barometers framed in conventional wooden cases survive which are fitted with the screw device. All the cistern-tube barometers in Patrick's later advertisement (Plate 8) have screw-type cisterns and the one which he expressly calls 'portable' is not the pillar barometer but Fig. 9.

Other makers sold these pillar barometers during the first quarter of the eighteenth century and many anonymous examples survive: a pendant barometer in a japanned case can be seen in the Victoria and Albert Museum[1] and I have seen several lacquered and walnut examples in private collections in recent years. Plates 110, 116, 118, and 120 show pillar barometers by Patrick and Quare which are described in Part II.

Plate 8 shows that in about 1710 Patrick was also offering four other types of barometer. Some further comments on these are necessary:

[1] Inventory No. W.65-1926.

'A diagonal barometer, the quick-silver moving at bottom 30 inches' (Fig. 11).

This instrument is remarkably similar to the barometer which was demonstrated by the elder Francis Hauksbee to the contributor to the 1704 volume of the *Lexicon Technicum* (Plate 86). Patrick possibly learned or copied the design from Hauksbee or even from the *Lexicon* itself. It is not clear however from Patrick's picture whether his barometer was based on Hauksbee's or Cassini's design (pp. 150–1). The cistern at the base of the vertical column is so similar to Hauksbee's drawing in the *Lexicon Technicum* as to suggest imitation: but the angle of the extended limb is too steep to allow it to act as a cistern gauge and the bulb at the top could conceivably be a cistern as proposed by Cassini. The answer could be either poor draughtsmanship or an attempt on Patrick's part, by the simple device of altering features of Hauksbee's drawing, to avoid the charge of plagiarism. This type of barometer did not at any rate achieve any success and its shortcomings are described on p. 151.

2 The diagonal, or angle, barometer

In his earlier advertisement (Plate 7 Fig. 2) Patrick illustrates a flamboyant version of the common angle barometer. He describes it as

> 'an excellent diagonal barometer . . . a looking glass commodiously plac'd on the same frame, between the barometer and thermometer, whereby gentlemen and ladies at the same time they dress, may accommodate their habit to the weather.—An invention not only curious, but also profitable and pleasant'.[1]

Three points should be noticed about this instrument. Firstly the cistern is not fitted with a screw: secondly the mercury moves over 30″, providing a magnification of ten times the ordinary movement: and thirdly the shape of the case, if the splendid decorative pediment is removed, is very similar to the later version (Plate 8 Fig. 1). It was presumably this later version, or its variant (Plate 8 Fig. 4), which Uffenbach described as a barometer which was 'bent and fastened into a mirror-frame': it cost fifteen guineas. Plate 8 Fig. 3 is a simpler version without mirror or thermometer. It is fair to assume that all three are mounted on walnut frames and all have screw-type cisterns. In Fig. 1 the mercury moves over 24″ (a magnification of eight) and in Figs. 3 and 4 it moves over 30″ but Patrick offered 'what scale you pleas to have it. Either 12 inches or 18 inches or 2 foot or 30 inches if desir'd'. Fig. 1 is of particular interest when compared to the barometer of Plate 108: it suggests that many of the drawings of Plate 8

[1] *A New Improvement of the Quicksilver Barometer, Made by John Patrick, in Ship-Court in the Old Baily, London* (c. 1700).

represent actual items of Patrick's stock.[1]

The angle barometer was expensive and not common at this period. Examples survive however and Edward Saul, writing in about 1710, recommended it as the most suitable type for the 'midland countries' where, owing to the height above sea level, the normal rise and fall could extend over only two inches.[2] It was a difficult instrument to fit into an acceptable design and a purchaser who wanted a barometer of pleasing appearance but modest cost would not choose an angle one. Patrick's idea of constructing his barometer round a mirror, itself an expensive article, and placing a thermometer also on the frame was cleverly calculated to attract richer patrons who wanted an instrument of 'figure and distinction' as well as of functional superiority.

Plate 13 illustrates an early angle barometer which is mounted on an oak frame veneered with walnut.[3] It is by an anonymous maker and is not in the healthiest condition, having lost its mirror, cistern covers (which were probably hemispherical), part of the moulded cornice and both barometer and thermometer tubes. There was also once a cover over the extreme tip of the arm of the tube (cf Plate 8 Fig. 4). The casework is however of good quality, with line inlays round the mirror and veneers of attractive colour and figure. The engraving is not exceptional but there is a typical formal acanthus design at the top of the thermometer plate: and the pierced brass clamp which holds the barometer tube to the frame is a pleasant feature (cf Patrick's barometer of Plate 108). The weather indications are engraved vertically on the silvered brass plates and read

Very Dry	Ha Frost
Setld Fair	Setld Frost
Fair	Frost
Change	able
Rain	Snow
Much Rain	Much Snow
Stormy	Weather

No inch digits are engraved but the scale covers the usual 3″ divided in decimals. The manual pointer is of brass and is sickle shaped. The tube is, unusually, bent to the left and the mercury can rise or fall over just under 18″. This barometer originally had a fixed cistern, presumably open and perhaps covered with pigskin, since there is no trace of a screw. It can thus probably be dated c. 1700 or a little earlier. The

---

[1] MacQuoid and Edwards in their *Dictionary of English Furniture* Vol. 1, *s.v.* 'Barometer' Fig. 6 illustrate a much damaged barometer by Patrick of the design of Plate 8 Fig. 4. (Collection of Albert Wade Esq.).
[2] *An Historical and Philosophical Account* p. 51.
[3] Museum of the History of Science, Oxford.

PLATE 13
Anon.
38·4″ × 21·8″
Museum of the History of Science, Oxford

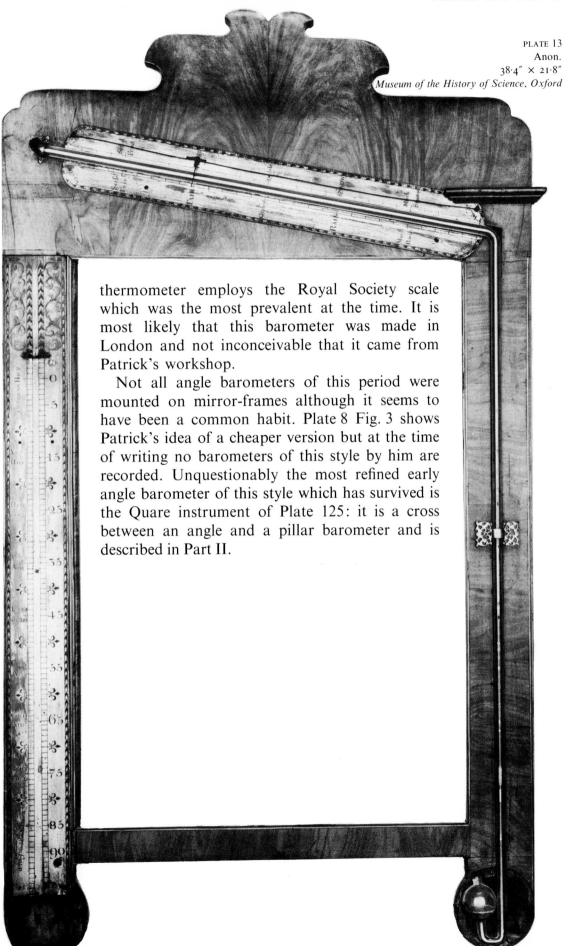

thermometer employs the Royal Society scale which was the most prevalent at the time. It is most likely that this barometer was made in London and not inconceivable that it came from Patrick's workshop.

Not all angle barometers of this period were mounted on mirror-frames although it seems to have been a common habit. Plate 8 Fig. 3 shows Patrick's idea of a cheaper version but at the time of writing no barometers of this style by him are recorded. Unquestionably the most refined early angle barometer of this style which has survived is the Quare instrument of Plate 125: it is a cross between an angle and a pillar barometer and is described in Part II.

Plate 14 shows a strange barometer mounted on a mirror-frame. I am perhaps mistaken in treating it as an angle barometer at all. The maker was more concerned with the design of his mirror-frame than with producing a barometer with an extended scale. The changing angle of the curve furthermore makes an accurate scale impossible to calculate. The tube is portable (the screw can be seen at the bottom on the right) and the silvered brass plates are engraved with a decimal scale and conventional weather indications. The spirit thermometer on the left, whose tube is extended up to the crest, uses a scale akin to Fahrenheit's second proposal of 1717. The frame is an elegant example of wood carving of *c.* 1720: it is now painted white and green.

An early and rare example of an ordinary cistern-tube barometer mounted as part of the decoration of a large giltwood mirror over-mantel can be seen in the Victoria and Albert Museum.[1] Such pieces of furniture demonstrate the curiosity of wealthy patrons about the comparatively new idea of the mercurial weather-glass.

3 '*A ship barometer a foot long*' (Plate 8 Fig. 2).

This was an invention of Robert Hooke but was described by Uffenbach (p. 36) as 'Halley's ship-barometer' because Edmund Halley had both given an account of it in the *Philosophical Transactions*[2] and used it during his southern voyage in 1699–1701. Strictly it is outside the scope of the present study but a brief explanation may be useful. It consisted of a sealed spirit thermometer (in which, as the temperature increases, the liquid expands and rises) and, beside it on the same frame, an air thermometer (in which, as the temperature increases, the air expands and depresses the liquid).[3] In Hooke's later modification of the invention the proposal was to note the station of the two thermometers at various temperatures when a standard mercurial barometer stood at 29·5″: this enabled an approximate scale of variation from the norms to be established. Halley found the device useful on his voyage because, using a fluid considerably more volatile than mercury, it gave early warning of approaching storms.

It was sudden changes of pressure which the mariner liked to be forewarned of, 'so that when Mr. Patrick the Toricellian Operator

[1] Inventory No. W.44–1927.
[2] Vol. 22 (1700–1) p. 791 *et seq.*: also in *Miscellanea Curiosa* (edited by Edmund Halley 1705–7) Vol. 1 p. 250 *et seq.* where it is illustrated in Plate 4 Fig. 1. Hooke's own original account was not published: according to Halley it was given in a lecture on 2 January 1668 and it appears in the Royal Society's *Classified Papers* Vol. 20 No. 48. Middleton who quotes it (*History of the Barometer* p. 375) suggests that Henry Oldenburg, who was in charge of the Society's publications, jealously refused to publish it. Hooke modified his design later in lectures given to the Society on 3 December

1690, and 5 and 12 December 1694. See also R. Waller's edition of the *Posthumous Works of Dr Robert Hooke* (1705) p. 553 *et seq.*
[3] This type of thermometer, in which air was enclosed in the upper sealed part of the tube and acted on the liquid in the lower part which was immersed in a cistern open to the outside air, was much used as a weather-glass before the mercurial barometer was commonly accepted. It was not accurate because there were too many variables: temperature changes affected the liquid as well as the air and the barometric effect also impeded its performance.

PLATE 14
Anon.
61″ × 31″
Mallett and Son (Antiques) *Ltd:*
from the collection
of the Hon. Mrs. Nellie Ionides

thought to improve this machine by substituting mercury instead of a lighter liquor[1] in his new marine barometer (as he called it) he render'd it unfit for the sea'. In his advertisement of *c.* 1700 Patrick had advertised a portable barometer 'with a marine barometer' fitted together in one frame. This refers to Hooke's design of marine barometer which, since this was only a foot or so in height, makes it absurd to suppose that the illustration of Plate 7 Fig. 3 is what it claims to be (see pp. 34–5).

There is in the Museum of the History of Science at Oxford an anonymous marine barometer of the Hooke pattern.[2]

This is probably the instrument described by Uffenbach as 'a newly invented barometer . . . etc.' (p. 36) although a vacuum and not air would have occupied the space above the mercury. There is little doubt that it is the barometer proposed by Guillaume Amontons in 1695.[3] This consisted of a tube of about 3·5 feet[4] in length but instead of being of even bore it was tapered, the thinnest part being at the sealed upper end (Fig. vii). The open bottom end was of only $\frac{1}{12}''$ diameter.[5] Considerable skill was needed to construct a conical tube of these measurements. There was no cistern; the mercury was suspended in the tube by the weight of the air, aided to some extent by the narrowness of the bore and the consequent capillary action. In Fig. vii A is the top sealed end of the tube, B the bottom open end. B–D measures say 28″ and C–A 31″. Owing to the tapering of the tube the same quantity of mercury is required to fill B–D as to fill C–A. Thus, when the atmospheric pressure is sufficient to sustain a 28″ column, the mercury will stand between B and D: when the pressure increases to 31″ it will rise to fill C–A. An exaggerated movement can therefore be achieved, i.e. between the points D and A. Desaguliers[6] suggested a movement of 31″ i.e. a magnification of about ten times the normal movement; but Patrick only claimed to achieve 12″ in his pamphlet of *c.* 1700 and it is unlikely that anyone succeded in drawing a tapered tube of nearly 60″ which Desaguliers' suggestion required.

4 *The 'Pendant barometer'* (Plate 8 Fig. 5).

[1] In, presumably, the air thermometer: Hooke himself (Waller *Posthumous Works of Dr Robert Hooke* p. 555) appears to have considered using mercury in this and positively recommended it in his proposals of 1668.

[2] Ascribed by the display placard to Patrick but this is conjectural.

[3] *Remarques et Expériences Phisiques* (1695) p. 121 *et seq.* In the *Philosophical Transactions* Vol. 31 (1720) p. 116 *et seq.* Edmund Halley made proposals for measuring heights with Patrick's pendant barometer and apparently considered Patrick to be the inventor: but it is likely that he had not read Amontons' book and had fallen for Patrick's self-confident advertising.

[4] Amontons *Remarques et Expériences Phisiques* p. 123: the measurements given by Amontons were in French feet each of which was equivalent to 1.0657 English feet.

[5] Desaguliers *Experimental Philosophy* p. 269: Amontons *Remarques et Expériences Phisiques.* p. 123 gives a diameter 'd'environ une ligne ou une ligne et demy'. Perhaps because he was a Huguenot Desaguliers did not explain that $\frac{1}{12}$ of an English inch was not the exact equivalent of 'une ligne' although the difference is immaterial.

[6] *Experimental Philosophy* pp. 269–70.

Amontons described this instrument as 'un nouveau barometre très simple et portatif à l'usage de la mer'.[1] According to Desaguliers it 'used to be made and sold by Mr. Patrick'[2] and had 'been much used within these 35 years, and especially at sea',[3] since it could be carried easily and inverted at will. The exaggerated movement of the mercury and the portability of this barometer in fact led to a temporary success: but as Desaguliers observed it had two important disadvantages. Firstly the narrow bore led to excessive capillary action which often hindered the mercury from moving at all: secondly the mercury tended to fall out of the tube altogether when it was jolted. The second problem could be solved by stuffing the base of the tube with cotton, but the first was insoluble and the invention was, like so many others, soon added to the list of ingenious but impractical ideas. The *Lexicon Technicum* of 1704 called it 'curious and nice' but Desaguliers said that 'it may do for seamen who are not very nice, but will not stand the examination of a philosopher'.[4] Perhaps the most concise judgement of it was that given by Ephraim Chambers in the first edition of his *Cyclopaedia* (1728) where it is called 'a machine rather pretty, and curious, than useful'.[5] It never achieved success as a domestic instrument and no examples appear to survive in this country.[6]

Wheel barometers do not appear among Patrick's wares. It is one of the strangest facts in the history of the domestic barometer that the wheel design, which accommodated itself most readily to pleasing decoration and proportion and which allowed more minute observations of pressure changes, remained rare in England until the nineteenth century. Expense has already been given as one reason for its neglect in the early eighteenth century. Another was the current opinion that wheel barometers were inaccurate. The contributor to the *Lexicon Technicum* of 1704 said of Hooke's wheel barometer that it did not answer 'fully the designed exactness, because the mercury is apt to stick about the sides of the glass, and would rise and fall in leaps, and all at once; and because also 'tis very difficult to adjust the ball and thread, etc. and that the instrument is very apt to be out of order, etc. 'tis now out of use'. Edward Saul thought that the pulley cord acted like a catgut hygrometer and shrank or expanded according to changes in the humidity of the air, thus moving the index without any change of the level of the mercury.[7] Edmund Halley on the other

FIG. vii. Pendant or Conical Barometer

[1] *Remarques et Expériences Phisiques* p. 121.
[2] *Experimental Philosophy* p. 269.
[3] *Ibid.* p. 270.
[4] *Experimental Philosophy* p. 270.

[5] *s.v.* 'Barometer'.

[6] Middleton *History of the Barometer* p. 119 reports an extant example at the Conservatoire National des Arts et Métiers, Paris, Inventory No. 1580: I have not yet seen it.
[7] Saul *An Historical and Philosophical Account* p. 94.

hand thought that the wheel barometer showed variations with great exactness, criticising it rather because it was 'only proper for a fixt station, nor easy to be removed'.[1] There are therefore very few wheel barometers of this period extant: and since those which survive were made for rich patrons it is no coincidence that they are of fine quality.

The wheel instrument illustrated in Plate 143 was made for William III and can thus be dated before his death in 1702: Tompion was well acquainted with Hooke's designs and made barometers, not necessarily of the wheel type, for him in 1675–6: but apart from the refinement of both case and mechanism he extended Hooke's scale of 200 divisions.[2] The 3″ scale which sufficiently covered alterations of air pressure in England was commonly accepted by 1690 and Tompion very naturally preferred a scale of 300 divisions, each inch being divided into 100 parts.

Also rare in this period were 'stick' barometers with siphon tubes and bulb cisterns. Although they were made in the early years they did not become common until the end of the eighteenth century.[3] An example of an early siphon tube can be seen in Plate 15[4] in the handsome instrument by Robelou dated 1719. The conical drawing of the bulb is characteristic of the period. The main panel has a black painted ground but the moulded edge of the case is red: the decoration is in gold. A recent author said of this casework that its japanning could stylistically be dated as early as 1680 and that it demonstrated the survival force of the popularity of Chinese lacquer furniture at the end of the seventeenth century.[5] The scale is divided into 36 divisions (i.e. 3″ divided into twelfths in accordance with French practice) the odd numbers being painted to the left of the tube and the even numbers to the right. The weather indications are given in Latin and English:—

Magna Siccitas	Great Drought
Tempus Constans	Settled Weather
Tempus Placidum	Fair Weather
Tempus Inconstans	Chang Weather
Pluvia vel Ventus	Rain or Wind
Magna Pluvia	Very Rainy
Procella	Storm

A manual pointer is fitted. The spirit thermometer is unusual in employing a scale very similar to Fahrenheit's first scale.

[1] *Philosophical Transactions* Vol. 31 (1720) p. 116: the paper has already been referred to in connection with Patrick's pendant barometer.
[2] See pp. 8–9.
[3] On the continent they appear to have been the commonest type from earlier in the century (see p. 7 Note 1).
[4] Science Museum, London: Inventory No. 1909–134. Robelou's name suggests that he was an immigrant Frenchman but I have so far been unable to discover more about him.
[5] Hugh Honour *Chinoiserie* (1961) p. 136.

PLATE 15
Isaac Robelou, Londini, 1719
37·5″ × 8·5″
*By courtesy of the Director
of the Science Museum, London*

CHAPTER 4

Period 1720–1790

THE EIGHTEENTH CENTURY was in many European countries a period of increasing prosperity. In England economic expansion took place as the country's maritime power and conquests overseas led to growing international trade. Meanwhile the population of England and Wales expanded from about five and a half million in 1700 to nine million in 1800. Helped by the growing demand for manufactured goods both at home and overseas and by important technological developments, especially in the fast growing metallurgical industries, England underwent the Industrial Revolution. Large new manufacturing towns such as Manchester, Sheffield and Birmingham and ports such as Liverpool grew up, creating new complex markets away from London.

Scientific instrument-makers prospered accordingly. Not only was demand for navigational, astronomical and surveying instruments increasing in England but export markets were also rapidly developing. By the middle of the century the leading instrument-makers' workshops were already well established as industrial concerns: by the end they enjoyed a reputation both in England and overseas which was second to none. To some extent, as Maurice Daumas argues,[1] English and Dutch makers benefited from the self-imposed restrictions which made the equivalent French industry backward and uncompetitive. He compares for instance the industrial workshop of Jesse Ramsden (1730–1800), in which some fifty workmen were employed, with the small establishments of the leading Parisian instrument-makers who employed only five or six. The division of labour and the quantity production of instrument parts, allied to a plentiful supply of more refined metals, enabled the English workshops to produce the large numbers of scientific instruments which were needed while the French makers could not begin to satisfy the demand.

[1] *Les Instruments Scientifiques aux XVIIe et XVIIIe Siècles* (1953) p. 126. The economic and social factors underlying the progress of the European instrument-making industry are admirably summarized in this book.

With the greater level of prosperity came a significant increase in the number of barometers manufactured for domestic use. At the beginning of the century they could be seen 'in most houses of figure and distinction': by the end they were found in many middle-class homes although not until the nineteenth century did the English bourgeoisie enjoy its greatest period of growth.

Although larger numbers of barometers were made there were surprisingly few improvements of design which became commonly applied during this period. The common domestic barometer was almost as rudimentary in 1790 as it had been in 1710: apart from the use of better materials and more advanced techniques of manufacture, the only significant improvements were the normal addition of a vernier to the scale and the rarer use of an ivory float designed to eliminate the inaccuracy caused by the variation of the cistern level.

Throughout the century barometers continued to be made and sold by a wide variety of tradesmen. Clockmakers and spectaclemakers remained important and among the most eminent of the clockmakers were George Graham (1673–1751), who succeeded to Tompion's business in 1713, and John Ellicott (1706–72). It is illustrative of the growing size of the important clockmakers' workshops that both these makers were Fellows of the Royal Society and cannot have possibly 'made' all the clocks and instruments which bear their names.[1] Other well-known clockmakers included John Hallifax (1694–1750) who worked in Barnsley and whose barometer cases were strongly influenced by his trade. Barometers of superb quality also survive by Daniel Delander (1674–1733) and John Whitehurst (1713–88) who was also a provincial clockmaker and who also became a Fellow of the Royal Society. Among spectaclemakers were James Ayscough (fl 1732–63) and his successor Joseph Linnell (b. *c.* 1740–fl 1764). It is unlikely that Ayscough did more than sell barometers, whereas the clockmakers could have produced at least the dials or plates in their own workshops.

It was the scientific instrument-makers who set the pace in the eighteenth century. In the early years their workshops were not very large but they continued, as in the seventeenth century, to make the optical, astronomical and mathematical instruments for which there was a steady demand. Men such as Thomas Wright (b. *c.*1686–fl 1748) and Francis Hauksbee the younger (1687–1763) supplied a fairly wide

(a)

MAKERS

1720–90

---

[1] An article by G. Buggins in *Antiquarian Horology* Vol. 4 (December 1964) p. 275 *et seq.* proves that the firm of Thwaites made clocks for Ellicott's successors in large numbers and suggests that Ellicott may also have employed them.

range of instruments including barometers and other physical instruments; but their establishments were probably akin to the workshops of the leading clockmakers of the late seventeenth century in which perhaps a dozen various workmen were employed. Much work—case-making, scale-dividing, etc.—was contracted out to specialists. Two particularly notable makers of this period were Jonathan Sisson (1690–1747) and Charles Orme (1688–1747). Sisson was born in Lincolnshire but was established in London by 1722 and became well known for his mathematical instruments and barometers. He was especially noted for his division of scales. His early association with George Graham demonstrates again how difficult it is to categorize any eighteenth-century maker in a particular trade. Charles Orme was born in Leicestershire and worked at Ashby de la Zouch. He apparently specialized in barometers and was well known in his day for the distinctive angle instruments which he made.

By the middle of the century the increasing commercial activity of the nation led to something of an explosion of demand for all sorts of mathematical instruments. This was not confined to England; London workshops were exporting instruments in large numbers to all parts of the commercially active world. Several makers advertised their wares in both English and French and such was their reputation that in 1764 William Small, a scientist at the William and Mary College, Williamsburg, Virginia, came to England in order to purchase astronomical instruments. The structure of the industry in fact became industrial because the demand for instruments could not possibly have been met without industrial methods—division of labour, quantity production of standard parts and mechanical methods of production. By about 1760 several English instrument-makers boasted semi-industrialized workshops and thus established themselves as the leading scientific instrument-makers in the world. It was not until the beginning of the nineteenth century that their position was seriously challenged.

Students of furniture will realize that this movement towards industrialization was not confined to instrument-makers. The same change occurred in the workshops of the leading cabinet-makers, many of whom of course supplied the frames for barometers. The best known example of an industrialized furniture workshop, because it is the most extensively documented, is that of George Seddon (1727–1801) who employed some four hundred workmen and had stock valued at £100,000 in 1790.

Among the leading instrument-makers of the latter half of the century were George Adams the elder (b. *c.*1704 –d.1772) and his son

George Adams the younger (1750–95), John Bennett (fl1743–68), John Bird (1709–76), Thomas Heath (fl1714 –d.1773), Benjamin Martin (1714–82), Henry Pyefinch (fl1739–90), Jeremiah Sisson (fl1747–70) the son of Jonathan, and Francis Watkins (*b. c.*1723– d.1784?): but perhaps the best known of the industrial workshops were those belonging to Peter Dollond (1730–1820) who came of Huguenot stock, Jesse Ramsden (1731–1800), Edward Nairne (1726–1806) and Thomas Blunt (fl1760 –d.1822) who were in partnership from 1774, and Edward Troughton (1753–1831) who expanded the firm of J. and E. Troughton after his brother John's death in 1784 until it became one of the leading nineteenth-century producers. The close links between several of these leading makers through apprenticeship, etc., are an interesting feature of the period.

It is notable that every one of the scientific instrument-makers so far mentioned worked in London except the specialist producer of barometers Charles Orme. Cross-country transport was not efficiently developed until the middle of the nineteenth century and London remained the supreme commercial centre to which foreign buyers came. Primitive transport however did not prevent the London makers supplying optical and mathematical instruments to provincial buyers. In 1765 for instance St. John's College Cambridge acquired instruments from Adams, Bennett, Bird, Dollond, Heath, Martin, Nairne, Sisson and Troughton.

Charles Orme and John Hallifax were early and comparatively rare examples of provincial makers but by 1790 there were local makers in many of the more prosperous towns and large industrial centres such as Birmingham, Bristol, Liverpool and Manchester. Many of these were of high calibre; worthy of mention are Joshua Springer of Bristol (fl1759–1808), John Russell of Falkirk, Balthazar Knie of Edinburgh, William Robb of Montrose, Batty Storr of York (1710–93) and the successors of John Whitehurst in Derby, his brother James and nephew John (1761–1834). Except for James Whitehurst and Storr these were all active well into the nineteenth century and much of their best extant work belongs to the next chapter. Several of them probably bought some of their materials in London and John Russell collected many of his both in London and in other towns in England.

To return to the large instrument-makers who dominated the industry in the eighteenth century, some idea of the range of instruments which they sold can be gained from Edward Nairne's trade card.[1] He advertised, in English and French, spectacles, reading,

---

[1] Reproduced in R. T. Gunther's *Early Science in Cambridge* (1937) p. 122: another trade card survives in the Science Museum, London.

burning and magnifying glasses, various telescopes, microscopes and other optical equipment, air pumps and fountains, apparatus for electrical experiments, barometers, thermometers, hygrometers, hydrometers, hydrostatical balances, quadrants, globes, marine compasses, lode-stones, nocturnals, sun-dials, drawing instruments, theodolites, spirit levels, 'and all other sorts of optical, philosophical, and mathematical instruments, of the newest and most approved inventions'; even rules and pencils.

It goes without saying that these large-scale and eminent makers, many of whom were scientists in their own right and Fellows of the Royal Society, did not necessarily produce fine instruments. They produced instruments to meet the requirements of a wide range of customers and many simple barometers constructed of standardized parts survive bearing their signatures. Bernoulli[1] went so far as to say that Peter Dollond's astronomical instruments were not of consistently high quality and that if a first-class instrument signed by Dollond came to hand it was probably not finished in his own workshop but in Ramsden's.

(b) BAROMETERS 1720-90	The straight cistern-tube barometer remained the commonest form of the instrument throughout the century. The scientist and lecturer J.T.Desaguliers, who like Dollond was a Huguenot and who was elected a Fellow of the Royal Society in 1714, said towards the middle of the century that 'the common barometer is the best and most lasting'[2] and dismissed the other established types as unreliable: in his view the wheel instrument was no good because the pulley did not respond evenly to movements of the mercury[3] and the angle instrument was 'more ingenious than happy' because its performance was spoiled by capillary friction; it was also impossible to read because the meniscus was never horizontal.[4] J.H.de Magellan, the Portuguese scientist, who became a Fellow of the Royal Society in 1774 and specialized in scientific instruments, commented in 1779 on wheel and angle barometers for curiosity's sake but clearly accepted the straight-tube instrument as the rule.[5] Finally in 1790 George Adams the younger, one of the leading instrument-makers of the day, wrote that 'various methods have been contrived for enlarging the scale of the barometer; they are, however, all of them replete with error; and

[1] Jean Bernoulli *Letters Astronomiques* (1771) pp. 68-9.
[2] Desaguliers *Experimental Philosophy* (1744) p. 272.
[3] *Ibid.* p. 264
[4] *Ibid.* p. 263.
[5] *Description et Usages des Nouvaux Baromètres* (1779) pp. 151-2.

though, in point of form, some among them may appear more elegant than the plain barometer, yet they cannot be depended upon . . .'[1] He came down solidly in favour of the 'plain barometer'[2] and the rarity of wheel and angle barometers at this date is suggested by the fact that he did not quote a price for them in his price list.

This does not mean that such instruments were not made during the period. As in John Patrick's day leading makers no doubt advertised and even stocked a wide range of instruments and the elder Adams was advertising wheel barometers at £8. 8s. 0d. and angle barometers at £5. 5s. 0d. in 1769.[3] Several other makers advertised them but did not quote prices. Many fine wheel and angle instruments, considerably 'more elegant than the plain barometer', survive. The magnificent wheel instrument by George Graham (Plate 82) which is now at Williamsburg is reminiscent of the earlier masterpieces by Tompion: and other handsome wheel instruments were produced by John Hallifax, John Ellicott (Plate 76), John Whitehurst, George Adams the elder (Plate 59) and many anonymous makers. The work of such makers gives point to J.A.de Luc's remark in 1772 that 'cet instrument est très susceptible de decoration'.[4] Fine angle instruments were made by Edward Scarlett (Plate 134), Charles Orme (Plate 104), Francis Watkins (Plate 152), Jeremiah (or possibly Jonathan) Sisson (Plate 136), Joshua Springer, John Whitehurst (Plate 157) and others; several distinguished angle instruments survive by lesser-known makers including the younger Whitehursts, John Wells of Birmingham, and John Berry of Manchester (fl 1738 –d. 1765). From the quality and rarity of extant wheel and angle barometers it is reasonable to assert that until very late in the century they were generally made for and sold to richer patrons: the elder George Adams' angle barometer in 1769 was, at £5. 5s. 0d., double the price of an ordinary barometer 'with thermometer'.[5] The case of the well-known wheel barometer which was supplied to Nostell Priory by Chippendale in 1769 cost £25.[6]

[1] *A Short Dissertation on the Barometer, Thermometer and other Meteorological Instruments* (1790) p. 6.

[2] *Ibid.*

[3] Catalogue of instruments attached to George Adams' *A Treatise Describing the Construction and Explaining the Use of New Celestial and Terrestrial Globes* (2nd edition 1769).

[4] *Recherches sur les Modifications de l'Atmosphere* (1772) Part 1 p. 21.

[5] *A Treatise Describing Celestial and Terrestrial Globes* (Catalogue of instruments).

[6] The case is a superb example of Chippendale's work: it is veneered with tulipwood, etc., and has gilt mounts. It will be illustrated in an article of mine in the *Journal* of the Furniture History Society 1966: see also R. Edwards and M. Jourdain *Georgian Cabinet-Makers* (1955) Plate 109. Chippendale's bill, dated 20 October 1769, survives at Nostell and reads: 'To a very neat case for a barometer made of fine tulip and other woods and very rich carvd ornaments gilt in burnish gold and plate glass in the doors.' See Part III, entry under Justin Vulliamy, who supplied the mechanism.

The variety and rarity of wheel instruments before the appearance of the 'banjo' shape make it impossible in fact to say that any particular design was in vogue for even brief periods. Wheel instruments of the eighteenth century tended to be characteristic of their makers: in notable support of this hypothesis is the clockmaker John Hallifax who almost invariably framed his barometers in a distinctive clock-like walnut case (Plate 84). Such instruments can only be dated by reference to the maker's dates or, if these are not available, to stylistic features of the case, a notoriously unreliable method. Some idea of the range of wheel barometers made by eminent makers in the period 1720–90 can be gained from Plates 59, 76, 82, 84, 85 and 158, all of which are described in Part II.

The same is to some extent true of angle barometers of the period. In the case of some makers—Charles Orme, Francis Watkins and the Whitehursts are good examples—designs were distinctive and proprietary. But because many angle barometers were literal extensions of the ordinary cistern-tube instrument they tended to have many features in common and they can therefore be treated together when the development of the instrument is being studied. Even Watkins, for all his distinctive ideas, used features of design in both frame-work and engraving which were characteristic of the decades in which he worked. This correlation of design is also exemplified by the Sisson barometer of Plate 136.

The familiar 'banjo' shaped wheel barometer probably originated in France. The design arrived in England towards the end of the eighteenth century but it did not catch the public fancy until after the turn of the century. Some early examples of about 1780–90 survive by English makers but there is no evidence to suggest that the many instruments by Italian makers which are sold today as being '*circa* 1780' were made until at least thirty years later. The 'banjo' instrument belongs to the next chapter. Plate 16 however shows an early example by an indigenous maker. It can be dated *c.* 1780–5. Its pine carcase is veneered with a dark mahogany reminiscent of George Adams' rare wheel instruments (Plate 59) which were made some ten years earlier. The mat brass centre of the dial, silvered chapter ring and pierced steel hands are also similar to Adams' style and are borrowed from clock designs. The lack of ancillary instruments gives the case an austere appearance but the brass bezel was once polished and a finial, now missing, was concession to decoration.

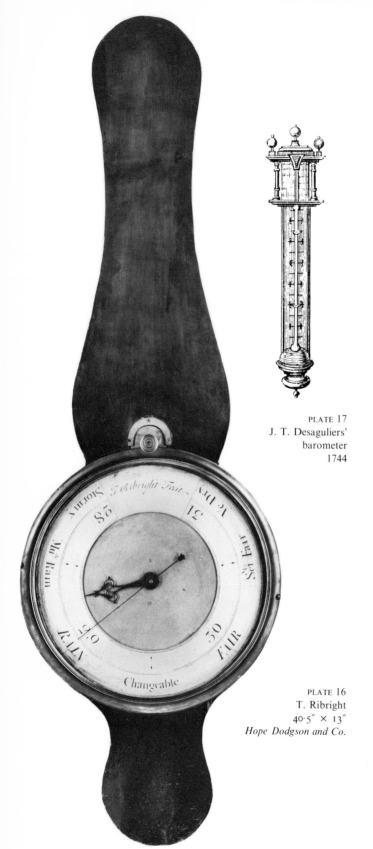

PLATE 17
J. T. Desaguliers'
barometer
1744

PLATE 16
T. Ribright
40·5″ × 13″
Hope Dodgson and Co.

The tube has been renewed but the brass pulleys of the main arbor and recording hand survive.

It had by 1730 become an established rule that the common barometer incorporated a screw beneath the leather-based cistern. As before, the tube was either attached to the frame with brass clamps and left exposed, or enclosed by a panel on the front of which was sometimes fixed a thermometer. The top of the case was variously treated but many extant examples (Plate 68) are still reminiscent of clock designs and the common idea of mounting three ball finials over a pillared hood was still apparently in use until the middle of the century: Desaguliers' illustration of the common barometer (Plate 17) was published in 1744.[1] This also depicts the turned cistern cover which was characteristic of the period (*cf.* Plate 68). The engraving of the register plates, which were usually of brass but occasionally of printed and varnished paper, was often fine and frequently incorporated the still popular acanthus motifs (Plate 70). The wording of the weather indications showed little variation from the previous period, the scale continued to be subdivided into decimals and a simple pointer was employed. In earlier instruments the thermometer which was sometimes, as in Desaguliers' illustration, mounted on the front of the case was still based on the Royal Society scale, i.e. 0°–90° descending, and its scale was frequently printed on paper which was often varnished. By the middle of the century the third Fahrenheit scale had been commonly adopted.

[1] A surviving walnut barometer which conforms closely to Desaguliers' engraving is illustrated in R. W. Symonds' *English Furniture from Charles II to George II* (1929) Fig. 252: another mahogany example by P. Sullivan 'at ye south back of St. Clements Church near Temple Bar London' survives in the National Maritime Museum, Greenwich (in store in 1964). According to the rate books Sullivan was active 1738–43.

After about 1750 the case and the engraving of the common barometer tended to become simpler. This was an inevitable effect of the increasing demand for instruments and the industrialization of instrument-makers' workshops. Standard components were used by several makers: and identical register plates for instance which were apparently engraved by the same craftsmen are found in instruments by different makers. Decorative engraving ceased to be commonly applied although one or two makers, including George Adams and Benjamin Martin, favoured a modicum of embellishment. Plates were still occasionally made of paper and enamelled plates[1] are also found: in neither case could scales be accurately enough drawn to permit the application of a vernier. Frames also assumed a number of fairly standardized designs and were almost invariably made of mahogany. It appears to have been the rule rather than the exception in about 1760 to panel the case, thus enclosing the tube, but not necessarily to mount a thermometer on the front. The familiar broken pediment was used (Plate 19) and cistern covers tended to be turned vertically rather than laterally (Plate 18) although this by no means meant the demise of the hemispherical cover (Plate101). Other features which appeared at this time were the oatbeard hygrometer (Chapter 1, pp. 12–14) which became so common in nineteenth-century wheel instruments, and the vernier (Chapter 1, pp. 9–10) which replaced the simple pointer and from now on became a necessary part of the common barometer. A 'bayonet' tube (Fig. viii) was also occasionally used. By this is meant an ordinary straight tube which was crimped below the register plates: in this way the lower part of the tube could be concealed behind a panel or brass plate on which a thermometer was frequently mounted (Plates 18, 101, 153). The barometer advertised by John Gilbert (fl1726–63) in his trade card (Plate 19) displays several of these features.

[1] For example on an open cistern barometer framed in an attractive mahogany case of 'Chinese Chippendale' style in the Victoria and Albert Museum, Inventory No. 363–1907 (in store 1963).

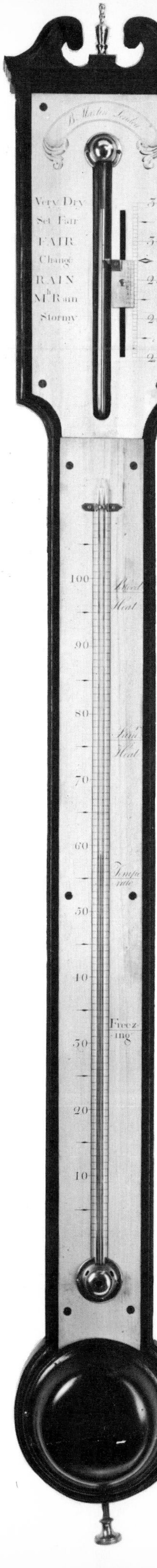

PLATE 18
B. Martin, London
38·2″ × 5·2″
Collection of
E. H. Goodison

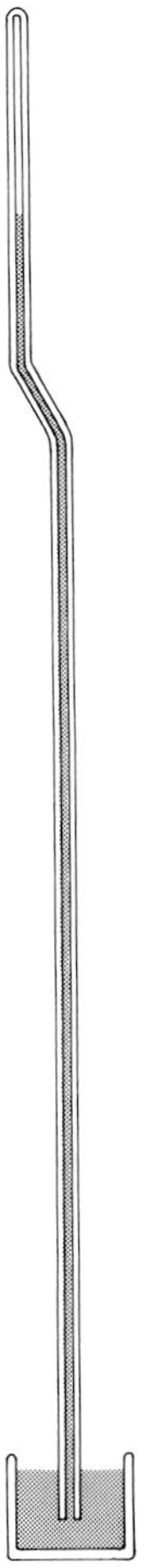

FIG. viii.
Bayonet
or crimped tube

John Gilbert

at the Mariner, in Postern Row, Tower Hill,

London.

Makes & Sells Wholesale and Retail,
All Sorts of Mathematical, Optical & Philosophical Instruments Viz.
Hadley's Sextants & Octants, in Wood and Brass, Davis's
Quadrants, Azimuth Steerage, Amplitude & common,
Compasses, Gunter Scales, Sliding D.º Reflecting Tellescopes
of various Sizes, Refracting D.º for Day & Night, Theodo-
lites, Circumferenters, Plain Tables, Perambulators, or Mea-
suring Wheels, Pentographas for copying Drawings, Parallel
Rulers, Cases of Drawing & Surveying Instruments, Universal
& Horizontal Dials, Globes of all Sizes, Spectacles, Concave, and
Convex Mirrours, Opera Glasses, Reading & Burning Glasses, Perspective Machines Double or Single, Electrical Machines, Barrell &
Hand, Air Pumps, Microscopes, Camera-Obscura's, Prisms, Barometers, Hygrometers, Hydrometers, Farenheits Thermometers, D.º
for Distillery, Brewery & Botany, Gauging Instruments, Rules & Scales,
of all Sorts in Wood, Brass & Ivory, with Various other Instruments not
mentioned. Books and Charts of Navigation.
N.B. Walking Canes Sold and Mounted, in the Neatest Manner.

The scroll pediment (Plate 18) became as familiar as the broken pediment and the simple rounded top (Plate 20) was also common by the third quarter of the century. All three styles survived strongly in the nineteenth century when they continued in use on both straight-tube and wheel instruments. Plates 18 and 20 are typical popular barometers sold by leading workshops in the decade c. 1770–80 and for a description of them the reader should refer to pp. 116 and 165.

Another form of case which became popular in about 1775 was the bow-fronted variety (Plate 21). The date, like so many, is necessarily approximate.

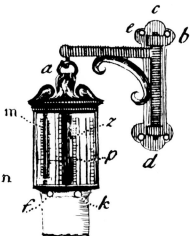

PLATE 22
J. H. de Magellan's
barometer
1779

There are however many bow-fronted instruments extant which can confidently be dated c. 1780–90. J. H. de Magellan[1] furthermore illustrated a barometer, or rather the top of one (Plate 22), which had a bow front and it is reasonable to assume that the design must have been current for some years before 1779 when he published his book. The tube was concealed in this design, as in Plate 21, behind a convex panel of polished wood, usually mahogany of the lighter and highly grained type. Plate 21 also exemplifies other typical features of

[1] *Description et Usages des Nouvaux Baromètres* (1779) Plate 4. Fig. 47.

Opposite PLATE 19
John Gilbert's trade card
Heal Collection:
by courtesy of the
Trustees of the British Museum
PLATE 20
Geo Adams, Fleet Street, London
36·4″ × 4·4″
Author's collection

PLATE 21
Stott, Dumfries
37·7″ × 5·4″
Collection of
Mrs Owen Hugh Smith

this design: the cistern cover is approximately square with bevelled edges which are inlaid with ebony and it is decorated with an urn in relief. The top is squared and moulded although some examples, as in Magellan's illustration, often carry a scroll pediment. A convex glass is set in front of the register plates necessitating a thumb screw, which was usually set below the plates, to operate the vernier. This took the form more often than not of a detachable key or ivory knob which was also used for adjusting the cistern screw. A thermometer was set sometimes on the left register plate, sometimes on the front of the case in a glazed case of its own. An unusual feature of the example of Plate 21 is its concertina cistern (Plate 24).

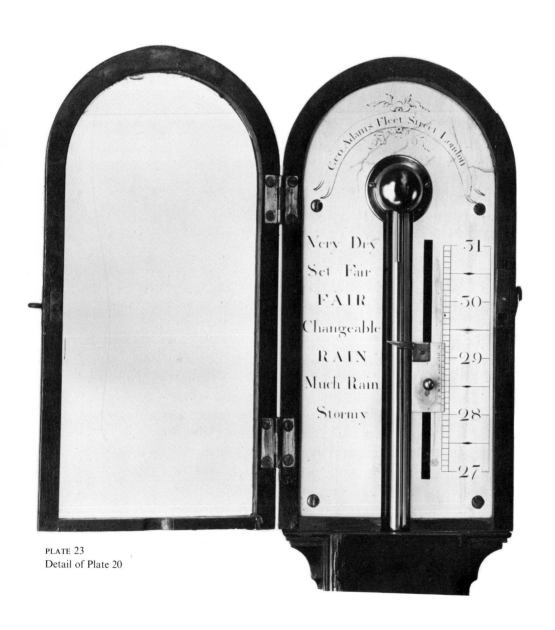

PLATE 23
Detail of Plate 20

PLATE 24
Concertina cistern of Plate 21

These brief descriptions of prevalent types of common barometer necessarily omit many details. Furthermore many barometers were made during this period, and indeed every period, which cannot readily be categorized. Several examples are illustrated in Part II and should be studied (Plates 62, 63, 65, 68, 69, 71, 88, 98, 101, 112, 153). Some of them reflect the excellence of eighteenth-century cabinet-making.

From the foregoing descriptions it is apparent that the domestic barometer of 1790 showed little advance over its counterpart of 1710. There were however a few significant improvements during the century. The most important of these was the general improvement of materials. Desaguliers had complained more than once in 1744 that the rough surface of the inner walls of the tube hindered the movement of the mercury.[1] The glass of 1790 was of better quality and tubes were of more even bore. Soda glass, i.e. glass compounded of sand and soda ash, which had been in general use in England from the sixteenth century, was commonly replaced by the stronger and purer lead glass (sand, potash and lead oxide) by about 1750. The mercury also was generally prepared with more care. Charles Orme appears to have been the first English maker to boil mercury in order to rid it of

[1] *Experimental Philosophy* pp. 263 and 274.

impurities and air bubbles.[1] By the middle of the century this was common but by no means universal practice. In 1794 the younger Adams, taking a leaf out of de Luc's work in 1772,[2] was recommending the boiling of the mercury as a matter of course. 'Choose a tube', he said, 'of not less than three feet long with a bore about three or four twentieths of an inch in diameter, but not more; and that it may be sufficiently strong, it should be nearly as thick on all sides as the diameter of the bore'. He also noted for the sake of the novice that when mercury boils 'its parts strike against each other, and against the sides of the tube with such violence, that a person unacquainted with the operation naturally apprehends the destruction of his tube'.[3] Instrument-makers in fact took a great deal more trouble in the construction of barometers towards the end of the century. George Adams the elder's equipment for filling a barometer tube[4] is a significant advance over John Smith's primitive methods: and whereas in 1710 it was wellnigh impossible to make two instruments of comparable performance a number of leading workshops in 1790 could supply barometers whose variations tallied sufficiently to satisfy at least some contemporary scientists.

Another improvement was the vernier which enabled readings to be taken to ·01″. In spite of its age this scale was not apparently applied to barometers until the middle of the eighteenth century, perhaps because it was recognized that until then the performance of the instrument was not sufficiently nice to justify it. By 1744 Desaguliers could assume its presence[5] although a vernier is not in evidence on the instrument which he illustrates (Plate 17). One incidental mystery, noted by Dr. Middleton,[6] is that the application of a vernier is not mentioned by J. A. de Luc in his extensive account of the development of the barometer in *Recherches sur les Modifications de l'Atmosphere* (1772). This may have been because de Luc[7] considered that he could observe readings by eye to an accuracy of almost $\frac{1}{32}$ of a line (i.e. 0·033″) and that the capillary adhesion of the mercury to the tube rendered any attempt at more precise subdivision ineffectual. Anyway by about 1760 the vernier was a common feature of domestic barometers although it could not be applied to instruments whose scales

[1] He also distilled it first. His innovation was reported by Henry Beighton in a paper submitted to the Royal Society in 1738 entitled *The Imperfections of the common Barometers, and the Improvement made in them, by Mr. Cha. Orme . . .* (*Philosophical Transactions* Vol. 40 p. 248 *et seq.*). See p. 173 *et seq.* For an account of the previous European development of this practice see Middleton *History of the Barometer* p. 243 *et seq.*
[2] *Recherches sur les modifications de l'Atmosphere* (1772) referred to by George Adams *Lectures on Natural and Experimental Philosophy* (1794)

p. 480: de Luc mentions boiling in Part 3 p. 24.
[3] *Natural and Experimental Philosophy* pp.480–1. Adams did not comment in these lectures, probably through ignorance, on the considerable danger to health involved in the operation. Mercury exudes toxic fumes at high temperatures.
[4] George III Collection, Science Museum, London.
[5] *Experimental Philosophy* Vol. 2 (1744) p. 272.
[6] *History of the Barometer* p. 197.
[7] *Recherches sur les Modifications de l'Atmosphere* Part 3 p. 21.

were printed on paper or painted on enamel. The division also of engraved scales was in general more accurately performed in 1800 than at the beginning of the century. A comparison of Quare's rather roughly engraved decimal divisions with Ramsden's work is sufficient testimony of this.

The old open glass cistern survived but with increasing rarity: a late example, covered with skin to exclude dirt, can be seen in the angle barometer by Finney of Liverpool in the Science Museum, London (Plate 25).[1] Open wooden cisterns by eighteenth-century makers also survive.[2] Some makers made closed cisterns of oak, usually in the form of a square box and without the portable screw because oak was too

[1] Inventory No. 1927–1911. The mahogany case is architectural in conception and the 3″ scale is divided in twentieths: the mercury moves over 18″, giving a magnification of 6 times.

[2] e.g. Victoria and Albert Museum, Inventory

No. 363–1907: the cistern is made of fruitwood. Another example signed by Deacon with an oak cistern but also with enamelled plates and framed in a simple sabicu wood case was sold at Sotheby's 31 May 1963 (Collection of the late the Hon. Mrs Nellie Ionides).

porous to contain the mercury when it was compressed. Charles Orme used cisterns of this shape, some of oak and some of boxwood (Plate 26). Boxwood was by far the commonest material used for the now common leather-based cisterns of the portable type (Plate 27): but some of the fine grained fruitwoods and even mahogany were useful substitutes, the disadvantage of mahogany being that it tended to split with age. A frequent variant was the concertina cistern in which instead of a leather base a leather sleeve was cemented between the top and bottom halves of the cistern (Plate 28). Cisterns are also found which are oval in section, a shape sometimes dictated by the design of the case. The use of a leather bag cemented to the tube and enclosed in a cylindrical box also persisted, especially it seems in Scotland.

Finally several attempts were made during the period to eliminate the cistern error and to 'zero' the scale. Most of these do not concern this study because they were never incorporated in domestic instruments; but two deserve mention. The problem has been stated already (p. 2): if the mercury rises in the tube it must fall in the cistern but unless the cistern level is constant the correct barometric height cannot be registered because the plates, which are engraved with the inches 28″–31″, are fixed. Originally the only recognized method of surmounting this problem had been to make the diameter of the cistern so large in relation to the diameter of the tube that movements of the cistern

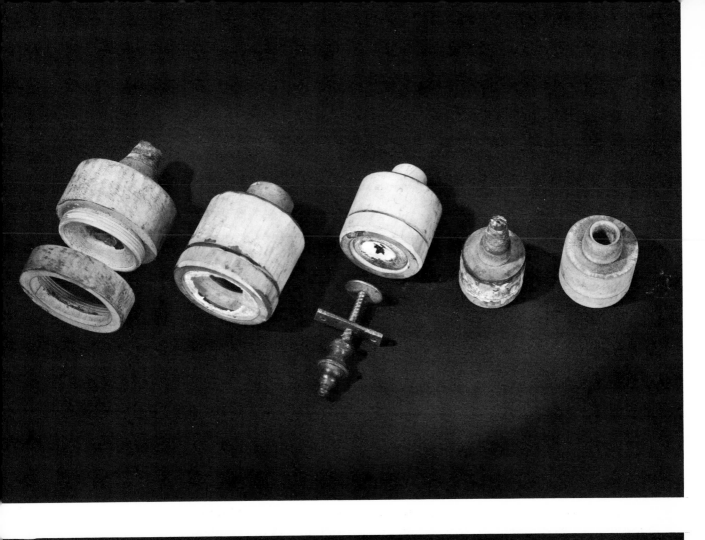

level were negligible. At the beginning of the eighteenth century for instance a drop of ·01″ in the cistern level when the mercury rose 1″ in the tube (i.e. the cistern area being 100 times the area of the tube) would have been thought unimportant. A wide cistern was still considered a serviceable answer in about 1760. Examples survive of instruments with exceptionally wide open cisterns by Ramsden, Sisson and Bennett.[1] In all three the tube is widened to a bulb at the top in order to dilute the effects of any air which may in time infiltrate and this bulb is protected by a brass cap attached to the plates.[2] The Sisson instrument (Plate 135) is fitted with a small microscope through which the mercury level is observed and an adjustable ivory scale at the base which shows the necessary correction to be made for the variation of the cistern level. These three instruments were clearly made for the use of meteorologists and not for ordinary domestic use but I have also seen an open cistern of 2·5″ diameter in a domestic angle barometer by Joshua Springer: the distinction between domestic and scientific barometers at this period was not at all finely drawn.

I think the only method which was employed at all commonly in domestic instruments was the incorporation of an ivory float in the cistern. The invention of this device has been attributed to Ramsden,[3] but George Adams the younger insists in his description that it was invented by his father.[4] It was only used in barometers 'of the best kind'.[5] A hole was made in the top of the wooden cistern: in this was screwed an ivory gauge (Plate 29) which consisted of a small cylinder cut open at the front and marked with an incision. Through this cylinder passed an ivory stem which was also marked with an incision and at the bottom of which was an ivory float. The float rested on the surface of the mercury and, when a reading was required, the mercury was screwed up until the incision on the stem of the float coincided with the incision on the cylinder. At this point the level of the mercury stood at the 'neutral' point, i.e. the point from which the inch measurements on the register plates were calculated. Thus a correct reading could be taken.

In Adams' description the upper part of the device is protected by a small tube of glass. It was unscrewed from the hole for transportation and its place taken by an ivory plug which, while the barometer was in use, passed its time as a finial 'between the scroles' of the pediment. In some extant examples the float itself can be screwed upwards to

[1] The first two in the Science Museum, London (Inventory Nos. 1893–143 and 1927–1910), the third in the Whipple Science Museum, Cambridge (Inventory No. 1090).
[2] This use of a bulb was proposed by Hooke in his modified design for a wheel barometer (p. 9).
[3] By Daumas in *Les Instruments Scientifiques* p. 274 among others.
[4] *A Short Dissertation* p. 8.
[5] *Ibid.*

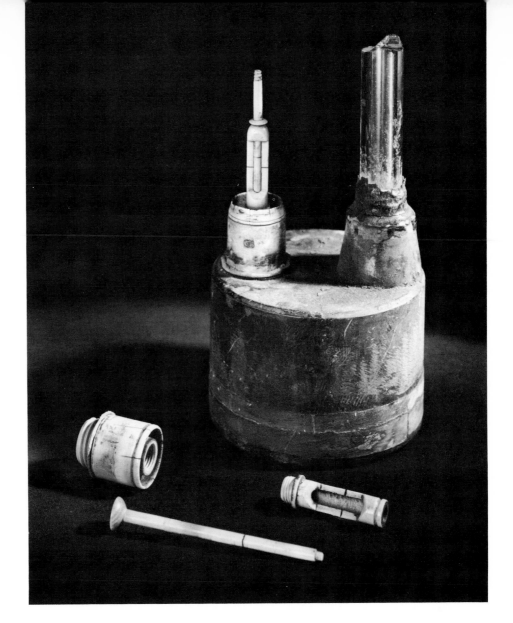

PLATE 29
Leather-based cistern
with ivory float

seal the hole in the cistern. This device, although rare in common barometers, is most frequently found in instruments incorporating an 'urn' type of cistern cover. It will be noticed that the tube is usually displaced from the centre of the cistern. Often the complete device has been discarded by a later repairer as being, presumably, inelegant and an ordinary cistern has been substituted: but traces of the hole in the cistern cover can often be detected.

The siphon tube was also used in domestic barometers, mainly in wheel instruments but also occasionally in simple instruments consisting of a tube attached to a board: but this type of tube did not really come into its own until the nineteenth century although one North country meteorologist in 1793 considered it 'usual'.[1]

[1] John Dalton *Meteorological Observations and Essays* (1793) p.2.

Perhaps a good way of closing this necessarily inadequate description of domestic barometers during the period is to summarize George Adams the younger's own description which was written in 1790.[1] He describes two instruments, the 'Common Portable Barometer' and the 'Best Portable Barometer'. The common instrument, which is described as answering 'for general and domestic observation', has a wooden cistern with a leather base which is covered with a 'neat mahogany cover, or box'. A screw of course is fitted. The bore of the tube can be assumed to have been between 0·15″ and 0·2″ (see p. 62). At the top of the mahogany frame which, judging from his price list, did not enclose the tube are the register plates which are of silvered brass. The right-hand plate is engraved with inches divided into decimals and is slit to take the vernier scale and pointer. The left-hand plate is engraved with the words

>Fair
>Changeable
>Rain

Although contemporary makers commonly employed this simple wording they also used the fuller wording quoted by J. H. de Magellan in 1779:

31	very dry
$30\frac{1}{2}$	set fair
30	fair
$29\frac{1}{2}$	change
29	rain
$28\frac{1}{2}$	much rain
28	stormy.[2]

This shows little variation from John Smith's version of 1688 (p. 22). The 'Best Portable' barometer has the same type of cistern but is fitted with the ivory float discussed above. The scale and weather indications are engraved in the same way, but the vernier has attached to it two pointers, one placed in front of the tube and the other behind it. This provided a more exact method of detecting the height of the mercury meniscus by obviating the effect of parallax.[3] On the left-hand plate is mounted a thermometer with a movable pointer and there is often also a scale affixed for correcting the reading of the barometer to allow for the thermal expansion of the mercury. Both pointers are operated by keys since a piece of glass is set in front of the plates to prevent the corrosion of the silvering.

For the common barometer Adams charged £2. 2s. 0d. His father had charged the same in 1769 when Henry Pyefinch was charging only

---

[1] *A Short Dissertation* p. 12 *et seq.*
[2] *Description et Usages des Nouvaux Baromètres* (1779) p. 140.

[3] *A Short Dissertation* p. 11 where the invention of this improvement is attributed to Ramsden.

£1. 11s. 6d. Both the Adams' price lists show that, as can be observed in a well-stocked antique dealer's show-rooms today, makers of their day did not conform to the simple dichotomy between the 'common' and the 'best'. Barometers incorporated diverse features, some of which the younger Adams attributed only to the 'best' instruments, according to the maker's whim. He himself indeed advertised

A plain portable barometer	£2.	2s.	0d.
Ditto with a thermometer	£3.	3s.	0d.
A plain barometer, covered frame and glass door	£2.	12s.	6d.
Ditto with a thermometer	£3.	13s.	6d.
A barometer with a long cylindric thermometer	£4.	4s.	0d.[1]

The importance of Adams' little treatise however lies in his differentiation between the common and the best instruments. The first, which is sufficient for domestic use and is therefore more properly the subject of the present study, is described as 'not sufficiently accurate for philosophical purposes'. This is significant if only because instruments which were considerably less accurate were being used for philosophical purposes only seventy years before. In other words from the latter half of the eighteenth century, stimulated no doubt by the requirements of meteorologists, makers began to differentiate between the two types of instrument: in the nineteenth century further steps were taken to make the barometer fit for use in scientific studies by the incorporation of devices and materials which were not used at all in domestic instruments. The gap never closed again, and the effects on the industry were far-reaching.

Adams' strictures on the inferior quality of many of the instruments sold in his day are reminiscent of Edward Saul's complaints at the beginning of the century. He criticized the poorly graduated and misplaced scales of some retailers' instruments, and the inadequate bore of their tubes which made the instruments behave like thermometers.

As a final postscript to this chapter I hope I have not given the impression that because it lacked innovation the eighteenth-century barometer is not worthy of attention. Far from it. Like all types of English furniture the domestic barometer achieved its zenith during this century and what it lacked in scientific accuracy it more than made up in exterior design. There are, as many of the illustrations of this book prove, very many superbly handsome old English barometers extant, the great majority of which date from this period of eighty years when the great cabinet-makers were active: and many of them

[1] *A Short Dissertation*, attached price list.

reflect the pleasing styles which have caused eighteenth-century English furniture to be so coveted. The common instruments discussed in this chapter are not truly representative of a period when an astonishing variety of individual pieces was produced.

CHAPTER 5

Period 1790–1860

DURING the nineteenth century the industrial movement begun in the eighteenth century gathered momentum. National wealth increased at a startling pace: between 1800 and 1850 exports rose six times in value and the population of the country roundly doubled. This growth affected not only London but also the large industrial towns in the provinces, especially in the midlands and north where the engineering and textile industries were fast expanding. Owing to the increasing international trade many ports—some of which, such as those in East Anglia, have long since lost their importance—prospered and grew into complex markets.

Hand in hand with the growth of national wealth and population went the increasing distribution of wealth. The growing middle classes took an interest in furnishing their homes comfortably. The expansion of the furniture industry was therefore assured: and the vast majority of domestic mercurial barometers which survive date from this period. They survive furthermore in very large numbers.

Almost any product suffers a deterioration of quality when it is produced for a mass market and the barometer was no exception. It is perhaps a sweeping judgement but it is true to say that as the nineteenth century wore on the quality of domestic barometers declined: and the dearth of inventiveness led to stereotyped designs in which only superficial variations were made. This was aggravated by the further standardization of component parts, an industrial development which had its parallel in the clockmaking industry.

Just as the eighteenth century was the period of the scientific instru-ment-makers the nineteenth century was dominated by the opticians and retailers of glass wares. It is not possible to name any hard and fast date when the predominance of one gave way to the other. It was a gradual process and it occurred for two reasons. Firstly the country-wide growth of demand led retailers in smaller towns to stock baro-meters which were usually constructed in the larger centres: and secondly, as I have said in the previous chapter, from the late eight-eenth century the domestic and the scientific barometer ceased to develop along the same lines. It might almost be said that the domestic barometer ceased to develop at all. Thus the scientific instrument-makers tended more and more to produce barometers exclusively for meteorological work or for studies of altitude which required an ever increasing standard of accuracy: they also, at the beginning of the century anyway, produced marine instruments and in this field too a standard of efficiency came to be required which emphasized differ-ences of design between domestic and other instruments. Because of this dichotomy the names of many of the big firms of instrument-makers which survived from the end of the previous century are not found on as many domestic instruments as one would otherwise expect. Many of them were however active until after 1850 and good domestic barometers survive, for instance, by Matthew Berge (fl 1802 – d. 1819), who succeeded to Jesse Ramsden's business in Piccadilly, Thomas Jones (1775–1852) who was originally one of Ramsden's workmen and who was well known for his marine and mountain barometers, and Dudley Adams (b. *c.* 1760 – d. 1826), who carried on the family business in Fleet Street until at least 1821. Other notable firms which continued to make barometers included Nairne and Blunt, W. and S.Jones, Dollond and J. and E.Troughton; and a large number of domestic instruments survive by Watkins and Hill (fl1819–56), the eventual successors of Francis Watkins.

There were many makers at the beginning of the century who appear to have been specialists in barometers. A notable example was Balthazar Knie (fl 1743 – d. 1817) who was mentioned in the previous chapter. A German by birth, Knie was originally a glass-blower and became the most renowned barometer maker in Edinburgh. Another Scottish specialist was the optician Alexander Adie (1774–1858) who became an eminent maker of both domestic and marine barometers, although his interest probably swayed towards the latter since he did a flourishing business with the navy. Adie was the inventor of the sympiesometer, a barometer in which the use of oil and hydrogen gas instead of mercury enabled the size to be greatly reduced.[1] Possibly his uncle John Miller (fl 1774 –d. 1825), who was also an optician and with whom he was in partnership for a time, specialized in barometers: interesting examples of his work survive.

Many clockmakers both in London and in the provinces continued to sell domestic barometers which fitted in well with their main trade. Particularly notable was John Russell of Falkirk (b. c.1745 –d.1817) whose distinctive wheel barometers were of a high degree of workmanship: other watch and clockmakers who sold unusually good barometers include William Robb of Montrose (fl1776–1816), who has been mentioned in the previous chapter, Richard Northen of Hull (fl1790–1841), and S.J.M. French (fl1810–44) who appears to have had Spanish connexions and who worked near the Royal Exchange. The young John Whitehurst carried on the family business in Derby until his death in 1834.

It was probably in 1810–20 that opticians and mirror and hardware retailers assumed a growing importance. It was during this decade that the familiar 'banjo' wheel barometer and the common nineteenth-century bulb-cistern 'stick' barometer began to dominate the field. The acceptance of these standardized designs was a reflection of the techniques of mass production which were applied to barometers. The leading makers began to produce them in larger numbers and to sell them wholesale to retailers—opticians, dealers in looking-glasses and picture frames, printsellers, artificial flower-makers, carvers and gilders—whose names appear on the instruments. This of course accounts for the almost identical instruments which are frequently discovered to be signed by different 'makers' and for the fact that on many instruments the engraving of the 'maker's' signature is inferior to the engraving of the scales.

This development was not confined to London. It is true that at any rate in the remoter areas of England the craft system survived well into and indeed beyond the nineteenth century: so incidentally did the popularity of weather lore and the use of primitive water weather-glasses. But in the larger industrial towns many retailers are found to have sold similar instruments and in many smaller towns opticians, hardware and furniture dealers sold barometers which were most unlikely to have been made on the spot.

Among London opticians who sold barometers at this period were Robert Bancks (fl1796–1834) who was optician to George IV both as Prince of Wales and King, James Smith (fl1817–28), William Harris (fl1799–1848), Thomas Rubergall (fl1802–54) and many others.

[1] Made principally for marine use, this instrument is outside the scope of the present study.

Provincial opticians included Adie and Miller, both of Edinburgh and already mentioned, Jacob Abraham of Bath (fl1805–41) who held appointments to the Dukes of Gloucester and Wellington, Philip Carpenter (fl1817–37) who opened a shop in London in 1830, and T. Saunders of Dublin (fl1794–1819). Some of these makers sold a wide variety of optical and mathematical instruments.

It is impossible to discuss the general hardware and other dealers without discussing the other well-known feature of the barometer industry in the nineteenth century, namely the huge influx of Italian 'makers'. Towards the end of the eighteenth century several Italian emigrants were established in Holland and France, working for instance as chimney-sweeps, plasterers and glass-blowers. It was clearly the last of these industries which led so many of them into the manufacture and sale of barometers. Among Italians in Holland at this time who are known only from their signatures on barometers Daumas lists Bianchi, Butti, Caminada, Pagani, Primavesi, Reballio, Sala and Taroni;[1] and among many other names which I have recorded from instruments of Dutch origin are Arzoni and Casartelli. All these names appear subsequently on English barometers, albeit with slight differences of spelling, and in view of the numerous coincidences it seems fair to assume that members of the Italian families established in Holland moved on to England. A similar movement appears to have occurred through Paris where coincidental names include Cazartelli and Ciceri. G. B. Torre, the original founder of the fine art dealers P. and D. Colnaghi, also came to this country from Paris where he owned a shop and sold prints and scientific instruments including barometers. Torre opened a shop in Market Lane, Pall Mall in 1767 but it is not known whether barometers were sold and it is almost certain that prints soon ousted rival wares. Many other Italian 'merchants' begin to appear in the London commercial directories from 1765 onwards but again they do not appear to have been instrument sellers.

One Italian maker of glass instruments who operated both in London and Paris by 1787 was C. Bettally. He had a shop in Charlotte Street in 1787 and in Oxford Street from 1788 and his trade cards (Plate 30) illustrate barometers in the French taste. Lord Bute bought a very fine barometer and thermometer from him in 1787 (Plate 42). Among other early arrivals who made or sold barometers appear to have been members of the Ronketti, Gatty and Sala families. J. M. Ronketti, who is variously described in the commercial directories as a maker of weather-glasses, artificial flowers and feathers, was

[1] Daumas *Les Instruments Scientifiques* pp. 331–2.

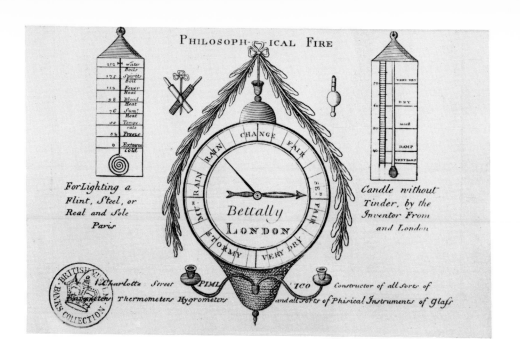

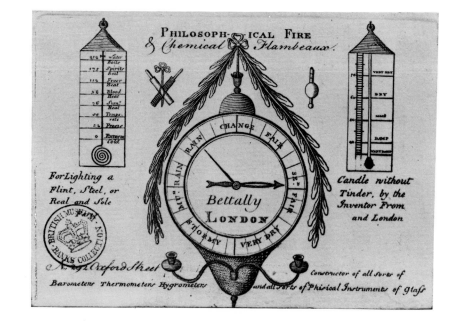

established in Holborn by 1790. He may before this have been in partnership with a Gatty (possibly James) since an early wheel instrument survives signed 'Roncheti and Gatty': but this may well have been a B. Roncheti who can also be dated early. Both Sala and Gatty are selected as early arrivals for stylistic reasons: the directories are regrettably unhelpful about both of them.

Among Italians listed in the London directories in about 1800, all of whom are either described as weather-glass makers or known to have sold them, are the following: F. Anone (1802), P. Barnarda (1803), J. Cetti (1803), Lione Somalvico & Co. (1805), P. L. D. Martinelli & Co. (1799), Dominick Manticha (1805), F. Pastorelli (1805), Charles Pistalla (1805), Stampa and Son (1802), C. Tagliabue (1799) and Tarone & Co. (1802). In the provinces are G. Bianchi of Ipswich (1805), S. Bregazzi & Co. of Derby (1809) and P. A. Tarone of Bristol (1809). Some of these makers may have been working before these dates; and others may have been omitted or hopelessly mis-spelt by the compilers of the directories.[1]

Very few of the early Italian makers are described in the directories as weather-glass or barometer makers. Among the makers mentioned above Barnarda, Manticha, Pastorelli, Pistalla and Ronketti are described as such; but I have already referred to Ronketti's other descriptions and he was no exception. Apart from artificial flower and feather makers other Italians carried on business as printsellers (Anone, Stampa, Martinelli), merchants (Tarone, Torre), looking-glass and picture frame makers (Cetti, Stampa), carvers and gilders (Martinelli) and opticians (Tagliabue).

From this time onwards Italian makers begin to appear thick and fast in the directories although for a time they are still outnumbered by their English rivals. In London in 1817 (the earliest nineteenth-century directory in which trades are classified) there were five barometer makers—J. Corti, Joseph Hicks, F. & J. Pastorelli, Ronketti & Co. and J. Somalvico—four of them Italian: but this is a misleading picture since there were forty-four mathematical instrument-makers and as many opticians, a large number of whose signatures appear on extant barometers: there were also forty looking-glass makers many of whom likewise sold barometers. In 1822 there were five Italian makers in Manchester and in 1828 there were nine Italians in London out of a total of eleven makers (F. Amadio, C. Coleman, J. Corti, della Torre & Barelli, P. & P. Gally, J. Noden, F. Pastorelli, J. Ronketti, C. Tagliabue, J. Tagliabue and another

[1] Early directories do not classify tradesmen by their trades: if his name is mis-spelt the chances of finding a known maker are minimal. I was for instance lucky to notice Manticha in the 1805 Directory: his name was spelt 'Monticha' and entered among names beginning Mo–.

J. Tagliabue). These figures must not be treated with entire confidence since the directories were still not comprehensive, but they give a useful indication of the state of the industry.

By 1840 it is fair to say that Italians dominated the industry. Up and down the country there were Italian opticians, hardware, mirror and picture frame dealers, carvers, gilders, glass-blowers and printsellers who sold barometers in increasing numbers as demand grew. The invasion was extraordinarily widespread and Italian names appeared in small country towns in distant counties as well as in the leading industrial cities. There can have been few comparable industrial movements in history, although the contemporary Italian invasion of the British ice-cream industry is perhaps analogous.

The variety of the wares which some of these 'makers' sold, especially in provincial towns where the demand for barometers could be expected to be small enough to dictate the stocking of other products, can be illustrated by the trade card of a Hull maker, Augustus Maspoli, who in 1837 claimed to be a 'Wholesale and retail manufacturer of looking-glasses, barometers, thermometers, telescopes, spectacles, picture frames, etc. . .' and who also sold clocks, watches, jewellery and musical boxes.[1]

It is almost impossible to say who made the barometers. Some of the Italian tradesmen described in the directories as barometer makers were probably glass-blowers by origin: it is therefore likely that they made the functional parts of the instruments and fitted them into frames supplied by the local cabinet-maker, together with the dials, bezels, hygrometers, levels, etc., all of which were probably supplied by specialists. Finally the 'barometer-maker' either retailed the instrument himself or sold it wholesale to other retailers whose names were duly engraved on the dial or level.

In 1817 there were in Leather Lane one barometer maker (J. Corti who advertised barometers retail, wholesale and 'for exportation'), five looking-glass makers, three of whose names appear on extant barometers, and two cabinet-makers. It was perhaps a microcosm of the industry, although Leather Lane itself cannot really be isolated from the many streets nearby—Brook Street, Charles Street, Cross Street, Warner Street, Eyre Street, Kirby Street, Greville Street, Saffron Hill, Hatton Garden, Turnmill Street, etc.: in this area of Clerkenwell, as the index in Part III of this book demonstrates, there was throughout the nineteenth century an extraordinary concentration of barometer 'makers'.

[1] Noted by E. G. R. Taylor in her *Mathematical Practitioners of Hanoverian England* (manuscript).

At the beginning of the nineteenth century the straight-tube barometers with leather-based cisterns described in the last chapter remained the most popular design. The simple mahogany case with rounded top, the tube either encased or exposed on a grooved frame, remained in vogue and in fact persisted throughout the century. As will be seen it was still commonly realized in solid rosewood, mahogany, or oak cases with glazed and slanted ivory plates at the end of the period under study.

One of the most characteristic designs employed in about 1810 for the cistern-tube instrument was a panelled mahogany frame with a turned cistern cover and scroll pediment. This design admitted of many little variations by way of embellishment; among which can be mentioned specially the application of carved ivory rosettes to the scrolls of the pediment, the use of ivory or wooden inlays on the cistern cover and wooden veneer inlays on the case. A common embellishment was an edging of ebonized veneer, a black border said by some to have been introduced by case-makers after the death of Nelson. A thermometer was commonly applied either on the plates or on the front of the case, and an oatbeard hygrometer was more rarely added above the plates. Charles Hutton, writing before 1795, said that 'the common chamber weatherglass is also usually fitted up in a neat mahogany frame, and other embellishments, to make it an ornamental piece of furniture. It consists of the common tube barometer, with a thermometer by the side of it, and an hygrometer at the top.'[1] His illustration of this instrument is reproduced in Plate 31. In spite of inadequate draughtsmanship and the impression that someone has hit it rather hard on the left side the illustration is instructive. The case is typical with a scroll pediment decorated apparently with ivory rosettes, although the hemispherical cistern cover, judging from extant examples, was not as common at this period as the shallower turned cover (cf Plate 36). The tube appears to be of bayonet form (cf Plate 18) and at the top it is covered with a polished brass cap (cf Plate 71). The plates are presumably of silvered brass and are screwed to the frame. There is a vernier and the weather indications are simple. A thermometer is affixed to the frame, its bulb protected by a pierced and polished brass cover (cf Plates 101, 154). An oatbeard hygrometer is added above the plates.

Instruments of this design survive in reasonable numbers although frequently with a broken instead of a scroll pediment and most usually with a shallower turned cistern cover and no hygrometer.

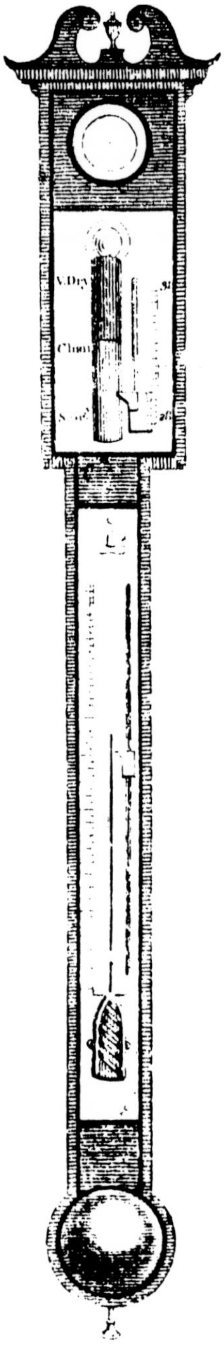

[1] Hutton *Mathematical and Philosophical Dictionary* s.v. 'Barometer'.

(b)
BAROMETERS
1790–1860

PLATE 31
Charles Hutton's barometer 1795

If the common straight tube was encased a glass cover or door was needed in front of the plates. One notable maker who often mounted a hygrometer above the plates was Dudley Adams. Examples are also extant by James Gatty, Charles Lincoln and many others.

Plate 32 shows a typical if undistinguished example by a successful firm of instrument-makers which can be dated c. 1810. The pine carcase is veneered with dark mahogany: apart from a straight-grained border there is no attempt at elaboration of the woodwork and embellishment is confined to the ivory finial. The door is hinged and the vernier is adjusted manually. The plates continue a design favoured for many years (cf Plates 18 and 20). The oatbeard hygrometer is unusually placed on the trunk and is detachable. Cases of this sort, but with the thermometer case (if a thermometer is attached) usually mounted on the front rather than set into the frame, were made until c. 1840.

Bow-fronted cases, which enabled the case-maker to display the lighter and highly-grained mahoganies to good effect, also remained in vogue.[1] Examples survive by Matthew Berge who thus continued a design favoured by his late master Ramsden. Cases of this design were made until late into the century but later examples reflect the ponderous well-being of the Victorian era. An example of c. 1825 by Watkins and Hill with a square moulded top of slight dimensions can be seen in Plate 154. Plate 33 shows one by Rubergall with a scroll pediment. It is very similar, but lacks a thermometer and

[1] The design was also favoured abroad: there is an example with a scroll pediment by Hohnbaum, Hanover, dated 1831 in the National Maritime Museum, Greenwich (Gabb Collection, Catalogue No. 0.12.: in store in 1964).

PLATE 32
Dring and Fage, London
37·8″ × 5·2″
Charles Stewart (Antiques) Ltd.
PLATE 33
Rubergall, London
38·5″ × 5·3″
Charles Stewart (Antiques) Ltd.

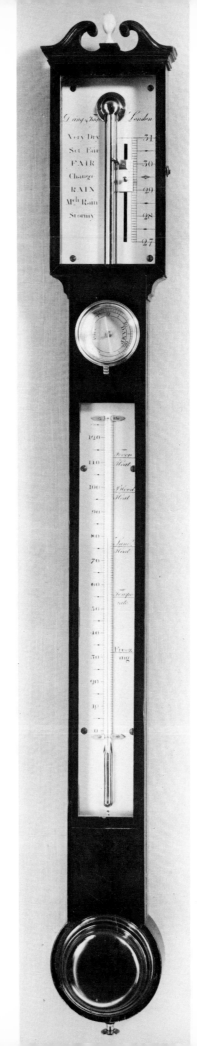

there are slight differences in the execution of the casework: the engraving of the plates is totally different in style. In both examples the key which operates the vernier is also used for adjusting the portable screw.

Fairly early in the century the siphon tube came to be used more frequently in 'stick' and angle barometers. Its appearance coincided with the earliest 'banjo' wheel instruments, which of course also used a siphon tube, and like the 'banjo' design it was popularized by the immigrant glass-blowers from the Continent where it had been common earlier in the century. Tubes of this type, with a bulb-shaped reservoir for the mercury (Plate 15), had been used in occasional 'stick' instruments from the beginning of the eighteenth century in England but were not popular because they ignored the problem of the variation of the cistern level and were not readily portable. In the nineteenth century domestic barometers came to be made in greater numbers than ever before and cheapness became a more necessary quality than accuracy or portability. The siphon tube was cheaper because the small cistern was an integral part of the tube and there was no device to make the instrument portable.

At first the reservoir for the mercury was pear-shaped and pierced in the side to admit the air: this is clearly the type John Dalton was referring to when he described the 'usual' siphon tube as having a 'pretty capacious' bulb which was pierced and had no neck.[1] Later it

PLATE 34
Bulb cisterns

[1] *Meteorological Observations* p. 2.

became more rounded and was left open at the top: later still a neck was added and by about 1860 an oval reservoir with a neck was favoured. These various bulb cisterns are illustrated in chronological order in Plate 34.

The earliest bulb-cistern barometers of distinctive design are probably the mahogany-framed instruments of which one is illustrated in Plate 96. The cistern cover is a rectangular box and opens on a hinge. The tube, which has a pierced pear-shaped mercury reservoir, is exposed and the paper plates, which are printed with the weather indications and some formal decoration, are faced for protection with glass and framed between pillars, the whole effect being somewhat Chinese. There were originally three finials but these are missing. Better examples of this type, with decorative carving on the hood and cistern cover, are to be found. Cistern covers are often oval but on the whole the basic design does not vary. Printed paper plates incidentally continued to be used spasmodically and were often finely executed: the barometer maker's name was subsequently either printed or written on. Instruments fitted with paper plates are even less accurate than domestic instruments with brass or ivory scales because the scale is not usually divided any more minutely and no vernier is attached.

By about 1820 (no date can be more than approximate) domestic 'stick' barometers with siphon tubes were common. Plate 35 illustrates a 'stick' barometer of the design which, with variations, came into vogue c.1800–10 after the influx of Italian makers. It combined the attractions of a reasonable price and a modest elegance which brought distinction to the domestic porch. The trunk of the frame is typically veneered with mahogany in herring-bone pattern: the square hinged cistern cover is reminiscent of the Manticha instrument of Plate 96 but its inlays give it more distinction. The survival of the earlier hemispherical cistern cover on a frame of this type is demonstrated by the Gatty barometer of Plate 78. Other typical features demonstrated by Plate 35 are the exposure of the tube on the trunk in spite of the glazed door which protects the silvered plates, the broken classical pediment, the brass finial (which is not original), and the manual vernier. The tube would originally have been of the bulb-cistern type with a pierced pear-shaped bulb.

PLATE 35
T. Roncheti, Bristol
38″ × 5·5″
Charles Stewart (Antiques) Ltd.

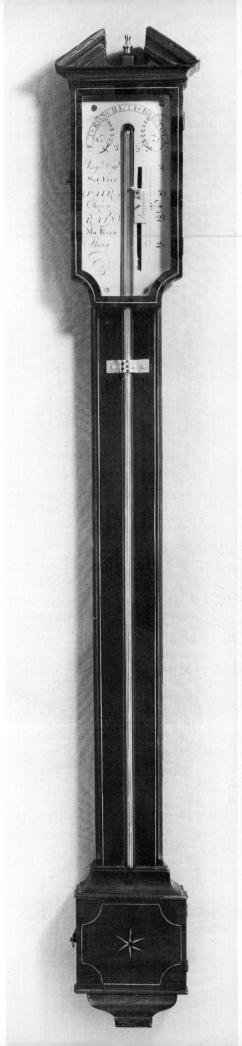

Another typical example is shown in Plate 36. The frame is again veneered with mahogany in herring-bone pattern but the chequered inlays are an improvement on the line inlays of the previous example. The shallow turned cistern cover became from *c*.1800 common and was often, as in this example, inlaid with blackened wood: other examples are found inlaid with ivory rings, etc. The engraved brass plates (Plate 37) carry the usual manual vernier (I have already drawn attention in Chapter One to the inaccuracy of this particular vernier, a blemish which hardly accords with the otherwise relatively good engraving) and a mercury thermometer.

PLATE 36
Frans Pelegrino
37″ × 6·2″
Author's collection
PLATE 37
Detail of Plate 36

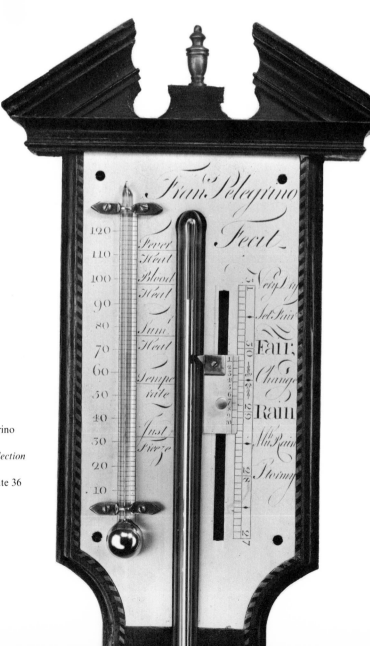

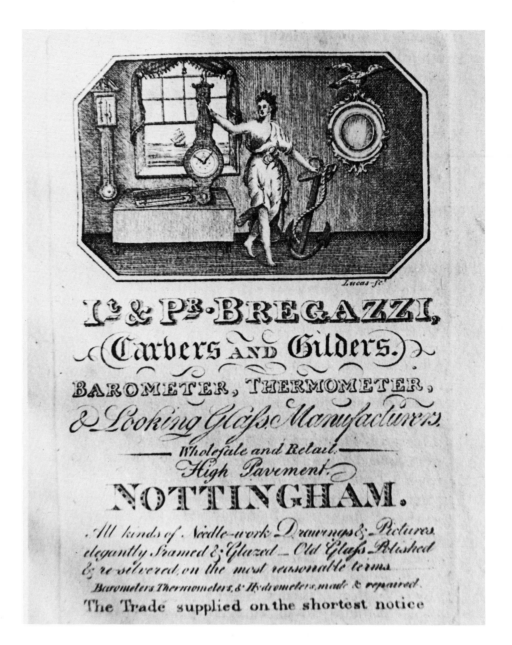

Innocent and Peter Bregazzi's advertisement of 1825 (Plate 38) shows that barometers of this design were still favoured a quarter of a century after its introduction: and similar barometers were sold by Augustus Maspoli at his address in Lowgate, Hull, where he was not in business until 1835. In fact countless examples survive of good, mediocre and poor quality, dating mostly from the first forty years of the nineteenth century. As with other standardized designs the close similarity between instruments bearing the signatures of different makers argues industrial methods of production.

This design appears to have generally lapsed by about 1840. From this time 'stick' barometers with scroll pediments also became rarer and the round-topped case began to predominate. This was produced in a variety of designs and a variety of woods, although mahogany continued to predominate, being slightly cheaper than rosewood and more elegant than oak (which did not have its vogue until the wave of Gothic taste later in the century). The simplest instrument of this period consisted of a solid mahogany board shaped with a round top and a body narrower than the 'hood' on which brass plates were mounted: this usually incorporated a siphon tube. More expensive instruments enjoyed a panelled case of mahogany, sometimes solid, sometimes veneered on pine or oak, with a portable cistern tube and ivory plates protected by thick glass: a small mercury thermometer was commonly mounted on the plates and a double vernier was not uncommon. One of these showed the reading of the day before, the other was adjusted to the present height of the mercury: and the plates were often from this period engraved with the words '8 (or 9 or 10) a.m. Yesterday' on the left and '8 (or 9 or 10) a.m. Today' on the right. The choice of time presumably depended on the purchaser's sleeping, or rather waking, habits.

In about 1869 Joseph Somalvico & Co. was offering barometers of 'Plain mahogany, round head, with door, shifting index, and portable tube', at thirty-five shillings and the same model in rosewood at thirty-six shillings. A rather more elaborate version was available at forty-five shillings with a panelled case, ivory plates, a thermometer mounted on the case, and plate glass: this was available in mahogany, oak, or rosewood.[1]

Ivory plates of the period are somehow intrinsically less attractive than the earlier engraved and silvered brass plates: they were in many cases carefully engraved although often they were crudely stamped with the weather indications and scales. It is worth noting also that they were frequently set aslant, a feature which became common from about 1840 in domestic instruments. It had been common in the slender marine instruments of the early years of the century.

An interesting summary of the types of 'stick' barometer which a leading London maker was offering at the end of the period covered by this study can be gained from the early catalogues of Negretti and Zambra. Their first *Illustrated Descriptive Catalogue of Optical, Mathematical, Philosophical, Photographic and Standard Meteorological Instruments* (Plate 102) ran to 181 pages and appeared in 1859.

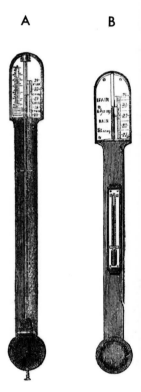

A   B

---

[1] Joseph Somalvico and Co. *Catalogue of Instruments* (undated but *c.* 1869 by which time the firm had moved from 16 Charles Street to 2 Hatton Garden).

It was later considerably enlarged as the firm's business and clientele expanded: but the later editions, while they demonstrate the persistence until the present century of the traditional barometer designs, do not concern the present study. The 1859 *Catalogue* advertised 2,134 items including a very wide range of scientific and domestic barometers. The stick, or 'Pediment',[1] barometers for domestic use were all portable and included the following:

		Each £ s. d.	Each £ s. d.
1.	Small portable barometer, mounted in mahogany frame, with ivory scale and sliding index		0 10 6
2.	Ditto larger size, with vernier reading to $\frac{1}{100}$th of an inch, thermometer, and screw to render it portable.		1 1 0
3.	Solid mahogany or rosewood barometers, with tube 0·25 in. diameter, ivory scale, thermometer, sliding vernier reading to $\frac{1}{100}$th of an inch, the tube visible throughout the whole length, and portable screw (Plate 39A).		2 2 0
4.	Ditto with tube covered and glass cover over the face, rackwork vernier, thermometer in front, with glass cover (Plate 39B).	2 10 0	
5.	Ditto ditto, with square moulded top and two verniers.	3 0 0	3 10 0
6.	Ditto ditto, bow-front, with 0·40 in. diameter tube, double rackwork vernier, the scales elegantly engraved on ivory plates, portable screw and thermometer, in oak, mahogany, walnut, or rosewood frame (Plate 39C)	4 0 0	5 0 0
7.	Portable rosewood barometer, elegantly fitted up, inlaid with pearl, thermometer in front, ivory scale, rackwork vernier reading to $\frac{1}{500}$th of an inch (Plate 39D).	4 0 0	5 5 0
8.	Portable barometer, Gothic pattern, in either rosewood, mahogany, or oak frame, ivory scales, with two rackwork verniers reading to $\frac{1}{500}$th of an inch, German silver fittings (Plate 39E).	5 5 0	6 0 0
9.	Large barometers, fitted in oak, mahogany, walnut or ebony frames, the tube 0·5 in. internal diameter, and the cistern presenting an area of 3 inches, to ensure uniformity in reading, engraved ivory or patent porcelain scales, and two verniers working by rack and pinion, reading $\frac{1}{500}$th of an inch.	6 6 0	8 8 0

PLATE 39. Negretti and Zambra's portable cistern barometers 1859

The list as a whole is not comprehensive and in a brief preface the makers emphasize that their selection is given 'only as being those most in demand': some notable features however emerge from it. Solid mahogany and rosewood were sometimes used in preference to veneers, decorative woods being in greater supply and therefore cheaper: oak and walnut are also mentioned. Many stylistic features

[1] The origin of this term is obscure. It is still commonly used in trade terminology for describing stick barometers: it may have been a corruption of the word 'pendant'.

survive from earlier years. The round and square moulded top are both mentioned (but not broken or scroll pediments), cistern covers are still turned and the bow-fronted case is still in use. Plates are principally made of ivory and a vernier, except on the first simple barometer, is a standard fitting: some verniers read to ·01″ and others to ·002″ and on some instruments there are two scales and verniers. Tubes vary from 0·25″ to 0·5″ in diameter and, except for item one, all are fitted with a portable screw although four of the illustrations do not show it. Item one, judging from its price and in spite of the title of this section of the *Catalogue*, is probably a siphon bulb-cistern tube: simple domestic barometers of this sort were still being made late in the nineteenth century.

Angle barometers were rarely produced in the nineteenth century. Early examples survive by among others Baptist Roncheti, William Robb and Balthazar Knie. Both Robb and Knie sold examples of a curious design (Plate 93) the aim of which was to avoid the asymmetric 'signpost' type of frame. It is possible that Knie, who was a renowned barometer maker, supplied barometers to Robb who was a clock-maker: at any rate examples of this type of tube survive in Germany[1] and it is interesting that Knie was of German origin.

Later in the century distinctive but rather ponderous angle baro-meters were made by Charles Howorth[2] and Samuel Lainton,[3] both of Halifax. These have mahogany frames, printed paper plates and two exposed siphon tubes with bulb cisterns which are too small in relation to the size of the tubes to allow accurate functioning. The work of these two makers is identical but I do not know which of them, if either, must be presumed the actual manufacturer.[4] Very few other makers seem to have sold angle barometers even in small numbers.

It is convenient at this stage to mention one further type of baro-meter—the 'double' or multiple tube variety—which enjoyed a small vogue at the beginning of the period under review. An example is illustrated in Plate 41 and it will be noticed that a spirit thermometer is also mounted on the frame. The barometer closely follows a design proposed by Guillaume Amontons in 1688. The aim of the design was to achieve portability by reducing the size of the barometer: this was done by splitting the mercury column between parallel tubes (two

[1] See p. 159 Note 1.

[2] Two in the Museum of the History of Science, Oxford, and one in the National Maritime Museum, Greenwich (Gabb Collection, Catalogue No. 0.4). These were all in store when I studied them. There is another in the Bolling Hall Museum, Bradford, also a single tube angle barometer with the address 'Pump Hill, Shibden, near Halifax'.

[3] Whipple Museum, Cambridge, Inventory No. 1130.

[4] Another Howorth angle barometer was sold at Sotheby's on 30 October 1964 (Lot No. 120). A thermometer was mounted between the tubes and its boxwood scale was signed by Lainton: Howorth's signature was on a piece of paper which was stuck over a previous signature on the barometer plates. It is conceivable that Howorth succeeded to Lainton's business but I have not yet been able to check this possibility.

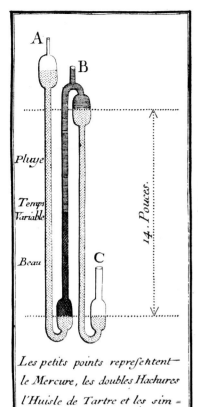

Les petits points representent—
le Mercure, les doubles Hachures
l'Huisle de Tartre et les sim =
ples Lignes l'Huisle de Karabe.

PLATE 40
Amontons'
double
barometer

PLATE 41
James Gatty
24·5″ × 5·7″
Author's
collection

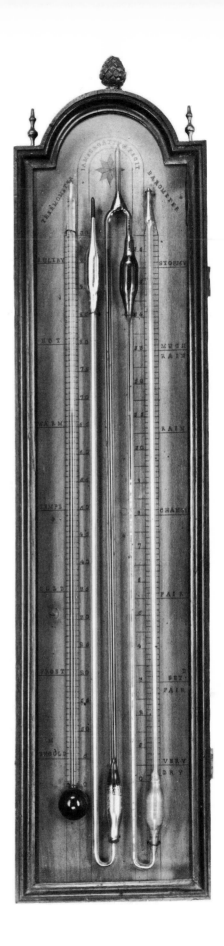

linked tubes of 14″ for instance being the equivalent of one of 28″). In order to achieve this a lighter liquid had to be inserted in a third tube in the centre. Plate 40 is from an account of the instrument written in 1723.[1] The three parallel glass tubes were cemented together and incorporated four identical glass bulbs or cisterns. The two outer limbs were filled with mercury which is represented in the drawing by dots and which extends into each of the four bulbs: the centre tube was filled with two oils—a coloured oil in the lower half and a colourless and lighter oil in the upper half. The completed

[1] A. Fortier de Virville *Construction d'un Nouveau Baromètre, avec la manière d'en pouvoir construire de telle grandeur qu'on voudra* (1723). De Virville says (p. 14) that the barometer was not entirely his invention and that the first idea was mooted by Amontons in the *Journaux des Sçavans* (Leipzig) July 1688.

tube was sealed at A and B but left open at C. The tubes were so constructed that the combined weight of the three liquids—mercury and the two oils—in the three tubes was equivalent to the weight of a column of mercury in an ordinary barometer. In fact however oil is so light in relation to mercury that the quantity used in such a short tube made only a minimal difference to the measurement: and for practical purposes, as the drawing suggests, makers were probably content merely to halve the normal mercury column of '28 pouces'.

The reading was taken from the intersection of the two oils. These could move over a considerable distance in the centre tube. If for instance the pressure was rising the mercury would rise in both the outer tubes and the effect would be to push the lighter oil upwards out of the cistern nearest to B and the heavier oil downwards into its own cistern: because the diameter of the cisterns was very much greater than that of the tubes the movement of the oils in the centre tube was magnified. As Plate 40 demonstrates the finer the weather (i.e. the higher the pressure) the lower the intersection of the two oils.

In so far as it employed liquids other than mercury and achieved an extension of the normal scale this instrument resembled in conception the double liquid barometer designed by Robert Hooke which employed only two parallel tubes; one of these was a full-length mercury tube and the other a thinner tube which extended above a glass cistern and was filled with water[1] It gained over Hooke's version because it was smaller and its size could be reduced still further by increasing the number of parallel tubes: it was also claimed that the thermometric expansion of the mercury was less marked since both mercury columns expanded at the same time thus exerting an equal and therefore ineffectual pressure on the oil in between.[2] This claim was unsound[3] however and the instrument had other disadvantages. Firstly, the liquids tended to encroach into the wrong tubes, especially if the instrument was inadvertently placed or carried at an angle. It was only portable in the sense that it could be carried: how it was carried was crucial. Secondly, the tubes once dirty were almost

[1] Proposed to the Royal Society on 18 June 1688 and mentioned by Thomas Birch *History of the Royal Society* (1756–7) Vol. 2 p. 298. Hooke's instrument was ingenious but the water in the narrow open limb tended to evaporate and to be affected by temperature changes. With oil substituted for water however it was applied commonly in the eighteenth century in Europe, especially by Dutch makers: examples of their barometers 'en contraleur', as they are called, are common, but since they do not appear to have achieved a foothold in England they are outside the scope of the present study. Even more similar to Amontons' design was Hooke's later three-liquid barometer in which an open cistern was attached to the top of the extended open limb. This limb was filled with two incompatible liquids, the line between which provided the point of observation—*Philosophical Transactions* Vol. 16 (1686) p. 241 *et seq.*

[2] De Virville *Construction d'un Nouveau Baromètre* pp. 19–20.

[3] De Luc in his *Recherches sur les Modifications de l'Atmosphere* (1772) Part 1 p. 31 complained of the double barometer that 'le chaleur produit des effets qu'il est impossible de determine pour tous les cas'.

impossible to clean and later repairers were not necessarily as competent as the original makers.

The example of Plate 41 differs from Amontons' instrument in one important respect. An extra limb has been added to the open cistern on the right. This was also filled with oil which has long since evaporated. Readings are taken from the station of the oil in this extra limb and not from the sandwiched oil which acts only as a buffer between the two columns of mercury. The scale is divided into sixteen inches each of which is subdivided into sixths. Between 'Very Dry' and 'Stormy' (i.e. the usual 3″ range of the common mercurial barometer) there are effectively fifteen divisions: the traditional scale is thus magnified five times.

Almost identical examples of this design survive signed by J. Gatty, Sala, D. Manticha, Baptis Ronchate, Torre and Silberrad. They all have the same plain arched mahogany case with a glazed door and three finials; and all, except the Manticha instrument which has varnished paper scales, have boxwood plates on which, as in Plate 41, the scales and weather indications are stamped. It is not known which, if any, of these makers made these instruments. The design was probably brought from Holland or even France, where earlier examples are known, by an early Italian immigrant.

The familiar 'banjo' wheel barometer was the most characteristic instrument of the nineteenth century. I have already said that the shape seems to have come from France where it was employed as early as c. 1760: a pleasant example made of oak with casuarina veneers and ormolu mounts by an anonymous French maker c. 1753 can be seen in the Wallace Collection[1] and there are many similar examples in private collections. The design arrived in England in about 1780: whether it was copied by English makers from French pieces imported by collectors or brought over by immigrant Italian makers is not clear; but the latter alternative seems probable. The barometer and thermometer supplied to Lord Bute in 1787 by C. Bettally (Plate 42) lack the usual base of the 'banjo' design but the similarity is obvious: and I have already observed that Bettally, whose name is clearly of Italian derivation, had a shop in Paris. This pair of instruments is of unusual distinction. The beautifully inlaid cases are veneered with satinwood: they were originally intended to be hung from the wall but have subsequently been fitted to Adamesque gilt and painted stands. The finials are both missing. The brass bezel and flat glass are typical features of the early application of the 'banjo' design but the 12″ silvered dial (Plate 43) is unusually wide. As can be seen the barometer

[1] Inventory No. F.69.

scale, which is divided in hundredths of an inch, and the weather indications are traditional. The pierced brass recording hand is

PLATE 42
C. Bettally, London, 1787
34·5″ × 16″
Mallett and Son (Antiques) Ltd:
from the collection of
Lord Robert Crichton-Stewart

PLATE 43
Detail of Plate 42
(barometer)

adjusted by the serrated brass knob to which it is attached by cord and brass pulleys. The inelegant tapered brass hand is another pointer: it is adjusted manually, the dial being pierced, and is a modern blemish which was probably installed by a repairer too lazy to open the dial (which has to be unlocked) in order to use the correct knob. The steel main hand has also been replaced. I do not know the purpose of the small dial above the arbor. It is operated by a rack and pulley wheel which is set in the same plane as the main arbor. It was inoperative when I saw it briefly and I did not have time to study the mechanism closely enough to reach a conclusion. It could be intended as the main indicator, with the hand on the main dial revolving once for each inch on the subsidary dial: but if so the eighty chief divisions of the main dial do not correspond with the 100 divisions of each inch against which the recording hand can be set. The tube is modern. The companion thermometer is fitted with a catgut hygrometer.

The instrument by Ribright (Plate 16) is an early example by an indigenous maker and it has been described in the previous chapter. It lacks the decorative inlays of Bettally's cases and the flamboyant ormolu mounts which an earlier French instrument would have had: but it displays many of the features typical of the early English application of the design—a ten-inch dial with brass bezel, rounded top and no ancillary instruments. Similar wheel barometers, but without the clock-like dial and hands, survive by Aiano, Roncheti and Gatty, all presumably Italian immigrants. The particular instruments by these makers which I have studied were all fitted with a thermo-meter and were embellished with inlaid paterae of coloured woods on either side of it. One of the Aiano instruments had a painted dial.

It was no doubt such instruments which in 1790 George Adams the younger called 'more elegant than the plain barometer' but dismissed because 'they cannot be depended upon . . . .'[1] They were still rare in his day and he did not even quote a price for wheel barometers: nor did W. and S. Jones in their catalogue of instruments which was appended to William Jones's 1799 editions of Adams' *Essay on Electricity* and *Lectures on Natural and Experimental Philosophy*. That the wheel barometer was not common in 1795 is also suggested by the passage from Charles Hutton's *Dictionary* quoted on p. 78. Hutton only illustrates a cistern-tube domestic instrument: the wheel baro-meter which he illustrates is Hooke's original design of 1665. I do not consider the evidence of Adams, Jones and Hutton conclusive. I think there were undoubtedly some wheel instruments on the market before 1800 but nothing like the number inferred either by previous writers

[1] *A Short Dissertation* p. 6.

or by many furniture dealers. That they were only introduced in quantity after 1800 is suggested by a writer who said in 1819:

> 'The wheel barometer has lately been obtruded upon the public by the strolling Italian hawkers in our streets; but the imperfect manner in which these barometers are constructed, as well as their defective principle, renders them mere mechanical pictures, and not scientific instruments, in the parlour'.[1]

Plate 126 illustrates a wheel instrument of the type which began to appear in *c.* 1795. It is veneered as usual with mahogany and bears some notable resemblances to the earlier type—the inlaid paterae on the case, the flat glass, silvered dial, brass bezel, etc.—but a broken pediment has replaced the rounded top and the dial has been reduced to 8″ diameter. The inlaid paterae follow a common design which appears for example, in Hepplewhite's *Cabinet-Maker and Upholsterer's Guide.*[2] A shell motif is also common. Contemporary barometers of almost identical design and quality survive by Francis Anone, Torre, and many other makers: and a closely similar instrument by Ronketti survives bearing his address in Peter Street, Bloomsbury to which he had moved by 1800. This design continued in common use for many years, and it would be a mistake to attribute all instruments of similar shape and decoration even to the same decade. Jacob Abraham of Bath advertised one in his trade card of 1833.

Another early example with an 8″ dial in a round-topped painted case is illustrated in Plate 97. The elegance of this instrument is apparent if it is compared with contemporary veneered examples of the same shape.

Occasionally cabinet-makers rejected the traditional pediment styles. The elegant barometer by James Gatty of Plate 80 is surmounted by three finials. A case of similar style with handsome satinwood veneers and a dark cross-grained border is shown in Plate 44. Its maker is recorded as working at 46 Lowgate, Hull, between 1803 and 1834 and he was at an unspecified address in Lowgate as early as 1790. Stylistically this barometer could have been made at any time between about 1795

[1] Abraham Rees *Cyclopaedia s.v.* 'Barometer'.

[2] 3rd edition 1794 Plates 70 and 71 (both engraved in 1787).

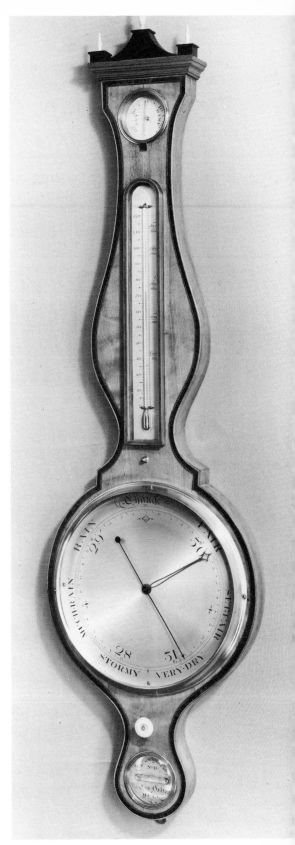

PLATE 44
Richd Northen and Son, 46 Low Gate, Hull
40·5″ × 11·5″
Charles Stewart (Antiques) Ltd.

and 1820 and the actual date of its manufacture is not material. The elegance of the case is matched by the subdued treatment of the silvered 10″ dial: this is an example of the 'banjo' design at its most pleasing.

Another early variation was the common scroll pediment which appeared on so many cistern-tube instruments. There are many fine wheel barometers extant dating from between 1805 and 1830 which display this feature. Not until later did it become common with an 8″ dial and an early example generally has a 10″ or even a 12″ dial and a convex glass. The case is almost invariably of mahogany veneer on a pinewood carcase, the border being in many good examples banded with satinwood or a pale alternative such as kingwood. The convex glass could not conveniently be pierced and a pulley and operating key are needed for the recording hand. An example of an instrument of about 1820 with a 12″ dial is illustrated in Plate 45. The casework and the engraving of the silvered dial are of high quality and the enamel-dialled clock is a pleasing feature. Similar barometers but of massive proportions with 14″ dials and brass pillars at each side of the trunk also survive from this period.

By about 1820 the 'banjo' barometer had become as popular as the common bulb-cistern 'stick' barometer which has already been discussed. I cannot hope to describe or even mention all the variations of embellishment and design which were used and must confine myself to generalizations which are as capable of contradiction as they are of confirmation. Cases were generally veneered with mahogany although satinwood and later rosewood were sometimes used. Designs incorporating the broken pediment were frequently decorated with inlaid paterae on either side of the thermometer and often too in place of the hygrometer and spirit level (cf Plate 126) which were by now standard parts of the design. Those incorporating a scroll pediment

PLATE 45
W. Horrod, 37 Laystall Strt, London
45·2 × 13·8″
Collection of Mrs. Owen Hugh Smith

frequently had a squared frame and the thermometer was often framed in a bow-fronted case of its own: Plate 46 shows a good example veneered with rosewood of about 1835–40. Other features which began to appear were clocks (Plate 45) and, more commonly in about 1840, convex mirrors which were usually placed above the dial and necessitated a shorter thermometer case (Plate 47): both of these features were reflections of the retailer's varied interests. The spirit level which became an almost invariable feature at the base of the barometer enabled the owner to set the instrument straight and the retailer to engrave his name without spoiling the engraving of the main dial (Plate 50). Thermometers and hygrometers were often detachable, the former usually locked in place by a sliding knob, the latter by a spring clip (Plates 44, 46, 47, etc.).

The silvered brass dials which were common at this period allowed engraving of great variety. Star designs, maps of the world, floral and geometric designs and masonic emblems are all found (Plates 45, 46, 51). The scale remained the traditional 28″– 31″, divided into twentieths or hundredths, and the weather indications likewise copied tradition. James Gatty was unusual in sometimes specifying horizontal engraving for his weather indications (Plate 80), the usual habit being to conform to the circumference of the dial (Plate 45). Dials were occasionally painted: John Russell's atypic instruments (Plates 129, 132) are the finest examples but dials of this sort survive by other makers and I have seen a well-designed and executed example by a Dumfries maker named McPherson.

Hands also admitted of some variety but Russell's elegant pierced steel and less elegant stamped brass hands were the exception rather than the rule. Simpler pierced hands were however common (Plates 46, 51). Main hands were often plain and made of blackened steel with arrow heads and crescent or round tails; and brass recording hands

PLATE 46
A. Tagliabue, 31 Brook Street, Holbn, London
40·5″ × 12″
Collection of Gordon F. C. Cole

displayed a similar simplicity. On instruments with flat glasses (usually those with 8″ dials and broken pediments) the recording hand is usually operated directly by a knob attached to it through a hole in the glass (Plate 126): on other instruments a cord pulley operating over two wheels is usual (Plate 44).

Not all the wheel barometers made during the nineteenth century were of the 'banjo' type and it would be impossible to catalogue all the styles which are found. Plate 48 shows a good example of a type which achieved modest popularity over several decades. The pinewood case is veneered with mahogany of pleasant figure and satinwood crossbanding. Several features, scroll pediment, silvered dial, detachable hygrometer and thermometer, are all shared with the normal 'banjo' style but there is no level. The scale is relatively inexact, covering only twentieths of an inch, and the hands are cut simply from brass. It is difficult to date this barometer; its makers were active practically throughout the period covered by this chapter.

Tubes and mechanism varied very little in nineteenth-century wheel instruments. A tube of about 0·2″ bore was common and although some makers attempted to improve the instrument's performance by using tubes of up to 0·6″ bore such tubes are rare. They occur more commonly on cistern-tube instruments but even these were not intended for domestic use. Pulley cords were customarily of silk, the counterbalance of glass (often a piece of snapped and filed thermometer glass) and the pulley wheel of brass. Sometimes pulley wheels of ivory or wood are found.

Thermometers contain either mercury or alcohol but more usually the latter, the scale

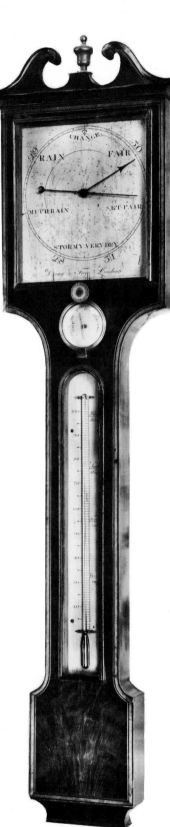

PLATE 47
Anon.
38″ × 10·3″
Charles Stewart (Antiques) Ltd.

PLATE 48
Dring and Fage, London
39″ × 9·5″
H. C. Baxter and Sons

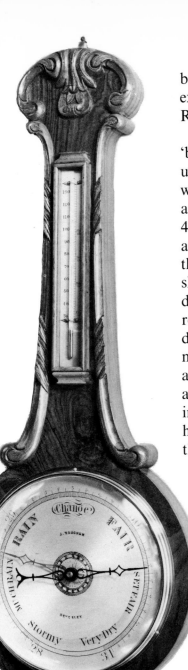

being most frequently Fahrenheit. Some examples are however found with duplicate Réaumur or, more rarely, Centigrade scales.

By about 1850 the most popular design of 'banjo' case appears to have been the plain unadorned case of mahogany or rosewood with a scroll pediment, 8″ dial, convex glass and convex mirror set above the dial. Plate 47 shows an example veneered with mahogany: the usual hygrometer and level are still there and the thermometer is somewhat shortened by the presence of the mirror. The design lacks elegance and there is little refinement in the casework: it reflects the degeneration inevitably caused by a mass market. Other characteristic designs of this and later decades are illustrated in Plates 49 and 50. The first is a heavy design fashioned in solid walnut with moulded edges: the hygrometer and level are dispensed with and the use of carved scrolls in the mouldings led

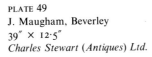

PLATE 49
J. Maugham, Beverley
39″ × 12·5″
Charles Stewart (Antiques) Ltd.

PLATE 50
J. B. Corti, Glasgow
40″ × 12″
Charles Stewart (Antiques) Ltd.

catologuists to describe this type of case as 'scroll pattern'. The same description was applied to the second example when its rather spiky form was embellished with mouldings. Both types were illustrated in Negretti and Zambra's 1859 *Catalogue* (Plate 52). As can be seen from Plate 52 D and E they were sometimes extravagantly inlaid with mother-of-pearl, brass, shells, etc., although in cheaper examples the cases were often painted in simulation of these inlays. More traditional designs were also inlaid and Plate 51 shows a good example veneered with rosewood and with mother-of-pearl inlays. Its case is basically very similar to the barometer of Plate 46.

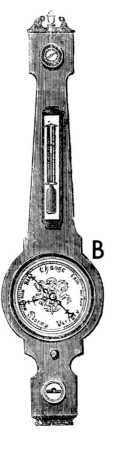
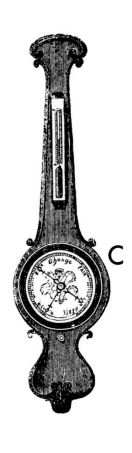

A B C

PLATE 52
Negretti and Zambra's
wheel barometers
1859

Negretti and Zambra's *Catalogue* gives a useful summary of the range of wheel barometers offered by a leading maker at the close of the period under study. These included:

	Each £ s. d.	Each £ s. d.
1. 8 in. Silvered brass dial barometer, mounted in common mahogany or rosewood frame, with or without mirror, hygrometer, and level (Plate 52A).	1 5 0	1 10 0
2. 8 in. Silvered brass dial barometer, mounted in common mahogany or rosewood frame, with or without mirror, hygrometer, level and square bottom (Plate 52B).	1 10 0	2 2 0
3. Ditto, superior finish, best engraving, and large tube (Plate 52B).	2 10 0	3 10 0
4. 10 in. Silvered brass dial barometer, in common mahogany or rosewood frame, with or without mirror, hygrometer, and level (Plate 52A).	1 15 0	2 5 0
5. Ditto, square bottom (Plate 52B).	2 0 0	2 10 0
6. Extra best ditto, both as regards frame, dial, engraving and tube (Plate 52B).		3 10 0

12 in. dial of the same patterns, from 15s. to £1. 5s. extra.

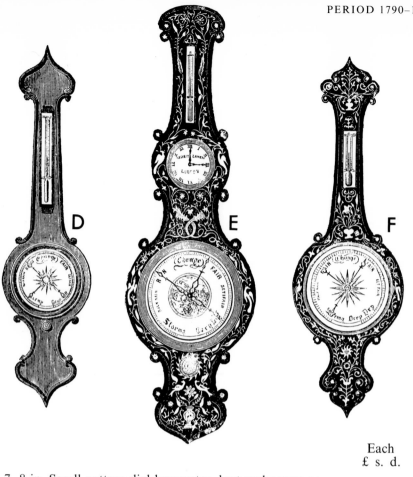

	Each £ s. d.	Each £ s. d.
7. 8 in. Scroll pattern dial barometer, best mahogany or rosewood frame, silvered brass dial, elegantly fitted up with thermometer (Plate 52C or D).	2 10 0	3 0 0
8. Ditto, with black enamel figures and divisions on porcelain dial, and thermometer in front (Plate 52C).		3 15 0
9. Ditto, rosewood frame inlaid with pearl, with silvered brass dial, and thermometer in front.	3 0 0	4 0 0
10. 10 in. ditto, best rosewood frame inlaid with variegated pearl and brass, the dial of silvered brass, with thermometer, double basil ring, and polished-edge plate glass, superior finish (Plate 52F). 12 in. dial ditto, at proportionate prices.		6 6 0
11. 14 in. best rosewood frame inlaid with variegated pearl and brass, the dial of silvered brass, and an eight-day pendulum clock fitted in the frame, thermometer, etc. (Plate 52E). Suitable for club-houses, mansions etc.	15 0 0	20 0 0

An almost infinite number of designs was available. The compilers were obliged to remark that barometers could 'be supplied to order of any style of architecture, so as to correspond with the furniture of libraries, halls, etc., or to drawing from design'. Barometers were 'mounted in so many varied styles, both plain and carved', that the selection given was confined only to 'those most in demand'.[1]

Those shewn in the *Catalogue* (Plate 52) are all basically 'banjo' barometers, which demonstrates the extraordinary persistence of this popular design. Plates 52A and B show two of the most popular forms of the design which were favoured from about 1840 onwards. Fig. A should be compared with Plate 47 and Fig. B with Plate 46. Unlike contemporary cistern-tube barometers, wheel barometers were still generally fitted with dials of silvered brass, the area being too large for the convenient use of ivory. The engraving was stylized and inelegant and matched the inartistic competence of the casework. A study of this *Catalogue* shows that domestic barometers were still commonly made of traditional materials and conformed to traditional designs. Even the oatbeard hygrometer was still a standard fitting.

In summary the nineteenth century was not notable for originality of design or for quality. Both suffered from the growth of a mass market. Ralph Fastnedge, who was speaking of furniture generally, said recently that 'deterioration in design and a poverty of invention became as obvious in case furniture as elsewhere'[2] and these words can certainly be applied to barometer cases.

As a scientific instrument the nineteenth-century domestic barometer is out of court altogether, the development of domestic and scientific barometers having parted in the eighteenth century. Real advances—such as Fortin's and Troughton's cisterns and Gay-Lussac's siphon tube—were made towards the design of an accurate barometer even early in the century but they were understandably neglected by makers of purely domestic instruments. The cheap barometers named after Admiral Fitzroy which were made mostly after 1860 and which fall outside the scope of this work have a specious air of efficiency but they cannot be called scientific instruments.

In 1823 J. F. Daniell (1790–1845), a Fellow of the Royal Society and Professor of Chemistry at King's College, London, wrote:

'In the shops of the best manufacturers and opticians I have observed that no two barometers agree: and the difference between the extremes will often amount to a quarter of an inch: and this with all the deceptive appearance which a nonius (i.e. vernier), to read off to the 500th part of an inch, can give. The common instruments are mere playthings.'[3]

[1] pp. 18–19.
[2] *English Furniture Styles from 1500 to 1830* (Pelican 1955) p. 275.
[3] *Meteorological Essays* (3rd edition under the title *Elements of Meteorology* 1845) p. 267.

More to the point, since he was talking specifically of wheel barometers which were not intended in the nineteenth century to have
scientific applications, J. H. Belville wrote in 1849:

> 'The wheel barometer, from its construction, cannot be trusted to
> for correct heights; it merely shows if the mercury be in a rising or
> falling state: it may rather be considered as an ornamental piece of
> furniture than as having the slightest pretensions to a scientific
> instrument'.

These writers' words demonstrate how far the required standards of
accuracy had advanced in 150 years and provide a fitting end to the
discussion.

[1] *A Manual of the Barometer* (1849) p. 14.

PART II

Important
Makers

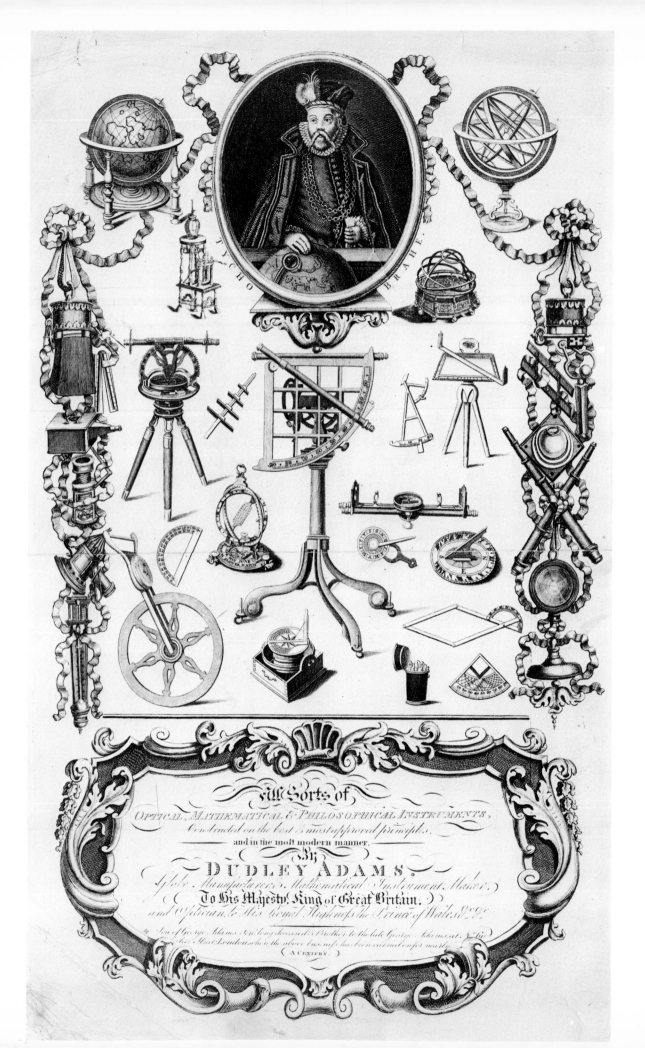

TYCHO BRAHE

All Sorts of
OPTICAL, MATHEMATICAL & PHILOSOPHICAL INSTRUMENTS,
Constructed on the best & most approved principles,
and in the most modern manner.
By
DUDLEY ADAMS,
Globe Manufacturer & Mathematical Instrument Maker,
To His Majesty King of Great Britain,
and Optician to His Royal Highness the Prince of Wales &c &c

Son of George Adams, Sen: long deceased & Brother to the late George Adams, at N°60
Fleet Street London where the above business has been carried on for nearly
A CENTURY.

DUDLEY ADAMS b. *c.*1760–d.1826

1. 53 Charing Cross (1793–5)
2. 60 Fleet Street (1795–1821)

THE YOUNGER SON of the elder George Adams, Dudley Adams had his own workshop at Charing Cross from 1793. He succeeded to the family business and the royal appointment when his brother the younger George Adams died in 1795. He specialized in astronomical instruments and globes and achieved three patents in 1797, 1800 and 1815 for improvements to telescopes and spectacles. He held appointments to the King and the Prince of Wales. He inherited from his mother his father's manuscripts and copperplates and re-edited his *Treatise Describing the Construction and Explaining the Use of New Celestial and Terrestrial Globes* in 1810. He did not inherit his brother's stock, library, or copyrights (which included his father's), which were sold at auction in 1796 to William Jones. There appears to have been a family dispute between George Adams' widow Hannah and Dudley over the auction. In his preface to the thirtieth edition of his father's book on globes (1810) Dudley Adams prefers to 'draw a veil' over the affair, regretting especially that Jones had acquired the library and copyrights: the latter enabled the new owner to republish a number of George Adams' treatises and to profit by the advertisements which he appended to them.

He may have continued to use his brother's name for a few years, since an 1801 directory lists 'George Adams' at 60 Fleet Street: but this may equally have been a misprint. Directories of 1800 and 1822 also give his address as 6 Jewry Street, which could have been either his residence or a branch shop.[1] Adams' later interests were various and not entirely practical: in 1820 he published a treatise enthusiastically entitled *Electricity is the Fountain, the great vivifying principle of nature; a source of life and health . . . etc.*, and he wrote a religious work which was published posthumously in 1827.

His trade card was beautifully engraved and examples of it survive in the Science Museum, London, and in the Heal Collection (Plate 53). A barometer of the pattern illustrated by Scarlett and Desaguliers (Plates 133 and 17) is included in the decoration of the card but this is

[1] R. S. Clay and T. H. Court say in their *History of the Microscope* p. 237 that he moved there in 1800 but this does not accord with most of the directories which give 60 Fleet Street as his only address to 1821.

unlikely to have been a type sold by Adams: it is stylistically sixty years out of date and the engraver was probably copying an earlier illustration.

A number of barometers survive signed 'Adams, Fleet Street' which can stylistically be attributed to Dudley Adams. Among these are mahogany screw-type cistern instruments similar to the household barometer illustrated by Charles Hutton (Plate 31),[1] i.e. with a mahogany panelled case, turned cistern cover, scroll pediment, brass or ivory finial, polished brass cover over the tip of the tube, silvered plates and vernier. Adams made many quite plain instruments of this design. One such instrument I have studied had the unusual feature of a glazed door made of cast brass (Adams did not apparently use bayonet tubes), as well as a thermometer on the case and a standard oatbeard hygrometer above the plates (cf. Plate 31 again). Another had neither of the ancillary instruments and had a more usual wooden framed door, but the mahogany case was of serpentine section.

He also sold cistern-tube barometers in the bow-fronted mahogany frames which were popular in the early nineteenth century (cf. Plate 33). There is an example signed 'Adams, London' in the National Maritime Museum, Greenwich.[2] The mahogany case is unusually slender and the extreme width of the hood is only 2·75″; the hood is glazed and surmounted by a square moulded pediment (cf. Plate 21) and a single finial. The top half of the urn-shaped cistern cover is missing. The silvered brass plates carry the usual seven states of the weather and a scale of 27″–31″ divided in decimals: and the vernier is operated by a key, which also operates the

[1] *Philosophical and Mathematical Dictionary* (1795) *s.v.* 'Barometer'.
[2] Gabb Collection, Catalogue No. 0.3: in store in 1964.

PLATE 54
D. Adams, Fleet Street, London
45″ × 13·5″
Reproduced by kind permission of His Grace
The Duke of Bedford

portable screw at the base. The tube is of about 0·2″ bore and is fitted to a normal leather-based cistern.

He does not seem to have made ordinary wheel barometers although the common 'banjo' case became popular during his career. But his signature appears on an exceptional pair of wheel instruments—barometer and thermometer—at Woburn Abbey (Plates 1, 54, 55). Although the casework belongs stylistically to the decade 1775–85 these instruments were not made before 1795 when Adams moved to the Fleet Street address. The case of each instrument is of mahogany veneer, now attractively faded, on a pine carcase. The thermometer case has fractionally darker veneers. The applied decorations —the formal statuesque figures on either side of the dial, the rams' heads, the eagle standing on a festoon of fruit and flowers, the pediment of scrolled foliage (Plate 56)—are of carved and gilt wood and strongly reminiscent of the designs of Adam. The centrepiece of the crest of each instrument is missing. The double twisted columns on either side of the case are also gilt. The cornice and most of the straight edges are of brass and the square bezel is also of brass, the main dial and subsidiary instruments all being glazed. A rectangular mirror is set in the base. The engraving is exceptional, the effect of applied spandrels in relief in the corners of the dials being achieved by skilful incision (Plate 58). The brass dials are silvered, most of the lettering being of great intricacy with silver highlights and extravagant flourishes. The engraving on the silvered thermometer and hygrometer plates is of the same high quality and the brass mounts of the subsidiary thermometers are beautifully pierced and engraved (Plate 57). In contrast to all this finery the barometer hands are

PLATE 55
D. Adams, Fleet Street, London
*Reproduced by kind
permission of His Grace the Duke of Bedford*

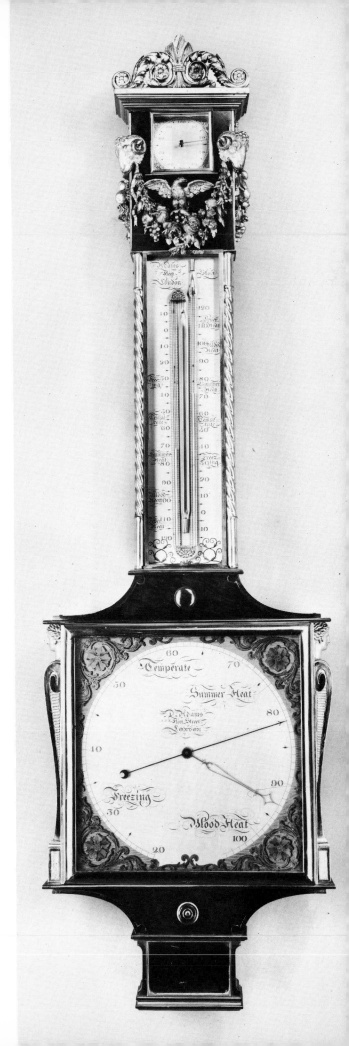

plain; the main hand being of blued steel, the recording hand of pierced brass. The mechanism of the barometer was renewed in 1904 and the original tube discarded: the brass pulley wheel appears to have been installed at the same date. The weather indications and the scale of the dial are conventional, the 3″ being divided into hundredths. The recording hand is operated by the knob beneath the dial through a cord and pulley wheels. The thermometer on the upper case of the barometer is mercurial with both Fahrenheit and Réaumur scales and a ring pointer, operated by the knob beneath it. The hygrometer at the top is of the oatbeard type with an engraved scale of 100 divisions and a manual recording hand.

These instruments are reminiscent of the brilliant workmanship of early makers such as Tompion and Graham. There are very few English barometers of their quality extant.

above: PLATE 56
Detail of Plate 55
right: PLATE 57
Detail of Plate 54
opposite: PLATE 58
Detail of Plate 54

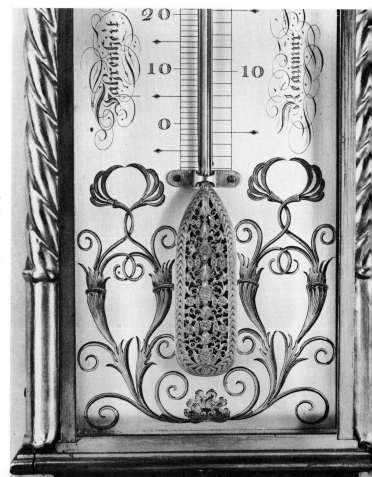

G E O R G E A D A M S (1) b. *c*.1704 – d.1772

1. Tycho Brahe's Head, Fleet Street
2. 60 Fleet Street

ONE OF THE most eminent of eighteenth-century instrument-makers, George Adams was principally known for his globes and microscopes, but a wide range of optical, mathematical and physical instruments was produced in his workshop. Their quality brought him an international reputation. He held the appointment of mathematical instrument-maker to the Prince of Wales, i.e. George III, before 1760 and later of course to the King. He was the father of George Adams the younger and of Dudley Adams.

The date of his birth is uncertain. He was apparently apprenticed in 1721 to a member of the Clockmakers' Company although he did not become a member himself until 1752. In 1735–6 he was making instruments for the East India Company and the flyleaf of his *Description and Use of the Universal Trigonometrical Octant* (1753) describes him as Mathematical Instrument Maker to His Majesty's Office of Ordnance. During the next eighteen years he published four or five treatises and pamphlets on instruments and globes, the most famous being *A Treatise Describing the Construction and Explaining the Use of New Celestial and Terrestrial Globes* which was published in 1766 and ran to thirty editions by 1810 when it was edited by Adams' second son Dudley. In the preface to this edition Dudley Adams gives the date of his death as 1773 but an advertisement in the *Daily Advertiser* of 28 October 1772 stated that Ann and George Adams (i.e. Adams' widow and elder son) were carrying on the business of the 'late Mr. Adams'.

The Prussian astronomer Bernoulli, who visited his workshop in 1769, said that it contained 'un nombre prodigieux d'instrumens de physique, de mathématique, de gnomonique, d'astronomie, etc.'[1] Several mathematical and scientific instruments by George Adams survive in public collections: and many can be seen in the George III Collection in the Science Museum, London. In the same museum there survives a manuscript which Adams wrote in 1761–2 explaining the pneumatic apparatus which he contributed to the collection. No barometers are mentioned in this manuscript.

[1] Bernoulli *Lettres Astronomiques* p. 74.

Adams often advertised his instruments in his treatises. Appended for instance to his *Description and Use of the Universal Trigonometrical Octant* (1753), which was 'given only with the instrument', is a three-page catalogue of 'all sorts of the most curious mathematical, philosophical, and optical instruments . . . [made] with the utmost accuracy and exactness, according to the latest and best discoveries of the modern mathematicians'. Included in this catalogue are 'curious barometers, diagonal, wheel, standard or portable, with or without thermometers', a phrase which is repeated on his trade card which survives in the Banks Collection.[1] A more detailed catalogue of Adams' instruments appears in the second edition of his *Treatise* on globes which was printed in 1769. It contains seven pages and includes:

	£	s.	d.
Barometers	2	2	0
Ditto, with thermometers	2	12	6
Ditto	5	5	0
Ditto, with hygrometers	5	15	6
A new invented barometer of a peculiar make	7	7	0
Diagonal barometers	5	5	0
Wheel barometers	8	8	0
Tripple diagonal barometers	16	16	0

The Portuguese scientist J. H. de Magellan[2] said that he had seen a static or balance barometer made by Adams in 1760:[3] he thought it to be one of the only two in Europe. It was certainly too rare to be included in Adams' price list.

According to the younger George Adams[4] his father was the first maker to apply a floating gauge to the barometer (Chapter Four, pp. 66–7): but this may have been invented, as Daumas[5] claims, by Jesse Ramsden who was at one time one of Adams' workmen. If Adams was the inventor the instrument could well be identified with the 'new invented barometer of a peculiar make' in the price list.

The appearance of 'tripple diagonal barometers' in the list is interesting. Adams seems to have received the idea of making an angle barometer with three tubes from Charles Orme.[6] I have not yet come across any angle barometers bearing Adams' signature but a triple tube barometer by Orme is illustrated in Plate 104.

[1] British Museum.
[2] *Description et Usages Nouvaux Baromètres* p. 156.
[3] For an account of the development of the balance barometer see Middleton *History of the Barometer* pp. 99–110.
[4] *A Short Dissertation* p. 8. The attribution is also made by Abraham Rees's huge edition of Chambers' *Cyclopaedia* of 1819 but the contributor had read most of the common sources including probably Adams' book.
[5] Daumas *Les Instruments Scientifiques* p. 274. Ramsden invented another type of gauge for zeroing the scale (p. 203).
[6] *Description et Usages des Nouvaux Baromètres* p. 152

There are many barometers of various designs extant signed 'George Adams': since both father and son worked at the same address and enjoyed the royal appointment it is regrettably difficult in many cases to assign authorship with confidence. The wheel instrument illustrated in Plate 59 can certainly be ascribed to the elder Adams. It was made after 1760 when the Prince of Wales came to the throne as George III and before 1772 when Adams died. It presumably cost £8 8s. 0d., or perhaps more since the wheel barometers advertised in the price list were probably of simpler design. This particular instrument has the unique feature of an engraved brass panel on the upper part of the case which gives in considerable detail a 'General State of the Weather' (Plate 60). The younger Adams, in his *Short Dissertation on the Barometer* of 1790 quoted this complete 'General State of the Weather' and said that he found it among his father's papers. He does not seem to have known of the existence of a barometer incorporating it; but the paper was almost certainly a meticulous copy—reproducing even the inaccuracies of the scale—taken before the instrument was sold.

The case is of dark mahogany and austere, the only decoration being the brass finial in the centre of the broken pediment. The dial and 'General State of the Weather' are both glazed and the case is hinged at the base (Plate 61) being locked in place by the two screws visible on either side of its upper part (Plate 59). The brass dial too is simple and the corners, where spandrels could easily have been fitted, are left plain. The centre is matted, the chapter ring silvered, and the engraving is of good quality. The main hand is steel and its plainness is in marked contrast

PLATE 59
Geo Adams, 60 Fleet Street, London
40·5″ × 11·3″
Private collection

to the pierced brass recording hand. The mechanism is of higher quality than is usual in domestic instruments and it is tempting to presume from this that Adams was trying to produce primarily a scientific instrument (hence also the meteorological instructions) in spite of the contempt with which contemporary scientists treated the wheel barometer. The tube is of 0·5″ bore which is unusually large for this period and the accurate transmission of the movement through the silk cord and double-grooved brass pulley wheel is helped by the simple and very lightweight main hand. The recording hand is operated by the knob above the dial: the cog of the brass gear wheel with which this connects when the case is closed can just be seen in Plate 61. The scale consists of the usual 3″ divided into hundredths and is repeated on the inner edge of the chapter ring for use with the recording hand. In between these two scales are engraved some weather indications and a series of numbers from 20 (at 'Harican') through 0 (at 'Varible') to 16 (at 'Clear Sky'). These numbers and indications are meant to tally with the table engraved in the panel on the upper part of the case. There is no doubt that this 'General State of the Weather' as it is headed was devised before the dial was made. In itself it is sensibly arranged with sixteen states of good weather and sixteen states of poor weather which with 'Variable' at zero in the middle, makes a total of thirty-three states. If the diallist had placed his 'Varible' at 29·5″, i.e. at the centre of the top of the chapter ring, he would not have made any mistakes: but 'Varible' is engraved at 29·67″ and, having divided the dial between 29·67″ and 31″ ('Clear Sky') into sixteen parts, the engraver found that he had space for twenty parts

PLATE 60
Detail of Plate 59

PLATE 61
Detail of Plate 59

between 29·67″ and 28″ ('Hari-can'). Hence the dial fails to correspond with the 'General State' table, the engraver being obliged to insert 'Heavy Storm' at state sixteen and demote the hurricane to twenty.

The paper quoted by the younger Adams gives not only an exact reproduction of the wording of the 'General State', but also the actual inches, to two places of decimals, with which the thirty-three states correspond on this barometer's dial. It seems inconceivable that the paper was the diallist's plan. Firstly it was palpably erroneous and secondly, if he used it, he failed to copy the words correctly. Hence my suggestion that the paper was a copy of the instrument and not vice versa.

A similar wheel instrument survives with a thermometer in place of the 'General State': this can likewise be ascribed to Adams. He may also have sold the two cistern-tube barometers of Plates 62 and 63 which I have arbitrarily ascribed to his son.

GEORGE ADAMS (2) b.1750–d.1795

1. Tycho Brahe's Head, Fleet Street
2. 60 Fleet Street

THE SON OF the elder man of the same name, George Adams succeeded to the business and royal appointment on his father's death in 1772. He also became optician to the Prince of Wales (later George IV) and was succeeded by his younger brother Dudley in both the family business and the appointments. His workshop continued, as in his father's day, to produce a wide variety of mathematical, optical and physical instruments: and he assumed and indeed exceeded his father's reputation for quality. Between 1784 and 1791 he published numerous pamphlets and essays on microscopes, astronomical and geographical studies, navigation, electricity and magnetism and his *Lectures on Natural and Experimental Philosophy*, first published in 1791, were re-published posthumously by William Jones who bought his stock, library and copyrights at auction after his death in 1795.

In 1790 he published *A Short Dissertation on the Barometer, Thermometer, and other Meteorological Instruments*. He calls it in the preface a 'hastily written tract' and published it because his large planned work on meteorology would need many years of preparation. In spite of its imperfections however it is a valuable source of information and evidence from it has been used extensively in Chapter Four. Besides the useful descriptions of contemporary barometers it contains a list, with prices, of meteorological instruments made and sold by him. These include:

	£	s.	d.
A plain portable barometer	2	2	0
Ditto with a thermometer	3	3	0
A plain barometer, covered frame and glass door	2	12	6
Ditto with a thermometer	3	13	6
A barometer with a long cylindric thermometer	4	4	0
A ditto with ditto, and De Luc's hygrometer	7	7	0
A barometer and thermometer, with a gauge, the indexes moving by rack-work	5	15	6
Ditto neater	6	16	6
A barometer for measuring the altitude of mountains, etc.	9	9	0
Marine barometers			
Diagonal, wheel, and statical barometers			

The lack of a price against the last four types suggests that they were not part of Adams' regular stock but that they could be made to order.

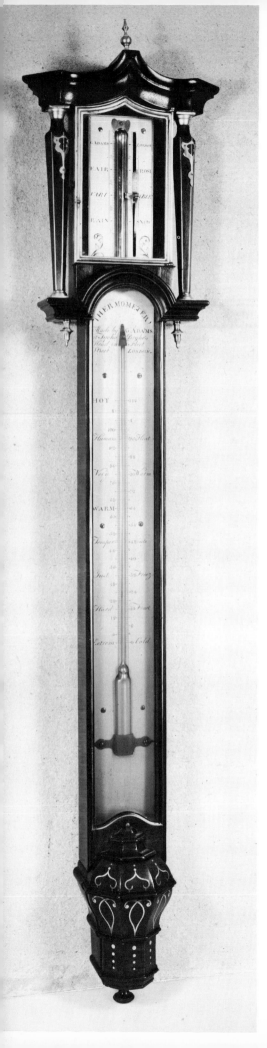

I have seen many cistern-tube barometers attributable to the younger Adams but none of any other type.

The list quoted above reappears in almost identical form in a fifteen-page catalogue of optical, mathematical and physical instruments appended to Adams' *Geometrical and Graphical Essays* (1791): as evidence of the growth of his business it is perhaps worth comparing it with the items extracted from a four-page list which was published in his *Essay on Electricity* (1784):

						£	s.	d.
Barometers	..	..	..	..	..	2	2	0
Ditto	..	..	..	..	..	2	12	6
Barometers and Thermometers from £3 3s. to						5	5	0
Marine Barometers	..	..	..	..				

The instrument illustrated in Plates 20 and 23 answers the description of 'a plain barometer, covered frame and glass door'. The dark polished mahogany was much favoured by Adams and several barometers survive mounted on frames of slightly different style but similar wood. The silvered brass plates (Plate 23) are of a style found on the barometers of many contemporary makers (*cf.* Plates 18, 32, 71) but the framing of the signature in a pennant is attractive. The portable tube has been renewed. In the Museum of the History of Science in Oxford there is a 'plain portable barometer': the tube is fixed to a plain mahogany frame and the engraving on the plates is simple with only

Fair	Frost
Change	able
Rain	Snow

The signature is again engraved in a pennant in the arch: a manual vernier is fitted. Unfortunately the instrument is in very bad condition and a siphon tube has been substituted for the original cistern tube and screw. An instrument incorporating features of both these designs—panelled case and glazed door, simple weather indications and manual vernier—but with a scroll pediment was sold at Sotheby's in December 1963. Adams in fact sold a large number of such stock instruments and many of them survive: a description of their points of variety would be tedious.

PLATE 62
G. Adams, London
37·5″ × 8·3″
Victoria and Albert Museum,
London: Crown copyright

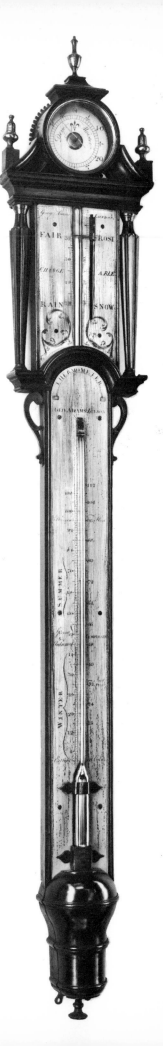

Besides these simpler instruments he sold several barometers in more elegant cases. I think it is correct to attribute
to him the instrument illustrated in Plate 62.[1] Certain
attribution is not possible and it may have been sold by
his father. The quotation of the Trade Sign ('Tycho Brahe's
Head') in the address engraved on the thermometer plate
is not conclusive either way: although hanging signs were
forbidden in the City in 1762 and three-quarters of the
houses were designated by numbers in the 1770 Directories
the use of signs, displayed on boards fixed to the outside
walls of shops, continued in the busier streets.[2] Dudley
Adams still maintained the board showing 'Tycho Brahe's
Head' after his brother George's death.

The casework is of mahogany. The angled architectural
cornice is a pleasing feature and the cistern cover and
tapered hexagonal pillars are dexterously inlaid with brass:
brass is also employed for the capitals, bases and applied
decoration of the pillars, for the glazed door and thermometer bezel, and for the finial and inverted mounts under
the cornice of the thermometer case. The barometer plates
are the poorest feature of the design: they seem too small
and are engraved with only three summer and winter
indications. The simple acanthus engraving is an attempt
to enrich them. The thermometer plate is also silvered and
is engraved with Fahrenheit's third scale. There is the usual
leather-based cistern and portable screw; and the tube,
which has been replaced, was probably of about 0·25″
bore. The manual vernier is moved by the hinged rod which
can be seen hanging downwards in the slot: a small knob
is missing from the end of the rod. Readings are taken by
adjusting the notch in the plate which is attached to the
vernier so that it coincides with the edge of the mercury
meniscus and not with its centre.

The barometer of Plate 63 shares many of these features.
It is less decorated, having none of the brass inlays, and its
silvered barometer and thermometer plates are left exposed:
but the case is broadly similar in conception. The mahogany
veneers are dark and unfigured in striking contrast to the
silvered plates. The finials, the capitals and bases of the
columns and the scrolls on each side of the case beneath

[1] Victoria and Albert Museum, Inventory No. W21–1961.
[2] Sir Ambrose Heal *The Signboards of Old London Shops* (1947) p. 2 *et seq.*

PLATE 63
George Adams, London
41·5″ × 6·8″
Private collection

the hood are all of brass. The register plates (Plate 64) are engraved as before with the simplest summer and winter indications and the 3″ scale is given on both sides of the tube. A curved pointer is attached to the ·01″ vernier. The tube is modern and is fitted to a leather-based boxwood cistern. The mercury thermometer employs the usual Fahrenheit scale and the oatbeard hygrometer in the crest uses the normal arbitrary 30° scale. The method of adjusting its pointer is unusual: a large brass cogwheel is set behind the case whose teeth can be turned manually. They also add decoration to the hood.

Like many eighteenth-century makers Adams also made instruments for export and I have seen a cistern-tube barometer with two separate scales—English inches and decimals and French inches and lines—signed by him. It was mounted on a simple frame veneered with mahogany with a broken pediment and shallow turned cistern cover. It can be dated *c.* 1790. Troughton was another contemporary maker who sold barometers with dual scales of this sort.[1]

[1] See p. 240.

PLATE 64
Detail of Plate 63

ALEXANDER ADIE   b.1774–d.1858

1. 94 Nicholson Street, Edinburgh (1804–7)
2. 96 Nicholson Street, Edinburgh (1807–10)
3. 8 Nicholson Street, Edinburgh (1810–11)
4. 15 Nicholson Street, Edinburgh (1811–18)

5. 35 Princes Street, Edinburgh (1818–34)
6. 58 Princes Street, Edinburgh (1835–42)
7. 50 Princes Street, Edinburgh (1843–58)

ADIE IS described in commercial directories as an optician and he held appointments as such to William IV and Queen Victoria. He was apprenticed to his uncle John Miller who died *c.*1825 and was his partner for a time at various addresses in Nicholson Street (1804–12). Instruments survive signed 'Miller and Adie'. He later took his son into the business. He was actively interested in meteorology as early as 1816 and although he later did a thriving business in marine barometers for the navy and in ordinary domestic cistern barometers he is chiefly known as the patentee and inventor of the sympiesometer: the patent was granted in 1818. This instrument is not strictly within the scope of this book, but it was made in large numbers by both Adie and others and it was intended for general, not only marine, use: examples are often to be found nowadays in antique shops and interested readers should refer to Dr. Middleton's work[1] where one of the very few accurate accounts of it can be found.

[1] Middleton *History of the Barometer* p. 378 *et seq.*

JAMES AYSCOUGH   fl 1732–63

1. Golden Spectacles and Quadrant, Ludgate Street
2. Great Golden Spectacles, Ludgate Street (1752)
3. 33 Ludgate Street

AYSCOUGH, the son of a Wiltshire clergyman, was an optician and probably did no more than sell barometers. He became a member of the Spectaclemakers' Company in 1740. His main wares appear to have been spectacles, lenses and microscopes and he wrote a pamphlet on a pocket microscope with his partner and previous employer

James Mann in 1743. A trade card in the Heal Collection[1] lists barometers and thermometers among his stock at the Great Golden Spectacles. Another trade card, in the Science Museum, gives his address as 33 Ludgate Street and advertises 'barometers, diagonal, standard, or portable': this advertisement was continued by his successor James Linnell who had been his apprentice from 1754 and whose own card can be seen in the Science Museum, London.

His claim to mention here rests on the exquisite barometer illustrated in Plate 65 which is signed 'J. Ayscough, London'.[2] There seems no reason to reject the attribution of this instrument to him even though his name is not signed in full. He is the only contemporary instrument-maker named Ayscough of whom we have any records and he advertised barometers. The mahogany carcase is fronted by a mirror which serves as a panel to conceal the tube. Set in front of the mirror and silhouetted in many places by it is an elaborate carved mahogany design of the greatest elegance which is composed of conventional scroll patterns, flowers, fruits, foliage and architectural columns in perspective. The cistern cover is in the form of a carved gilt face representing the sun, in deliberate contrast perhaps to the icicles above the thermometer. The instrument is seen to best advantage when hung opposite a source of light as in the photograph: the intricacy of the carving is not only more easily observed but is also thrown into high relief by the reflection of light behind it. The silvered barometer and thermometer plates are set behind glass: the barometer scale is unusual in extending from 26″–31″ but the vernier, which has a sickle-shaped pointer and is operated by a knob which is fitted to the right of the case at the foot of the plates, cannot be used below 27·5″. The weather indications are standard. I have not seen the cistern but a portable screw is visible beneath the sun's chin. The mercury thermometer is headed 'Fahrinheit's Scale', i.e. the third scale which is given from 5° to the unnecessary height of 212°: the plate is embellished with engraving round the edge.

[1] British Museum.

[2] Victoria and Albert Museum, Inventory No. W27–1926. It is a pity that owing to the fragility of the frame this barometer is displayed in a sealed glass case. Its release would improve its appearance.

PLATE 65
J. Ayscough, London
41″ × 7·3″
*Victoria and Albert Museum,
London:
Crown Copyright*

JOHN BENNETT

fl 1743–68

The Globe, Crown Court, between St Ann's, Soho, and Golden Square

BENNETT held appointments to three members of the Royal Family. He was a well-known optical, mathematical and physical instrument-maker and his trade card is illustrated in Plate 66.

The instrument hanging on the left of the design bears a strong resemblance to the barometer by Sisson of Plate 135 but the scale shows that it is in fact an alcohol thermometer: the same instrument appears in the trade cards of several contemporary makers. The barometer on the right is a decorative object: it is portable but the engraver has omitted any sort of pointer or vernier.

It is I think reasonable to attribute to him the interesting barometer signed 'Bennett, London' in the Whipple Science Museum at Cambridge.[1] It is closely similar to the Sisson instrument of Plate 135. The mahogany case follows the same design with a

[1] Inventory No. 1090. It is illustrated in Gunther's *Early Science in Cambridge* p. 94 and was in store when I studied it in 1963.

hemispherical cistern cover, the top of which can be lifted off. The tube is protected by a mahogany sleeve and the bulb at its top has a mahogany cover. The silvered plates carry a conventional scale but the manual vernier covers 2·1″ (having twenty divisions) and it is attached to a hinged pointer: this pointer is notched, possibly to allow observation of both the centre and edges of the meniscus. A second pointer can be used for recording the previous reading. As in the Sisson barometer the cistern is open and measures 3·9″ in diameter: and a similar ivory scale and vernier allow an accurate computation of the cistern level.

J O H N   B I R D   b.1709–d.1776

1. Sea Quadrant, Court Gardens, Strand
2. Sea Quadrant, near the New Exchange Buildings, Strand (1748–63)

BIRD WAS an optical and mathematical instrument-maker who came to London from Durham in 1740. He gained experience in the workshops of George Graham and Jonathan Sisson, for whom he was working in 1740. He was an accomplished and well-known maker and published two treatises on astronomical instruments: he also produced navigational instruments, barometers, thermometers etc., being especially noted for his scales.

Professor Taylor[1] has recorded a 'Bird' barometer and thermometer among various instruments left by a William Wales: and a number of barometers survive with the signature 'Bird' which were probably made in his workshop. There is a mahogany cistern barometer in the Museum of the History of Science at Oxford: the case has been almost completely renewed but the original urn type cistern cover is intact together with an ivory float of the type described in Chapter Four (pp. 66–7). Dr. Middleton[2] mentions an open cistern barometer made by Bird for a certain Roger Pickering who said in a paper submitted to the *Philosophical Transactions*,[3] without unfortunately describing it in detail, that it gave readings to ·0025″.

[1] *Mathematical Practitioners of Hanoverian England* (manuscript).
[2] Middleton
History of the Barometer pp. 198–9.
[3] Vol. 43 No. 473 (1744) p. 5.

THOMAS BLUNT fl 1760–d. 1822

22 Cornhill

A MATHEMATICAL and optical instrument-maker, Blunt was the son of a Surrey shoemaker. He was apprenticed to Edward Nairne in 1760 and became free of the Spectaclemakers' Company in 1771. From 1774 they were partners in the well-known firm of Nairne and Blunt. According to Professor Taylor[1] the name of the partnership was used until 1822 in spite of Nairne's death in 1806 and Blunt's own name was used by his successor T. Harris until 1827: but Blunt appears in several directories after 1801 under his own name and is styled 'Mathematical Instrument Maker to His Majesty'. In 1805 he had a son with him in the business, Nairne having presumably retired.

He was an instrument-maker of distinction: he was associated with the Portuguese scientist J. H. de Magellan and devised some of the features of Magellan's 'New Barometer', which was designed for measuring heights etc., and a description of which the inventor published in 1779.[2]

[1] *Mathematical Practitioners
of Hanoverian England* (manuscript).
[2] *Description et Usages des Nouvaux Baromètres*
pp. 90, 92, etc.

Several domestic barometers survive signed 'Blunt, London' which can be ascribed to him. They can probably but not necessarily be dated after Nairne's apparent retirement in 1805. There is a mahogany cistern barometer in the Museum of the History of Science at Oxford: the case is panelled and has the black edging fashionable at the beginning of the nineteenth century but it is in poor condition and the pediment is missing. There is a manual vernier: and a thermometer is set on the front of the case with a hygrometer above it.

Blunt favoured round-topped mahogany cases (*cf.* Plate 20) but his cases were not always panelled. One cistern barometer which I have studied was of rich mahogany with a herringbone inlay and had a brass sleeve encasing the tube: another had an ebonized inlay and an exposed tube. Both were portable with oval cistern covers, standard plates and manual verniers. His trade card (Plate 67) illustrates a barometer on the right but its design harks back to a period long before Blunt was working. Another barometer can be seen hanging on the wall of the shop which is depicted on the card: this is badly drawn but could be interpreted as a siphon or cistern-tube instrument in a mahogany case with a broken pediment (*cf.* Plate 36).

Two fine angle barometers similar to Plate 134 and signed by Blunt are extant:[1] in style they seem too early for Blunt to have been the original retailer and it is conceivable that his signature was added when they were repaired.

[1] One illustrated and the other mentioned in R. W. Symonds' *Furniture-making in 17th and 18th century England* (1955) Figs. 362, 363 and p. 235 (see p. 219).

J O H N   C U F F   b. *c.*1708–d.1772

Reflecting Microscope and Spectacles, Serjeants Inn Gate, Fleet Street

A WELL-KNOWN optical instrument-maker, Cuff was especially noted for his microscopes and astronomical instruments. He was apprenticed to James Mann who was also the master and subsequently the partner of James Ayscough. He published pamphlets on microscopes in 1742 and 1744 and was Master of the Spectaclemakers' Company in 1748–9. Like most of his rivals he made instruments both for the trade and for sale in his own shop. His trade card, a copy of which survives in the

Heal Collection,[1] advertised 'all types' of optical instruments, microscopes etc., and many other scientific instruments including barometers and thermometers.

I have only seen one barometer which can be ascribed to him: it is illustrated in Plate 68. The panelled pine case is veneered with highly figured burr walnut: the plain cistern cover is in surprising contrast to the moulding of the edges of the case and the arched cornice. The three brass ball-shaped finials were a favourite stylistic feature of about 1730 (*cf.* Plates 17, 69). A glazed brass door protects the silvered brass plates: these are engraved with conventional weather indications but are enriched at the bottom with some brass foliate decoration. The instrument is portable, with leather-based cistern and screw, and the manual pointer is made, as frequently, in the shape of a sickle. The high quality and the balanced proportions of the case make this instrument one of the best examples of a cistern-tube barometer of its period. It is probable that like other leading spectacle and optical instrument-makers of the eighteenth century Cuff regularly stocked barometers among his wares: but this appears to be the only example known at present. Its quality induces the hope that others may come to light.

[1] British Museum.

PLATE 68
Cuff
40″ × 5″
Collection of Ronald A. Lee

DANIEL DELANDER b. 1674–d. 1733

1. Devereux Court
2. Temple, Fleet Street (from 1712)

A CLOCKMAKER of some repute, Delander was apprenticed in 1692. He was elected to the Clockmakers' Company in 1699. According to F. J. Britten[1] he had at one time been one of Thomas Tompion's servants. Several clocks of good quality survive bearing his signature.

Only one barometer signed by Delander is known. This is illustrated in Plate 69. Now in a private collection, it hung originally in Clumber Park, the home of the Dukes of Newcastle. It can be assumed that Delander made it for the Duke of Newcastle, who also patronized John Whitehurst, in about 1725–30. The oak case is veneered with ebony which, as can be seen in the illustration, contrasts strikingly with the silver colour of the mercury and the silver inlays on the trunk and cistern cover. The two brackets, which clamp the tube to the trunk and are decorated with chased leaf motifs, are also of silver, as are the capitals, bases and reedings of the Corinthian columns and the little rosettes above them: the register plates and the signature plate above the hood are silver and the three ball finials (cf. Plates 17, 68) are of brass with applied silver decoration. The engraving of the register plates (Plate 70) is particularly worthy of notice. The common acanthus motif is used to unusually good advantage: and the flourishes are finely drawn. The scale is that commonly used on cistern barometers at the time—28″–31″, each inch divided into decimals and twentieths—and there is nothing unusual about the weather indications except that they include the directions 'Riseing Fair or Frost' and 'Falling Rain Snow or Winds' which were popular with makers such as Patrick and Quare (Plates 110, 116). The instrument is portable, with leather-based cistern and screw, and the manual pointer is made in the form of a leaf.

The workmanship of this barometer is exceptional and it is fair to say that it is one of the finest cistern-tube barometers extant. The combination of silver mounts and ebony or ebonized casework had often been used for both bracket and long-case clocks by leading clockmakers of the previous generation (Fromanteel, Knibb, Tompion and others) and the effect is one of sober opulence. Another barometer which uses the same contrast to equally fine effect can be seen in Plate 113.

[1] *Old Clocks and Watches and their Makers* (3rd edition 1911) p. 648.

PLATE 69
Delander
43″ × 5·4″
Private collection
PLATE 70.
Detail of Plate 69

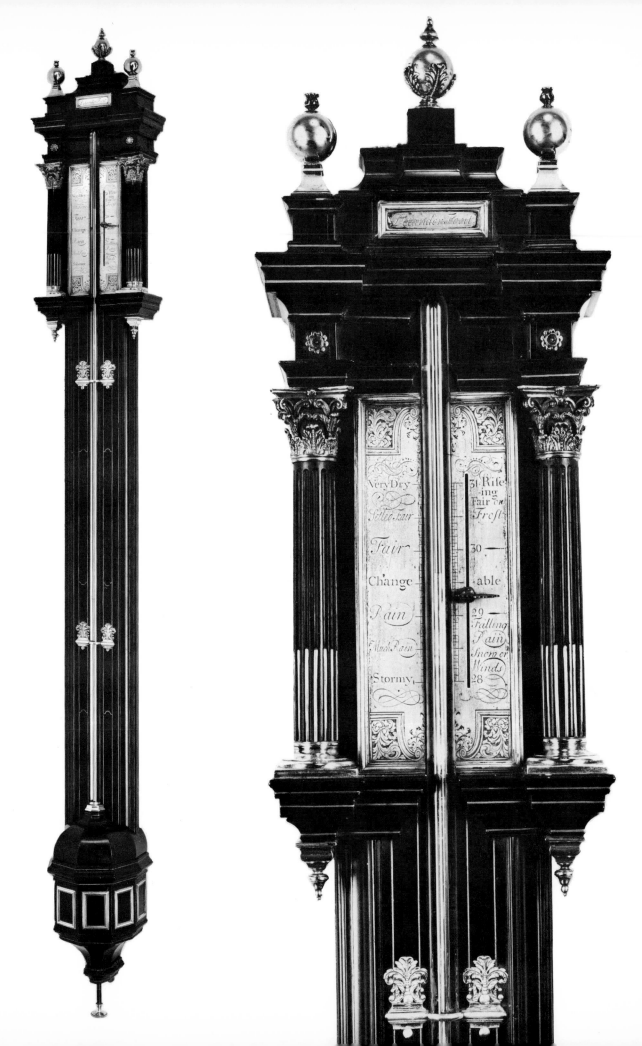

GEORGE DOLLOND b. 1774–d. 1856

1. 59 St Paul's Churchyard (1804–56)
2. 61 Paternoster Row (1854–6)

THE NEPHEW of Peter Dollond, his real name was Huggins; he changed it to Dollond for business reasons. He was apprenticed to his uncle in 1788 and became his partner in 1804. He continued the family reputation for optical and mathematical instruments and held the appointment of Optician to William IV. He was elected F.R.S. in 1819 and published a number of works on instruments. By 1821 he was in sole charge of the business which still survives under the name of Dollond and Aitchison Ltd.

Apart from selling Adie's sympiesometers in London, Dollond sold a wide selection of meteorological instruments. Barometers sold by the firm were almost invariably signed 'Dollond' and, as with the Adams, Sisson and Whitehurst families, attribution of individual instruments must rely on the evidence of stylistic features. Large numbers of Dollond barometers are extant but except in a few instances it is not possible to state without doubt that an instrument derived from the Dollond workshop under Peter's or George's direction. Certain instruments however were clearly sold after 1820 when Peter Dollond died and can be attributed to George: these include standard mahogany wheel barometers with scroll pediments and 10″ or 12″ dials which were almost certainly only retailed. One 10″ instrument which I have studied had a round-topped case with satinwood banding and the hygrometer set immediately above the dial.

Many other barometers survive which could have been made before or after 1820: but since Peter was seventy-four years old when in 1804 his nephew became his partner it is perhaps fair to attribute to George, who was presumably the more active partner, most of the instruments produced by the firm from the turn of the century. A favourite design during this period was the bow-fronted case similar to Plate 33 veneered with mahogany and topped by either a scroll or a square moulded pediment: an ebonized urn-shaped cistern cover usually conceals the portable cistern, the plates are silvered and there is a key operated vernier. Many of these are found in private collections. There is one in the City of Gloucester Museum but the bottom of it was unfortunately reconstructed by an ignorant and tasteless restorer before it was bequeathed to the Museum: the case has a scroll pediment with an ivory finial and a thermometer is fitted to the plates.

Another type, also portable, of which I have seen many examples is housed in a flat panelled mahogany case with a scroll pediment, turned cistern cover and a glazed door: a manual vernier is fitted and a thermometer often mounted either on the front of the case or on the register plates.

Dollond's instruments varied widely in quality as can only be expected of a large workshop catering for all types of customer.

PETER DOLLOND b.1730–d.1820

1. Vine Street, Spitalfields (1750)
2. Golden Spectacles and Sea Quadrant, near Exeter Exchange, Strand (1752–63)
3. 59 St Paul's Churchyard (1769–1820)
4. 35 Haymarket (1784)

THE ELDEST SON of John Dollond the elder, who was a Huguenot silk weaver, Peter worked originally in the family business. At the age of twenty however he set up as an optician and he later became the most eminent optical instrument-maker of the late eighteenth century. The 1763 Directory describes him as 'Optician to His Majesty and the Duke of York and sole maker of the refracting telescopes invented by the late Mr. John Dollond who obtained his Majesty's Royal Letters Patent for the said invention': the patent was dated 1757 and Peter's right to it was unsuccessfully contested by most of his leading rivals in 1764. In 1752 his father, a keen amateur physicist, joined him and they were partners until his father's death in 1761. From 1766–1804 he took his younger brother John into partnership and after his death his nephew George. For a period after 1784, the firm had a shop in the Haymarket. Among his workmen was Jesse Ramsden who became his brother-in-law. In 1799 he was Master of the Spectaclemakers' Company.

J. H. Bernoulli, who visited his workshop in 1769, called it 'très considerable' and listed several astronomical instruments on offer. He also added that Dollond's instruments were not of consistently high quality and that if a first-class instrument signed by Dollond came to hand it was probably not finished in his own workshop: he often maintained his reputation by having frames and scales etc. made by Ramsden 'qui passe pour un des meilleurs artistes de Londres, dans ce genre'.[1] J. H. de Magellan[2] said that Dollond made barometers to his new design, as did Nairne and Blunt.

[1] *Lettres Astronomiques* pp. 68–9.
[2] *Description et Usages des Nouvaux Baromètres* p. 142.

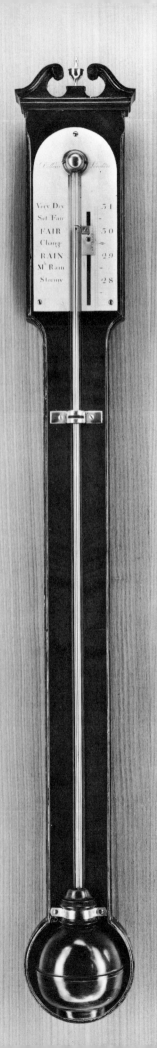

As I have said in the context of George Dollond, attribution of instruments is not easy because they are usually signed 'Dollond', or sometimes 'Dollond London' or 'Dollond Fecit' neither of which is any more helpful. Having however allocated to George the barometers made in the nineteenth century, I can arbitrarily attribute to Peter (although George was in his workshop from 1788) those of the more distinguished eighteenth century. Plate 71 illustrates an example. It is a relatively simple instrument—the case is not panelled for instance—but the mahogany veneer is of fine figure. The tube is portable but the screw at the base is missing. The register plates are of a standard design and quality found on the barometers of many instrument-makers of the later half of the century. Identical plates are fitted to barometers, for example, by George Adams the younger and Benjamin Martin: it is very likely that the same engraver executed them all. The plates are also arched whereas squared plates would have better suited the design of the case. Many contemporary makers, including Adams, Martin and Dollond himself, sold round-topped barometers during this period and the use of arched plates in this example is odd.

Examples by Dollond similar to the Adams barometer illustrated in Plate 20 are extant, but employing mahogany of lighter colour. One example in a private collection which I studied still had its original tube of 0·375″ bore, the leather-based cistern being of boxwood.

There is an interesting barometer by Dollond in the Museo di Storia della Scienza at Florence,[1] but I have only seen a photograph of it. It is suspended in a stout four-legged frame which can be screwed to the floor and a lead weight at the base is meant to keep the instrument vertical. This suggests that it might have been designed for marine use. The round-topped case is of mahogany and a glazed door protects the silvered plates to which a manual vernier is fitted. Dr Middleton[2] reports that the cistern is of the closed portable type but that the adjusting screw has been lost.

The same author also mentions a mahogany portable barometer signed 'Dollond, London', which he dates *c.* 1780, in the Conservatoire National des Arts et Métiers, Paris.[3] This again I have not yet seen: it has silvered plates and a vernier giving readings to ·01″.

Peter Dollond does not seem to have employed the better cabinet-makers as did some of his contemporaries. Unless notable examples of casework bearing his signature come to light in the future it can be assumed that his workshop sold mostly functional barometers and did not cater for the customer who wanted an elegant piece of furniture.

[1] Inventory No. 1160.
[2] *History of the Barometer* p. 152.
[3] *Ibid.* pp. 205 and 459.

PLATE 71
Dollond, London
39·3″ × 5″
*English Scottish
and Australian Bank Ltd.*

JOHN ELLICOTT b.1706–d.1772

17 Sweetings Alley, Royal Exchange

ONE OF THE most famous of English clockmakers, Ellicott was also a mathematician and physicist of great ability. He was in business as a clockmaker by about 1728: he succeeded his father John who, coming originally from Bodmin, was admitted to the Clockmakers' Company in 1696 and died in 1733. He was Clockmaker to George III and is best known for his invention of a compensated pendulum in 1752. He submitted a paper on a pyrometer for measuring the expansion of metals with heat to the Royal Society in 1736 and was elected F.R.S. in 1738: later he submitted other papers on clockwork and served on the Society's Council for three years. His friends included many of the eminent astronomers and scientists of the day and he had an observatory and laboratory at his house in Hackney. He took his son Edward into partnership three years before his death and was succeeded by him.

A number of barometers were sold from his workshop and, like his clocks, they are usually of the highest workmanship. Some long-case clocks survive with wheel barometers set in the door. R. W. Symonds illustrated one in *A Book of English Clocks* (1947)[1] and in *Furniture-making in 17th and 18th century England* (1955).[2] Another, with a similar dial, is fitted to the clock illustrated in Plate 72. The tall case may originally have been surmounted by a decorative design in walnut with finials[3] but it is otherwise in excellent condition. The movement is in perfect order and the dial

[1] Plates 60B, 61.
[2] Figs. 316, 317, 318.
[3] This could have followed the design of the clock by Ellicott which is illustrated in R. W. Symond's *A Book of English Clocks* (1947) Plate 52: *cf.* also Plate 74.

PLATE 72
John Ellicott, London
92·5″ × 21″
Author's collection

engraving, brass spandrels and pierced steel hands are all of good quality. The burr walnut veneer and restrained mouldings of the case are typical of Ellicott's casework of about 1740 and the trunk and base are further enriched by lines of chequered inlay. The siphon barometer tube (the original was 35″ in length and approximately 0·5″ in diameter) is set in grooves carved in the oak body of the door and is concealed by a detachable oak panel. There is a double grooved brass pulley wheel of half an inch diameter and the recording hand (the pierced hour type hand) is operated by the knob below the dial to which its arbor is connected by the usual cord and wheels. The visible parts of the barometer (Plate 73) betray Ellicott's trade: the finely pierced hands, the mat brass centre of the dial and silvered chapter ring are traditional features of clock design. The dial is glazed and the bezel measures 9·5″ in diameter. The scale spans the usual 28″–31″ but each inch is divided unusually into forty parts: the scale is repeated on the inner edge of the chapter ring for the sake of the recording hand. There is nothing unusual about the weather indications.

A similar clock of larger proportions is illustrated in Plate 74. Various features of the clock and dial work differ from the previous example, as can be seen by comparing the illustrations. The casework and the figure of the veneer are of remarkable quality but the frets are missing from the hood (cf. Plate 72) both below and above the arched cornice and the pillars are probably not original: in spite of these blemishes the overall effect is majestic. The barometer set in the door is also of grander proportions, the bezel measuring nearly 12·5″, and the dial glass 11″ in diameter (Plate 75). Many of its features differ slightly from the previous example. The scale is of only half the accuracy, each inch being divided into twentieths. The chapter ring is wider and the weather indications are engraved round the circumference. This feature is not entirely successful since although their larger size enhances their legibility only three out of seven states of the weather are engraved the right way up: and the fact that the inches 28 and 31 are not upside down makes the design inconsistent. A better balance is achieved in Plates 73 and 76. The pierced hands are both expectedly longer than those of Plate 73 and different in design. The mechanism is similar to

PLATE 73
Detail of Plate 72

PLATE 74
John Ellicott, London
99·7″ × 20·8″
*Victoria and Albert Museum, London:
from the collection of C.D. Rotch.
Crown copyright*

that of Plate 72 but the pulley wheel is only 0·25″ in diameter: the tube has been renewed. On the inside of the door is pasted an old but undated 'Advertisement concerning the Barometer' which consists of weather observations made by a certain Thomas Ellinett of Charing Cross, Norwich: it is possible that the original owner lived in Norfolk. So far as I know the barometer is the only one by Ellicott in a public collection in this country.

Plate 76 illustrates the only Ellicott barometer I have seen which was not mounted on a clock. The case is of pleasant design and is also veneered with burr walnut. The carcase of the upper part of the case is of oak whereas the dial is backed by walnut: the carcase is in fact composed of three separate pieces which are clamped together by the brass plates visible above and below the dial, and I think it is fair to surmise that because this frame seems specially devised wheel barometers on their own did not form part of Ellicott's stock in trade. The barometer dial was probably made with the intention of fitting it to a clock. Its chapter ring and hands are almost identical in design, size and choice of materials with the example of Plate 73 and the only differences are minor points of engraving (e.g. 'Settd Fair' instead of 'Set Fair', the positioning of 'Rain' and 'Fair', and the arrangement and shape of the inch digits). The fact that the instrument is not mounted on a clock has led to the painting of the signature on the lighter veneer at the base.

It is strange that Ellicott did not specify a more exact scale on his wheel barometers. He was a leading physicist of his day and Tompion had divided his scale into ·01″ forty years earlier (Plates 143 and 146). Possibly he realized that the unusually long cord necessary when the pulley wheel was set so far above the short limb of the siphon tube prevented great accuracy. He may also have recognized that Tompion's accuracy was more apparent than real since it depended on imperfect materials.

I have seen no cistern-tube barometers by Ellicott although I have been shown one poor counterfeit which is now in the U.S.A. It is reasonable to assume that he sold cistern-tube barometers since an example is illustrated on a trade card

opposite PLATE 75
Detail of Plate 74
PLATE 76
John Ellicott, London 1740
43·5″ × 8·8″
Collection of Mrs S. T. Cook

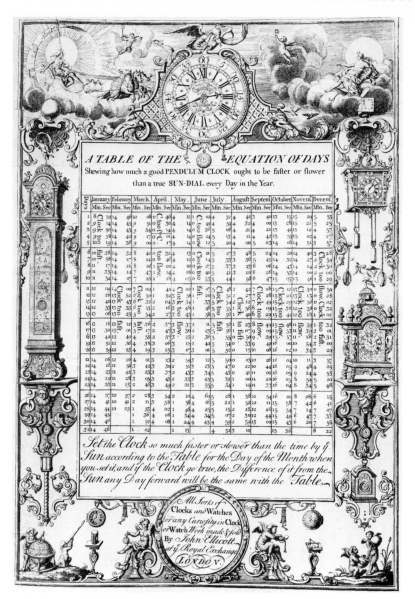

which principally advertises his equation clocks and which survives in the Heal Collection (Plate 77).[1] It is a portable barometer of the pillar type which was common in the early eighteenth century (Plate 116) but the trunk is entirely of spiral form and looks like a piece of barley sugar: the plates are set in an arched glazed hood. It is impossible to say whether this barometer represented a type sold by Ellicott or was a fanciful invention of the designer of the card: but since most of the clocks advertised by the same card are extravagant distortions of Ellicott's usual work the second alternative seems more likely.

[1] British Museum.

JAMES GATTY

130 High Holborn

I HAVE so far been unable to discover exactly when Gatty was working since the commercial directories are woefully silent. For the same reason it is not known whether he was an optician by trade or whether he was one of the many Italian glass-blowers who set up retail businesses in London in about 1800. His address in Holborn is omitted from the early street directories but he could possibly be identified with a James Gattey who is listed as a silversmith and pawnbroker of 64 Tooley Street as early as 1802. Possibly too he was originally in partnership with a Ronketti since an early wheel barometer survives signed 'Roncheti and Gatty'. If so, this could have been J. M. Ronketti or Bapt. Roncheti.

Gatty deserves special mention because the barometers bearing his signature which survive are generally of high quality. Plate 78 shows a 'stick' barometer which is now in the City of Gloucester Museum. The mahogany veneered case is of conventional design but the cistern cover is hemispherical: the more usual shape is seen in Plate 36. The chequered inlay is attractive but by no means a rarity; the shaping of the protective glazed door in order to conform with the narrowing of the trunk is an elegant and unusual feature. The engraving of the silvered plates (Plate 79) is of good quality and the duplicate weather indications for summer and winter are not common at this period. The original siphon tube had a diameter of 0·625″—unusually large for an instrument of this type—but the bore may have been only 0·25″

I have also seen a mahogany cistern-tube barometer by Gatty with a bayonet tube. The case was

PLATE 78
Jas Gatty, London
38·5″ × 5·2″
City of Gloucester Museum: from the collection of S. Marling

PLATE 79
Detail of Plate 78

of very good quality with a border of crossbanding: there was a scroll pediment and, unusual on a bayonet-tube barometer, the plates were protected by a glazed door.

Gatty is best known however for his wheel barometers which can rightly claim to be among the most handsome banjo barometers ever made in this country. One of them is illustrated in Plate 80. The slender shape of the case is most elegant and the veneer is of exceptional quality. There is some disagreement among furniture dealers about the identity of the wood used for this veneer. Some believe it is amboyna: but amboyna is a light coloured wood and it is most probably burr yew. The argument against yew is based on the fact that its knots, while they are often clustered, seldom cover a large area; but none of the veneered areas on this instrument is extensive and there is one place (above the thermometer to the left) where there are practically no knots. The attractive crossbanding round the border of the case is of kingwood and it is emphasized by three line inlays on the inside and one on the outside edge: the sides of the case are veneered with mahogany and the pedestals of the finials are likewise of mahogany. The thermometer case, which is detachable and locked in place by the sliding brass knob beneath it, is also faced with crossbanded kingwood. The engraving of the silvered dial which is just under 10″ in diameter is of above average quality and the unusual horizontal setting of the weather indications is a notable feature. The scale is traditional and the inches are divided into hundredths but the numbering of the 0·1″ divisions is uncommon. The blued steel main hand is conventional and the recording hand is of pierced brass. The tube has been replaced and the recording hand and hygrometer are both set by keys operating through cord and wheels. The alcohol thermometer uses the usual Fahrenheit scale and the hygrometer is the usual oatbeard type. Other almost identical instruments survive in private collections and their quality is consistent.

PLATE 80
Jas Gatty
130 High Holborn, London
41·5″ × 11·5″
Private collection

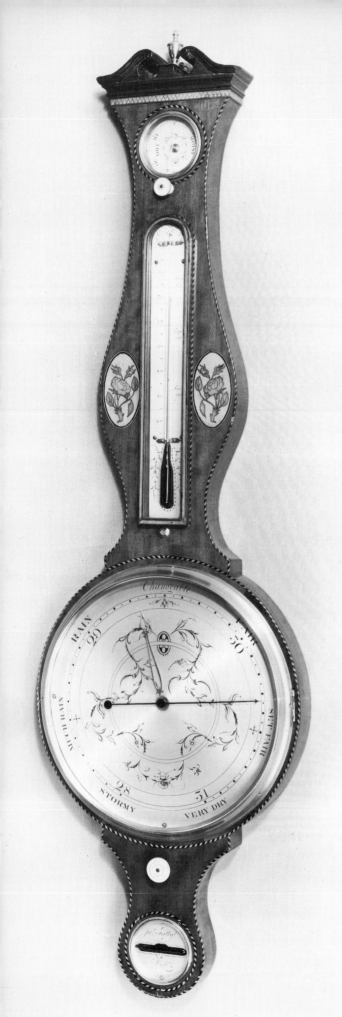

A wheel barometer of very different appearance is illustrated in Plate 81. The ancillary instruments are the same, the thermometer is detachable, and the dial again measures about 10″ in diameter; but the case, which is veneered with an attractive light-coloured mahogany, is highly decorative. It lacks the elegance of Plate 80 owing partly to the treatment of the top; it is in fact some 2″ shorter than the previous example, there being less space allowed for the hygrometer, and the moulded scroll pediment gives the impression of interrupting rather than containing the curves of the case. The decoration however makes up for any shortcoming on this score and the bordering of each dial in addition to the case with a chequered inlay is unusual. The tooth design of green and yellow woods beneath the cornice of the pediment is not uncommon (cf. Plate 126). The floral engraving of the silvered dial is equally elaborate and would perhaps be more emphasized if there were no floral paterae inlaid on the case. The scale is in twentieths but unusually signified with dots instead of line divisions. The main hand is of steel and the recording hand, which is operated by the detachable ivory knob below the dial, is of brass. The brass bezel is hinged. The mechanism has been entirely renewed.

Gatty also sold 'double' barometers of the type described on pp. 86–9. An example of his in an arched mahogany case with box-wood plates and an alcohol thermometer is shown in Plate 41 and an almost identical example can be seen in the City of Gloucester Museum.

PLATE 81
Jas Gatty
39″ × 11·8″
Collection of the Stock Exchange, London:
gift of H. A. F. Goodison

GEORGE GRAHAM
b. 1673 – d. 1751

1. Dial and Three Crowns, Water Lane, Fleet Street
2. Dial and One Crown, Fleet Street (from 1720)

GRAHAM was the leading maker of clocks and astronomical instruments of his generation in England. He was born in Cumberland but came to London as a boy and was apprenticed in 1688, becoming a member of the Clockmakers' Company in 1695. He became one of Thomas Tompion's assistants in 1696, married Tompion's niece and was in partnership with him 1711–13. On Tompion's death in 1713 Graham took control of the business which remained in Water Lane until he moved to the other side of Fleet Street in 1720. He was elected F.R.S. in 1721 and served on the Council of the Royal Society in 1722 as well as being Master of the Clockmakers' Company. His workmen included John Bird and probably Jonathan Sisson, both of whom inherited Graham's reputation for astronomical instruments.

Graham's renown was international. He was best known for his clocks and watches, for his inventions of the dead-beat escapement and the mercury-compensated pendulum and for his improvement of the cylinder escapement; also for his astronomical instruments, including the famous iron mural arc at Greenwich made for Halley in 1725, and his zenith sectors. He contributed some twenty papers to the *Philosophical Transactions*; these were not confined to these two subjects but included treatises on the compass, weights and measures etc.

Only two barometers carrying Graham's signature are readily traceable (Plates 82 and

PLATE 82.
Geo Graham, London
45·5″ × 15·1″
*Department of Collections, Colonial Williamsburg, Virginia, U.S.A.:
from the collections of Percival Griffiths and J. S. Sykes*

83). Other wheel instruments may be in existence: during the sale of the Earl of Macclesfield's library in 1765 a 'wheel barometer by Graham' remained unsold,[1] and during the sale of the Duke of Sussex's furniture at Christie's on 4 July 1843 a 'Barometer by George Graham in ebony case' fetched £4 4s. 0d.[2] Either or both of these may well be the instrument illustrated in Plate 82. Another reference to a wheel barometer appears in a paper submitted by Graham to the Royal Society on 11 January 1721.[3]

The shape of the wheel instrument of Plate 82 is most unusual but wheel barometers of this date are so rare that almost every extant example is unique. The extension below the dial is made necessary by the length of the barometric tube and gives the design an appearance rather similar to the so-called 'Act of Parliament' clocks. The austerity of the ebonized pearwood is relieved by the curved mouldings (except in the glazed dial frame there is not a straight vertical line in the whole design) and by the applied gilt brass mounts on the door; it is strongly reminiscent of clock case designs of the first half of the eighteenth century, even down to the false keyhole. The dial, with its silvered chapter ring, matted brass centre and chased brass spandrels, also reflects traditional clock design. The dial and scale are however more similar to the work of the elder George Adams (Plate 59) than to that of Graham's former master and partner Tompion (Plates 143, 146). As in the Adams instrument the usual barometric inches are divided into hundredths: but there is also an unusual alternative scale engraved on the inner circumference of the chapter ring which ranges from 0 at 29·5″ both clockwise and anti-clockwise to 150 at 28″/31″ which share the same point. This scale should be compared to Tompion's numbering of his scale from 0 to 300 but Graham preferred to specify 150 degrees of good and 150 degrees of bad weather on each side of 29·5″, i.e. 'Changeable'. Another unusual feature is the single weather indication. The steel main hand is simple and lightweight in order not to impede the delicate operation of the instrument: the brass recording hand is operated by the brass knob above the signature, to which it is connected (as in George Adams' instrument) by brass gears. The date can be set manually on the two subsidiary silvered dials which, like the adjustment and 'strike-silent' dials on many earlier and contemporary clocks, replace the bulk of two of the spandrels. I cannot unfortunately give further details of the mechanism of this exceptional barometer since it is in the U.S.A. and I have not yet had an opportunity to study it in person.

[1] Britten *Old Clocks and Watches* p. 291.
[2] Lot 97: the purchaser's name was Foster.
[3] *Observation of an extraordinary Height of the Barometer, December* 21, 1721. (*Philosophical Transactions*, Vol. 31, p. 222).

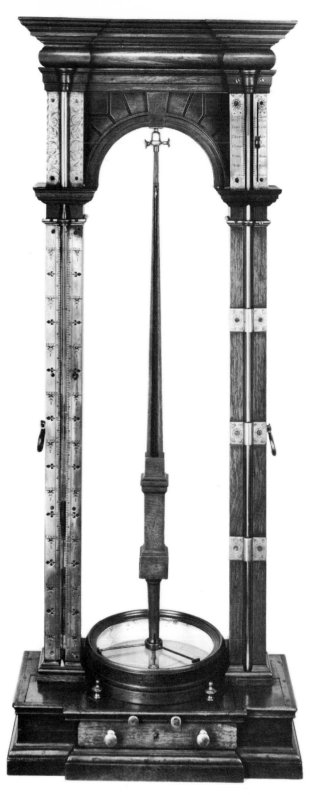

PLATE 83
Geo Graham, London
38″ × 15″
By courtesy of the
Director of the Science Museum, London

The earlier straight-tube instrument of Plate 83 is equally unusual.[1] A thermometer, a hygrometer and a barometer are set in a carefully made walnut frame of architectural design. The shape of the frame is dictated by the suspended catgut hygrometer in the centre. The design of the frame and the relatively inferior quality of the engraving on the thermometer and barometer register plates suggest that Graham was principally concerned in this instance with making the hygrometer, which follows a proposal made by William Molyneux to the Royal Society.[2] This involved the suspension of a metal weight on a whipcord which wound and unwound according to the humidity of the surrounding air: attached to the weight was a horizontal index hand which traversed a dial on which the scale was engraved. The cord was to be cut to a length which did not allow the hand to move over more than one revolution of the dial, a measurement which could only be found by trial and error. A similar method is employed in the manufacture of the popular 'weatherhouses' of the present day. Although Hooke considered gut 'nothing neer so exact or so tender'[3] as a wild oatbeard it was used occasionally by makers other than Graham, notably by Francis Hauksbee the younger who made gut hygrometers for the illustration of William Whiston's lectures in 1713. Later in the century Benjamin Martin also reverted to the use of gut but his method was less efficient than that of Molyneux (Plate 100).

In Graham's hygrometer the gut is suspended inside the tapered wooden spindle which is anchored to the keystone of the arch. Three guide rods at the base (of which one is

[1] Science Museum, London, Inventory No. 1928–705.
[2] *Philosophical Transactions* 172 p. 1032.
[3] *Micrographia* Obs. 27.

missing) keep the device in the exact centre of the horizontal dial so that the gut can hang free through the pierced glass and dial. A lead weight is attached to the bottom of the gut below the dial and is accessible when the drawer-like front of the pedestal is slid sideways. The silvered brass dial is engraved with divisions numbered from 1 to 12 and these are subdivided into fifths. At 12 are engraved the words 'Increse Shows Dry' and at 6 'Decrese Shows Wett'. There is also a subsidiary dial engraved with the figures 1 to 8. This was presumably intended to record the revolutions of the main hand but its precise mode of functioning is obscure since the mechanism has been badly tampered with. At present the left-hand adjusting knob of the pair visible below the hygrometer operates nothing since its spindle has been cut: and the right-hand knob is connected not only to the recording hand on the main dial, which is correct, but also to the hand of the subsidiary dial, which is not.

The hygrometer dial is well engraved and is signed 'Geo Graham London'. The fact that Graham's signature does not appear on the accompanying thermometer and barometer and the difference in quality between them and the hygrometer suggest that Graham had no hand in the manufacture of them: but these indications are not conclusive. The barometer tube is fixed to the right-hand column of the arch with engraved brass clamps and the floral engraving is repeated on the register plates. The barometric scale covers the usual 28″–31″ (although these are not engraved) and each inch is divided in decimals. The weather indications are also unusual:

Very dry	Great Frost
Fair	Cold
Clear	Air
Chang	Able
Rain	Snow
Much	Rain
Storm	Tempest

These should be compared with the contemporary and more usual summer and winter indications on the instruments illustrated in Plates 9 and 109: the use of 'Much Rain' for the winter as well as for the summer state is unsatisfactory. The pointer is missing from the recording index which slides in the groove on the right-hand plate. The tube is not original: nor is the conventional leather-based cistern which can be inspected by removing the panelling of the podium. There is no trace of the original application of a screw device for portability; but the carrying rings fitted to each side of the arch suggest that the instrument was meant to be portable, and the original cistern was probably either a sealed wooden box or a bowl covered with skin to prevent leakage. The alcohol thermometer fixed to the left-hand column of the arch is based on the first scale proposed by Fahrenheit in about 1709 (p. 11) and endorses the supposition that this barometer was made between 1713, when Graham inherited Tompion's business, and about 1725. The engraving on the brass plate at the top, which consists of formal acanthus motifs and is intended to balance the barometer plates, lends stylistic support to this estimate. The scale extends not between Fahrenheit's extreme fixed points but from 'Extrm Hot' at 80° through 'Temperate Air' at 0° to 'Extrm Cold' at 80°.

The case of this instrument is of great interest as an example of architectural cabinet-work: but since the hygrometer is of even greater scientific interest it seems correct that the instrument should be displayed in the Science Museum—which cannot be said of some of its neighbours (Plates 15, 96).

JOHN HALLIFAX b.1694–d.1750

Barnsley

THE HALLIFAX FAMILY originated from John Hallifax's grandfather who changed his name from Waterhouse in the seventeenth century. Son of the vicar of Springthorpe, Lincolnshire, John Hallifax moved to Barnsley and set up in business as a clockmaker, probably after his father's death in 1711. His local reputation as a clockmaker was second to none and it was engraved on his tombstone that 'few in these times had attained to his abilities and virtues', etc. He had seven children and was succeeded in the business by his fifth son Joseph (1728–62): his fourth son George had moved to Doncaster by 1750 where he became a prosperous clockmaker and later Mayor. His third son Thomas went to London after being apprenticed to a grocer in Barnsley and became an eminent banker, Lord Mayor and later a member of Parliament. The Hallifax family are beyond the scope of the present study but it is interesting to note also that John Hallifax's uncle was a D.D. (as was his last son Ben) at Oxford and Chaplain to William III; and that his

cousin's sons became respectively Bishop of St Asaph and Gloucester and Physician to the Prince of Wales, later George IV.[1]

Hallifax's barometers are mostly of distinctive design although they vary considerably in quality. Plate 84 illustrates a particularly fine example. The general design of the case is closely related to the style of contemporary clock cases, Hallifax being clearly influenced in his specification by his proper trade. The walnut veneers are well arranged and of rich colour and are skilfully defined by the triple line inlays on the trunk and squared base. The built-up mouldings of the hood, which is decorated with chased brass finials of traditional urn design, may seem heavy to modern eyes but were a frequent feature of clock cases of the period (Plate 74). The pillars of the hood and the arched dial are also clock-like features. As in this example Hallifax did not usually hinge his glazed 'doors' but attached them by screws, since the hand of a barometer does not need regular manual adjustment. The centre of the arched brass dial plate is engraved with acanthus motifs and the spandrels are of finely chased brass: the chapter ring and signature disc in the arch are, unusually, of silver. The cursive script of the weather indications and signature are typical of Hallifax's engraving, the modest flourishes compensating to some extent for the unexceptional quality. The weather indications themselves are a combination of normal summer and winter states, 'Very Dry, Settled Fair or Frost, Fair or Frost, Changeable, Rain Wind or Snow, M. Rain Wind or Snow, Tempestuous'. The scale, consisting of three concentric rings, is typical of almost all Hallifax's barometers. The centre ring represents the usual barometric inches 28″–31″ which are divided into decimals, the divisions being signified by the numbers 1–9 in each inch: the actual inch digits are engraved in the outer ring in order to avoid confusion in the

[1] An account of the family's achievements can be found in Joseph Wilkinson's *Worthies, Families and Celebrities of Barnsley and District* (1883).

PLATE 84
Jno Hallifax, Barnsley
48″ × 10·3″
Collection of
F. R. Poke

numbering, but they bear no relation to the outer ring and their position is indicated in the centre ring by symbols each consisting of four arrow-heads in the form of a cross. The inner ring represents an arbitrary scale numbered from 1 to 30 whose actual divisions are engraved in the outer ring: because there are 30 these divisions also represent decimals of an inch and since they are set between the decimals of the centre ring the overall effect of the dual scale is tantamount to dividing each inch into 20 parts. The scale is as rare as it is cumbersome. Hallifax may have favoured it because he preferred a separate recording dial on the trunk of the case to a recording hand on the main dial, the extensive numbering being designed to save the observer the trouble of counting unnumbered divisions: but a good engraver could have surmounted this problem with greater clarity. The pierced steel hand is also typical of Hallifax. The recording dial on the trunk has a silver chapter ring on which the triple scale is repeated and a simpler pierced steel hand. The mechanism of this instrument has been renewed with the exception of the wooden pulley wheel and now employs a standard siphon tube of about 0·2″ bore.

Several similar walnut barometers by Hallifax survive in private collections. The overall design of their cases is strikingly similar although measurements differ slightly: the design of their hoods includes variations of shape, finials differ in number, shape and material, and the trunk inlays are sometimes of chequered or herring-bone design. Dials often have a matted brass centre but almost invariably have silvered brass rather than silver chapter rings and chased brass spandrels. One example I have studied dispensed with spandrels in favour of engraved foliate motifs. The engraved script on most examples is not of high quality. Another common feature is the use of a six-pointed star inlay of woods in the centre of the recording dial. The maker's signature is always engraved on a convex disc in the arch of the dial: it usually takes the form 'J. Hallifax Barnsley Invt & Fect' but 'Jn Hallifax' 'John

PLATE 85
John Hallifax, Barnsley
46″ × 8·6″
Victoria and Albert Museum, London:
Crown copyright

Hallifax' and 'Johannes Hallifax' are found. An illustrated example, which used to be in the Percival Griffiths collection, can be seen in R. W. Symonds' *English Furniture from Charles II to George II* (Fig. 213) or in the *Dictionary of English Furniture* (2nd edition, *s.v.* 'Barometers' Fig. 14). Another example survives in the Victoria and Albert Museum.[1] This has a case similar to the one in Plate 84 but is 3·5″ taller, has a star inlay in the centre of the recording dial, cross-grained mahogany inlays instead of line inlays on the trunk, and wooden finials which are not original: the veneer on the trunk has also suffered some damage and the recording hand, which on most of Hallifax's barometers is liable to damage because it is not protected by glass, has been replaced by an inferior substitute. The dial embodies slight variations of design and the chapter ring is of silvered brass. I have so far traced a dozen of these instruments of which this is the only one in a public collection.

The barometer illustrated in Plate 85 is also in the Victoria and Albert Museum.[2] The casework lacks the extravagance of Hallifax's more characteristic instruments. The walnut veneer is however finely figured and the six-pointed star inlay in the centre of the recording dial is composed of two shades of wood. The moulded mahogany cornice below the domed top is a later addition. The dial is glazed for protection and has a brass bezel. The chapter ring is of brass and was originally silvered: the engraving of the weather indications is more elaborate and of better quality than on most of Hallifax's barometers, compensating partly for the plainer case. The scale is if anything less confusing than the more usual scale of Plate 84: there are only two rings, the inner of which is numbered from 1 to 30. Unlike the inner scale of Plate 84 this scale corresponds to the decimal divisions of the barometric inches, 30 (and 0, but this is not engraved) being placed at 28″ and 31″, 10 at 29″ and 20 at 30″. The outer ring, on which for convenience the inch digits are again engraved, also shows decimal divisions and as before enables readings to approximately 0·5″. The simplicity of the steel hand is another peculiarity of this instrument. The recording dial at the base repeats the scale of the main dial and should also be silvered: the hand is probably not original. The mechanism of the barometer consists of the usual siphon tube, which has been renewed, but instead of a pulley wheel a sort of balance is used. The thread to which the float is attached is tied to one end of this balance and a compensating wire weight to the other end. At the point of balance, which is at the axis of the arbor of the indicating hand, a small cylindrical box is fitted behind the dial: this houses a simple gearing mechanism in order to translate the tilt of the balance into the full circle which the hand must traverse on the dial.

[1] Inventory No. W.10–1960.   [2] Inventory No. W.11–1960.

A very similar barometer by George Hallifax, John's son who emigrated to Doncaster, survives in a private collection. It has the same type of mechanism and the differences of detail include a finial, a more elaborate indicating hand of the type in Plate 84, less elaborate engraving on the chapter ring and a veneered surround of cross-grained walnut. The maker has also spoilt his scale. He has used a recording dial as in Plate 85 but on his main dial the 1–30 scale does not correspond to the decimal divisions of the barometric inches. The existence of this barometer suggests that the example by John Hallifax was made late in his career and that George was using pieces of his father's stock: but this is conjecture.

Finally a remarkable barometer which is no less than 71″ high and 11″ wide also survives in a private collection, having been once in the Percival Griffiths collection. In style it is somewhat similar to Plate 84 since the dial is arched and the hood built up with moulded walnut veneers: but there is no recording dial and the absence of this makes the likeness to clock designs more striking. The casework is of good quality with herring-bone inlays framing the figured walnut veneers on the trunk and squared base: but the chief attraction of this barometer is the engraving of the dial. This is arched in form with the usual spandrels (only roughly finished), silvered chapter ring, and convex disc in the arch on which the signature 'Johannes Hallifax Invenit & Fecit' is engraved. The centre of the brass dial is engraved with formal foliate designs and above the arbor there is a rather unflattering representation of Hermes the messenger of Zeus (cf. Plate 10). On the chapter ring moreover between the weather indications are engraved various pictures of the weather: particularly attractive among these is a picture of clouds and a hand (presumably Zeus's) pouring rain out of a jug, which is engraved between 'Rain or Wind' and 'Very Rainy'. Although I was brought up on more modern gods this was how, as a child, I used to imagine that rain occurred.

FRANCIS HAUKSBEE (1) fl 1700–d. 1713

1. Giltspur Street
2. Wine Office Court, Fleet Street
3. Hind Court, Fleet Street

HAUKSBEE was an instrument-maker of considerable contemporary repute. He was elected F.R.S. in 1705 and was an acknowledged expert on pneumatics and meteorology, submitting a large number of papers to the Society. In 1704 he instituted a series of 'physico-mechanical' lectures at his house, for which the complete range of demonstration instruments was made in his workshop. These lectures, given successively by James Hodgson, William Whiston and Humphrey Ditton, continued until his death and were then given by J. T. Desaguliers on behalf of his widow. An idea of the broad scope of the lectures can be gathered from Hauksbee's *Physico-Mechanical Experiments on various subjects* published in 1709. The traveller von Uffenbach visited his workshop on 28 June 1710 and again on 28 October: on the second occasion he found him in and Hauksbee demonstrated many of his experiments to the visitors.[1]

The lecture courses made Hauksbee's workshop well known and must have stimulated his trade. He appears to have had an especial reputation for air pumps, surgical cupping-glasses[2] and barometers which were stated to show 'the most minute variation of the air's pressure, whereby the alterations of the weather more suddenly nicely and truly are discovered'.[3]

No signed barometers appear to be extant[4] but it can be assumed that Hauksbee made cistern-tube instruments for the lectures and, probably, for sale. He made a type of angle barometer, an illustration of which appears in the *Lexicon Technicum* of 1704 (Plate 86): 'the

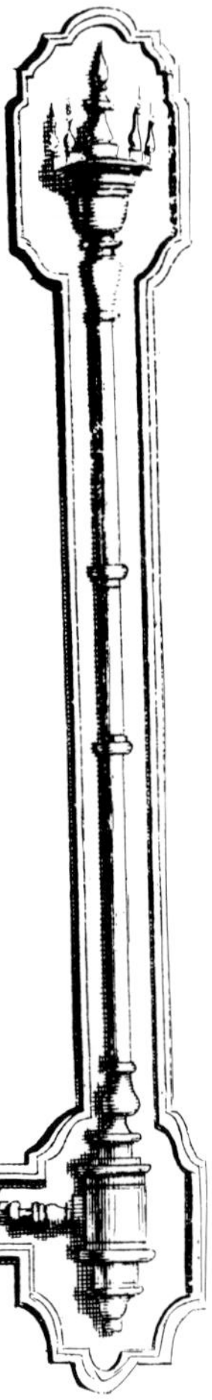

Mr Hawksbee's Barometer, rising & falling 60 Inches

ingenious Mr. Hauksbee' demonstrated this instrument to the contributor. It is based on the cistern-tube principle, a glass tube being fixed

[1] Quarrell and Mare *London in 1710* pp. 77 and 169.
[2] Harris *Lexicon Technicum* Vol. 1 (1704) s.v. 'Barometer'.
[3] Quoted by Taylor *The Mathematical Practitioners of Tudor and Stuart England* p. 296: I do not know the source but imagine it is one of the lecture sheets which has eluded me.
[4] Unless I am wrong in attributing the barometers mentioned on p. 152 to his nephew.

PLATE 86
Francis Hauksbee's diagonal barometer 1704
By courtesy of the Trustees of the British Museum

to the side of the cistern and extending at a slight angle to a distance of 60″. The scale is fixed along this limb. The contributor observed that 'it may very easily be made for 100 or 200 inches, if a strait small thin glass tube can be blown or drawn of that length, and that it were as easily manageable'. Unfortunately these were impossible conditions. The narrow bore caused by extensive drawing increases the likelihood of a break in the mercury column through capillary action; and the almost horizontal tube must have made reading the instrument impossible since the mercury meniscus would have rested at an angle. The principle of this instrument was very similar to that of the 'square' barometer invented by J. D. Cassini (1625–1712) in about 1673 but the latter employed a cistern at the top of the vertical tube—a more sensible idea altogether.[1] John Patrick also advertised such 'diagonal' barometers: but he presumably followed rather than preceded Hauksbee since the contributor to the first volume of the *Lexicon Technicum* was acquainted with Patrick and his wares but mentioned only Hauksbee in this context.

[1] See Middleton *History of the Barometer* p. 114 *et seq.*

FRANCIS HAUKSBEE (2) b.1687 d.1763

Near St Dunstans Church, Crane Court, Fetter Lane

HAUKSBEE was a nephew and probably at the beginning of the century an apprentice of Francis Hauksbee the elder. In 1710, when von Uffenbach visited his uncle's workshop, he may well have been the 'cousin' said to have been present.[2] He was certainly working independently by 1712 however, for in that year, copying his uncle's precedent, he instituted a series of lectures which were given by Humphrey Ditton until 1713 and by William Whiston thereafter. In 1723 he became 'Clerk-Housekeeper' to the Royal Society which had moved from Gresham House to Crane Court in 1710. He appears to have enjoyed a fair reputation and in 1724 his meteorological instruments were recommended by the Secretary of the Royal Society as being sufficiently accurate for those who wished to send their observations to the Society.

Hauksbee, like his uncle, made and sold a wide range of mechanical, optical and meteorological instruments, including all the instruments used for illustrating Whiston's lectures. He performed the experiments

[2] Quarrell and Mare *London in 1710* p. 77: the suggestion was made by E. G. R. Taylor in *Mathematical Practitioners of Tudor and Stuart England* p. 296.

himself, the complete range of which can be found in Whiston's explanatory and introductory notes *A Course of Mechanical Optical Hydrostatical and Pneumatical Experiments* published in 1714. Among the instruments which he made and sold were 'several sorts of barometers' constructed, as his advertisement claimed of all his work, 'according to their latest and best improvements'. Among the diagrams illustrating the lectures are various cistern-tube instruments, an angle barometer and a wheel barometer.

I have only been able to trace two extant barometers signed by Francis Hauksbee[1] and I think both should be attributed to the younger man. They are both portable cistern-tube barometers, each set in an ebonized fruitwood frame with an arched and moulded hood and turned pillars; the edges of the trunk are moulded, the cistern cover is similar to Plate 88 and there are brass capitals and bases to the pillars. The one at Althorp has three spherical brass finials on squared podia and inverted acorn finials beneath the pillars but these are all missing from the other. The chief interest of these barometers lies in their scale. This represents the normal barometric inches which are divided into decimals, but on each register plate there is a dial with fifty divisions. The steel hands of these dials, which are moved manually (the Althorp barometer has a special finger grip on each hand), operate grooved pointers on each side of the tube; each pointer moves $0.5''$ as its controlling dial hand is turned through one revolution of the dial. Readings can thus be taken to $0.1''$. The only weather indication given is 'Variable' but the words 'Fair if ☿ Rise' and 'Foul if ☿ Fall' are engraved at the top and bottom of the plates respectively. Mr. Smith's barometer has a spirit thermometer mounted on the trunk with the so-called Royal Society scale[2] engraved on brass plates: the Althorp barometer has no thermometer but is panelled and has a wooden sleeve concealing the tube.

[1] One in the collection of the Earl Spencer, Althorp, Northampton, the other in the collection of D. W. Smith.
[2] See p. 11.

PLATE 87
Heath and Wing's
trade card
Banks Collection:
by courtesy of
the Trustees of the British Museum

THOMAS HEATH fl 1714 –d.1773

Hercules and Globe, next door to Fountain Tavern, near Exeter Exchange, Strand

HEATH was one of the most notable instrument-makers of his day. His trade card advertised all sorts of optical, astronomical and mathematical instruments as well as globes, mathematical books and weather-glasses. He was also a prolific advertiser in newspapers. In 1740 he took Tycho Wing into partnership and the firm, known as Heath and Wing, remained in business until Heath's death in 1773. On 7 October of that year the *Morning Post* advertised the sale of Heath's stock-in-trade and announced Wing's retirement. It appears that T. Newman took on the business since he described himself as 'successor to Heath and Wing'.

One of Heath and Wing's trade cards which survives in the Banks Collection[1] includes among the various instruments illustrated a cistern-tube barometer with a broken pediment (Plate 87): it has a screw device for portability and an interesting H-shaped pointer which presumably makes it easier to observe both the centre and edges of the meniscus. In the Museum of the History of Science at Oxford there is a cistern-tube barometer of similar design signed 'T. Heath' (Plate 88). It is unfortunately in very bad condition but the illustration, which is scarcely better, hints at its erstwhile quality. The mahogany case incorporates a broken pediment with brass finial and a type of cistern cover which was typical until about 1780 (*cf.* Plates 68, 152): the arched cornice above the thermometer is also found in the work of other makers (*cf.* Plate 62). The applied carvings at each edge of the case appear originally to have been gilt and there are traces of gilt also on the raised rings of the cistern cover, the moulded edges of the frame and the cornices above both the thermometer and the barometer plates. The plates were originally silvered. The scale covers 4″ and is divided into decimals: and the weather indications are normal. The vernier suggests that this barometer was made late in Heath's life but the use of the Royal Society scale for the thermometer at this date is unusual. The thermometer tube is missing but it would originally have been a spirit thermometer with its bulb concealed under the top of the cistern cover. The portable barometer tube has been replaced.

I have seen one angle barometer signed by T. Heath but the mahogany case was unfortunately in irreparable condition. The original cistern seems to have been a large one and may have been open. The brass plates had summer indications above and winter indications below the tube; and the scale, reading to ·01″, was extended over 24″. There was a manual pointer above the tube.

[1] British Museum.

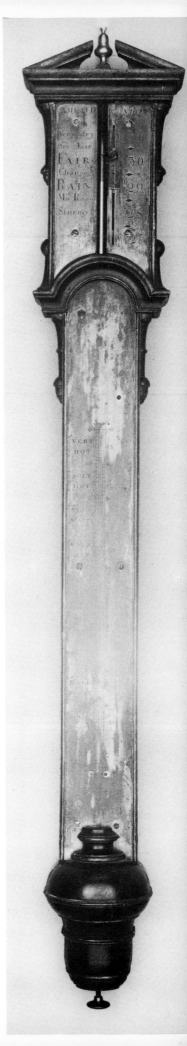

PLATE 88
T. Heath, London
37″ × 6·1″
*Museum of the History
of Science, Oxford*

THOMAS JONES b. 1775 – d. 1852

1. 120 Mount Street, Berkeley Square (1806)
2. 21 Oxenden Street, Piccadilly (1811–14)
3. 62 Charing Cross (1816–50)

BEFORE 1800 Jones was one of Jesse Ramsden's workmen. During the next fifty years he became one of the most eminent of instrument-makers: all forms of optical, mathematical and physical instruments were made and sold in his workshop. He was patentee of a dividing instrument in 1811 and was well known for his astronomical and meteorological instruments. He was elected F.R.S. in 1835.

Jones made marine barometers, as did his namesakes William and Samuel who were not related, and a typical marine barometer bearing his signature can be seen in the Science Museum, London.[1] Mountain barometers were another of his specialities and a *Companion to the Mountain Barometer*, containing directions and tables, which he published in 1817, survives: in the preface to the first edition he claimed to have made between three and four hundred of these, following a design of Sir H.C. Englefield, since its introduction in 1806 besides others of 'former construction'. He also made portable siphon-tube barometers of the type devised by J. L. Gay-Lussac (1788–1850) in 1816.[2]

Many of his domestic instruments are of high quality. Plate 89 illustrates a portable cistern barometer in a bow-fronted mahogany case which is a conspicuously fine example. The general design of the case is of a type often adopted by nineteenth-century makers which enabled well-figured mahogany to be displayed to its best advantage: the urn and black linear inlays on the cistern cover and the bow-fronted thermometer case were also frequent features. The weather indications engraved on the usual silvered plates are standard but the scale is very unusual (Plate 90). The barometric inches are not divided into decimals (the lack of divisions lending a certain sober elegance to the design of the plates) and the normal vernier is also dispensed with. Readings to ·01″ are achieved however by moving the pointer, whose operating knob can be seen on the right, to the level of the mercury: this simultaneously moves the hand of the dial above the plates to which it is geared. The mechanism and the quality of the engraving of the divisions are typical of this maker's work.

[1] Inventory No. 1908–83.
[2] For an account of this see Middleton *History of the Barometer* p. 140 *et seq.*

It is not relevant to the present study. An example by Jones survives at the Kew Observatory.

opposite: PLATE 89
Thomas Jones, 62 Charing Cross, London
39″ × 4″
Collection of Gordon F. C. Cole
opposite right: PLATE 90
Detail of Plate 89

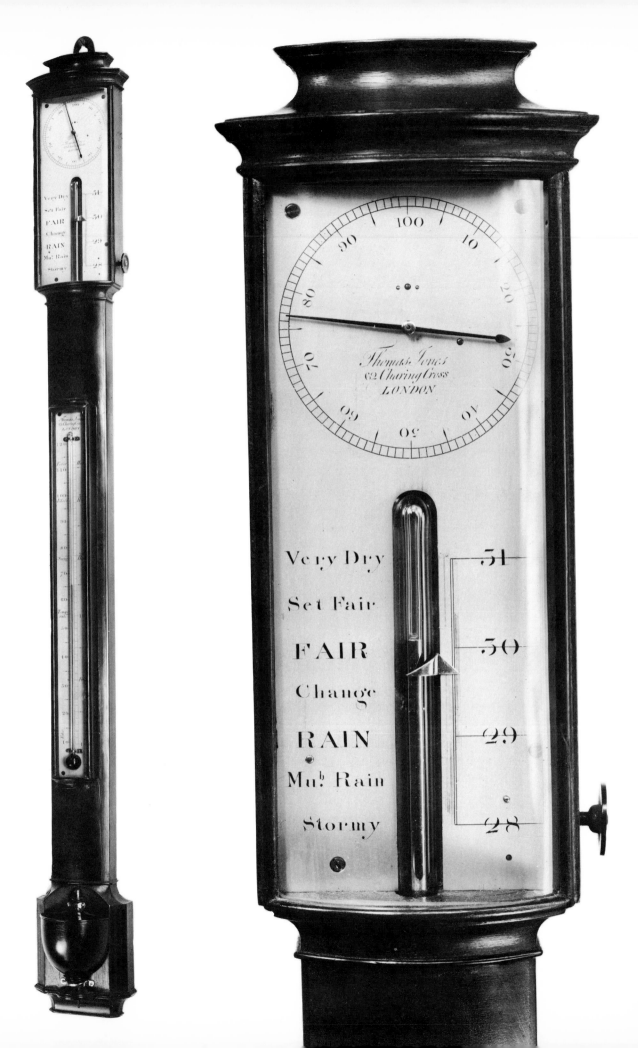

WILLIAM AND SAMUEL JONES   fl 1784–1860

1. 135 Holborn Hill (1794–5)
2. 32 Holborn Hill (1801–5)
3. 30 High Holborn (1802–60)

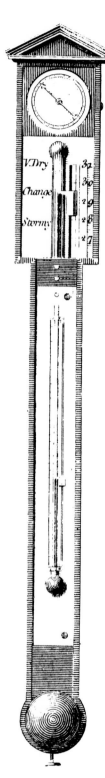

WILLIAM and Samuel succeeded their father John Jones (1739–87) who worked as an optical and mathematical instrument-maker at 135 Holborn Hill 'near Furnival's Inn'. William (1763–1831) was a pupil of Benjamin Martin and worked for a time in the workshop of George Adams the younger. In 1782 he wrote a *Description and Use of a New Portable Orrery* which was published by his father at 6d.: by 1784 he was in partnership with his father when the second edition was sold by 'Jones and Son' at 1s. Appended to the third edition of 1787 (1s. 6d.) was a four-page catalogue of optical, mathematical and philosophical instruments including

	£	s.	d.		£	s.	d.
Barometers of the best sort .. *from*	1	11	6	*to* 3	3	0	
Barometers, thermometers, and hygrometers, all in one neat mahogany frame .. .. *from*	3	0	0	*to* 4	14	6	

Similar barometers were again advertised in a list of instruments made and sold by J. Jones and Son which was appended to William Jones's 1788 edition of Martin's *Description and Use of the Pocket Case of Mathematical Instruments*.

By 1794 the firm appears in the directories under the names of the two brothers and the name W. and S. Jones remained well known as one of the leading and most prosperous firms in the instrument industry for most of the nineteenth century. It produced a wide variety of instruments and the catalogue appended to the sixth edition of William Jones's *Description and Use of a New Portable Orrery* (1812 and now 3s.) ran to fourteen pages, even then omitting 'a great variety of other articles too numerous to be included'. The firm followed common practice in selling scientific books and William Jones re-edited a number of books by previous authors. Among these were works by Benjamin Martin and George Adams the younger, Jones having purchased the latter's stock, library and copyrights (but not his copperplates or manuscripts which were secured by Dudley Adams) at auction after Adams' death in 1795.

PLATE 91
William and Samuel Jones's
barometer 1819

Charles Hutton, whose *Mathematical and Philosophical Dictionary* (1795) itself appeared in the firm's catalogues, said that they made 'two excellent marine barometers' and one was illustrated in Abraham Rees's *Cyclopaedia* of 1819.[1] In the 1799 editions of Adams' *Essay on Electricity* and *Lectures on Natural and Experimental Philosophy* the firm was advertising

	£	s.	d.	£	s.	d.
Barometers, plain mounted .. .. *from*	1	18	0 *to*	2	12	6
Barometers, thermometers, and hygrometers all in one neat mahogany frame *from*	4	4	0 *to*	6	6	0
Barometers for measuring the heights of mountains .. .. *from*	7	7	0 *to*	10	10	0
Marine barometers, diagonal, wheel and statical ditto						

These also appear in the 1812 catalogue which is identical except for the prices: these are '£1 18s. to £3 0s. 0d., £4 4s. to £6 16s. 6d. and £4 4s. to £10 10s. 0d.' for the first three items, the fourth remaining unpriced. The description of the second item suggests the cistern-tube barometer illustrated by Charles Hutton (Plate 31), and since Hutton seems to have known the firm his illustration may well be a drawing of one of their actual barometers. Abraham Rees explicitly illustrated one of their domestic barometers (Plate 91) in 1819[2] and apart from the different pediment it is very similar to Hutton's version. The compiler remarked that the thermometer and hygrometer were detachable and could be used apart. Also in 1812 the firm advertised *A Concise Explanation of the Barometer, Thermometer, and Hygrometer, with rules for predicting Changes in the weather*: it was sold in a small box for 6d. or on a varnished pasteboard for 1s.

By 1843 wheel barometers naturally appear among the standard stock-in-trade as the following extract of the firm's catalogue shows:

	£	s.	d.	£	s.	d.
Best constructed barometers, plain mounted varnished frames .. .. .. *from*	2	5	0 *to*	3	0	0
Barometer, thermometer, and hygrometer, all in one neat mahogany frame .. *from*	4	14	6 *to*	6	16	6
A new stick barometer for ascertaining the heights of mountains, depths of valleys, etc. .. .. *from*	4	4	0 *to*	6	16	6
Ditto with folding portable staves, gimbals, etc.				7	17	6
Marine barometers on springs, for floor or partition				7	7	0
Adie's sympiesometer				4	4	0
Hook's wheel barometer, less correct than the above common form .. .. *from*	3	3	0 *to*	6	6	0

I have seen various extant domestic barometers made by the firm. Like other leading 'industrial' firms of the nineteenth century the partnership seems to have concentrated more on producing a quantity of useful and accurate instruments rather than a few elegantly designed ones: and it is sufficient to let their catalogues speak for them. Among barometers I have studied have been standard mahogany cistern-tube instruments with scroll pediments or rounded tops and glazed doors (*cf.* Plates 20 and 32), and a number of plain mahogany wheel barometers with the usual scroll pediment and 8″ dial. I have also seen a cistern-tube barometer in a bow-fronted mahogany case with an urn-shaped cistern cover (*cf.* Plate 33) and an ivory float of the type introduced by the elder George Adams, and several more elegant examples of the same design without the float.

[1] Vol. 4 of Plates *s.v.* 'Pneumatics' Plate 10 Figs. 86 and 87.   [2] Rees *Cyclopaedia* Vol. 4 of Plates *s.v.* 'Pneumatics' Plate 9 Fig. 84.

BALTHAZAR KNIE fl 1743 –d. 1817

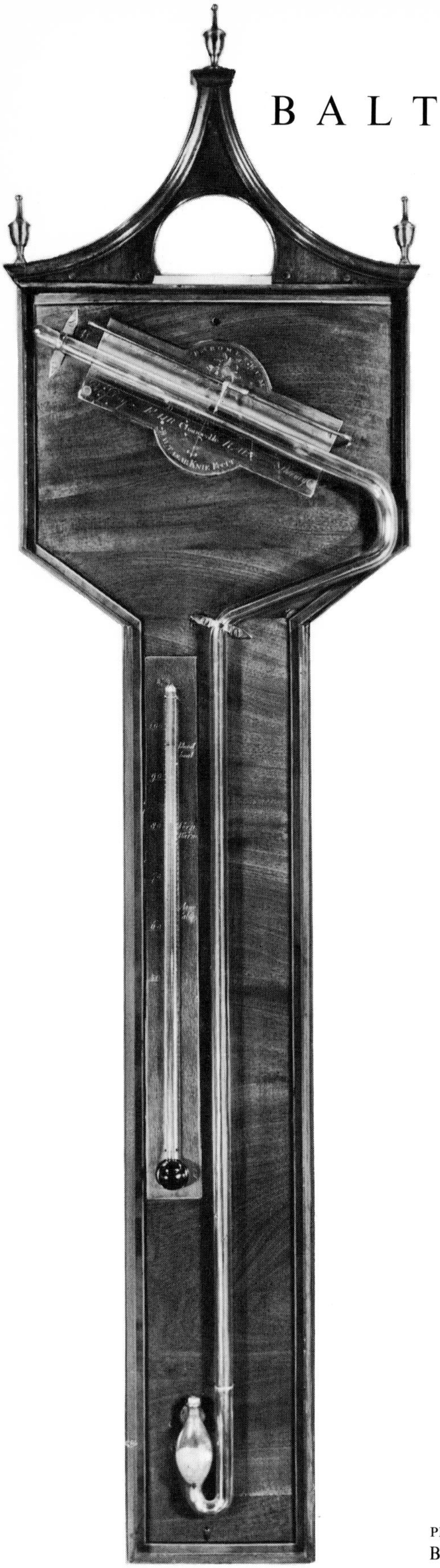

Lawnmarket, Edinburgh

BORN IN Germany, Knie appears to have been a glass-blower by trade. He settled in Edinburgh in about 1774 and opened a shop near the well on the north side of Lawnmarket. In a trade advertisement dated 1793 he claimed that he made and repaired barometers and thermometers of various constructions and in particular that he made 'a double weather-glass, invented by Mons Reamuer [*sc.* Réaumur] of Paris': he also stated that he had been 'in practice of this business for upwards of forty years . . . in various parts of Europe'.[1] In an 1809 *Directory* he is styled as a 'weather-glass maker' and according to one authority he introduced the manufacture of barometers to Edinburgh, but there seems to be no evidence for this. The same authority quotes an interesting excerpt from the *Edinburgh Evening Courant*—'Friday next being the Equinox, Mr. Knie desires you to take notice of the barometer. If the mercury be marked fair it will be fair for some time, but if it is marked rain or changeable it will be rain or changeable for some time'.[2] Knie retired in 1815 and his 'elegant and valuable' stock of barometers and thermometers which was valued at £309 14s. 0d. was dispersed by lottery.[3]

This 'elegant and valuable' stock, judging from extant examples of Knie's work, included many different designs: some of these are technically ingenious and almost all of them are well-designed and pleasant pieces of furniture. Plate 92 shows an

[1] This advertisement was quoted by John Smith in an article in *The Weekly Scotsman* (10 December 1898), a cutting of which is pasted to the back of the barometer illustrated in Plate 92.
[2] John Smith *Old Scottish Clockmakers* (1921) p. 217.
[3] *Ibid.*

PLATE 92
Balthasar Knie
43·5″ × 11·1″
Royal Infirmary, Edinburgh

example of one of his typical angle barometers. The rejection of the extended arm which is more usually found in angle barometers was clearly an attempt to produce a more harmonious design: angle barometers tended to look too much like signposts unless they were set in a square frame, and their lack of symmetry did not allow them to become popular pieces of furniture. Knie's design overcame this problem at the expense of a considerably less extensive scale. The design appears to have originated in Germany and Knie presumably brought it with him.[1] The case is of rich brown mahogany with line inlays round the inside edge of the rim. The tent-shaped crest is also of mahogany and the finials are of brass. The brass register plates are now polished but were originally silvered. The weather indications, which are not entirely clear in the photograph, read above the tube 'Settled Fair' and 'Much Rain' and below the tube 'Very Dry, Fair, Changeable, Rain, Stormy': the word 'Barometrum' is engraved in the arch of the upper plate which is decorated with a pleasant floral design, and on the lower plate is the signature 'Baltasar Knie Fecit'. The scale is engraved below the tube and consists of the usual 28″–31″ divided into decimals. A manual brass pointer is fitted to a brass rod above the tube. The tube itself is not original: the case has been hollowed further behind the bulb by the repairer who has also been obliged (since he found the tube difficult to reproduce) to move the position of the brass clamp below the plates. The alcohol thermometer's register plate should also be silvered and a hygrometer was originally fitted in the semi-circular glazed cavity in the crest: the hole for its adjusting key can be seen immediately beneath it on the case.

Two very similar barometers survive in the U.S.A. signed by William Robb of Montrose. In spite of superficial differences it is very likely that Robb bought his pair from Knie and, like many recorded

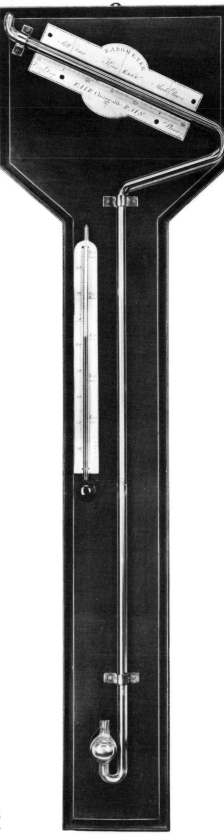

PLATE 93
Knie, Edinr
36″ × 10·5″
Author's collection

---

[1] Examples survive in the Deutches Museum, Munich (Inventory No. 6281) and the Landes Museum, Zürich (Inventory No. L.M.7663). The latter is mounted on a frame slimmer than those used by Knie with a gilt border: the tube is bent the other way and its cistern, which is almost certainly of the bulb type, is protected by a rectangular wooden cover.

'makers', acted only as the retailer. Other examples of this design by Knie survive of almost identical dimensions. Plate 93 shows one mounted on a case of darker mahogany which, like the Robb instruments, lacks the crest at the top: the register plates are also simpler (Plate 94), the signature 'Knie, Edinr' replacing the floral engraving on the upper plate. The manual pointer is missing: the holes which used to hold its wire are visible in the photograph. Another example is owned by the City of Gloucester Museum: as in Plate 92 this has a well-figured mahogany case but has a fretwork scroll pediment which is not contemporary. The brass plates, instead of each having one bulge or arch (Plate 94), have three which give the effect of waves. The weather indications are similar to those of Plate 92 but 'Change' is substituted for 'Changeable': as in Plate 93 the signature is inscribed above the plates but is decorated with an engraved six-pointed star and above it, following the convex line of the middle wave, is engraved the word 'Barometerum'.

Plate 95 illustrates a straight-tube barometer by Knie. The carcase of the case is mahogany, as in the angle barometers discussed above, and the similarity of the style of the casework is striking: the edge is banded, for instance, probably with tulip-wood, and has a raised rim. The patera on the oval cistern cover is very finely executed in sycamore and ebonized fruitwood. The finial is not original and is too small. The polished brass plates would again have originally been silvered and a

PLATE 94
Detail
of Plate 93

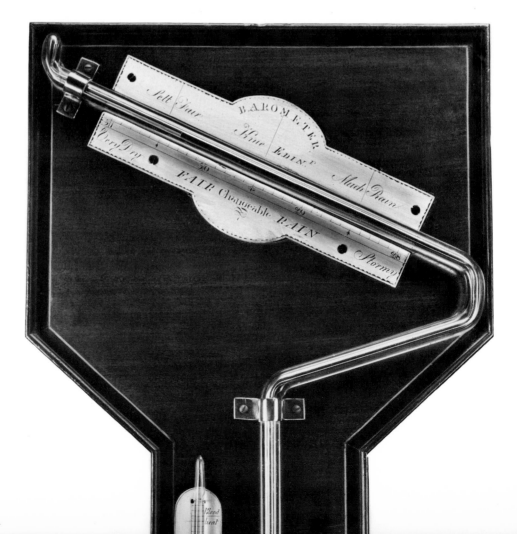

pleasing swag of floral engraving decorates the word 'Barometer' in the arch: this practice of giving the instrument its name seems to have been a habit of Scottish makers (*cf.* Plate 128) although some English makers also indulged in it on occasion (Plate 99). Because the plates are now polished the weather indications, above which is engraved the signature 'Knie Edin', are not easy to see at a glance and do not come out clearly in the photograph: they read 'Very Dry, Set Fair, Fair, Change, Rain, Much Rain, Stormy' and the scale, which is engraved as usual to the right of the tube, covers 27″–31″ and is divided into decimals. The manual vernier makes possible readings to ·01″ The use of an arched brass plate in a frame which does not strictly demand it should be compared to the Dollond barometer of Plate 71. The siphon tube is a new one with a bulb cistern and the original neat cavity in the wood of the base has been roughly enlarged to house it. There is no trace of a portable screw and the cavity suggests that there was originally some sort of conventional wooden cistern but whether it was closed or open is not deducible.

Knie also made wheel barometers. I have seen a good example of an instrument similar to Plate 126 with a broken pediment and 8″ dial. The case was finely made and had a shell inlay above the dial instead of on each side of the thermometer. The inlay at the top represented a vase of flowers and at the bottom consisted of a geometrical pattern: and the case was edged with a chequered banding of black and yellow woods. Another most unusual wheel barometer which is now in America was housed in a case which took the form of a four-sided steeple, not unlike a Roman burial monument; the barometer dial was resting on a square plinth and above it rose the steeple, on the face of which was fitted a tapered thermometer case. From the minute photograph I have of this remarkable barometer the casework appears to be excellent.

In modern times a general ignorance about Knie has led to neglect of his work. Judging from the barometers which survive he fully deserves his contemporary reputation.

PLATE 95
Knie, Edin.
41·2″ × 6·2″
Randolph

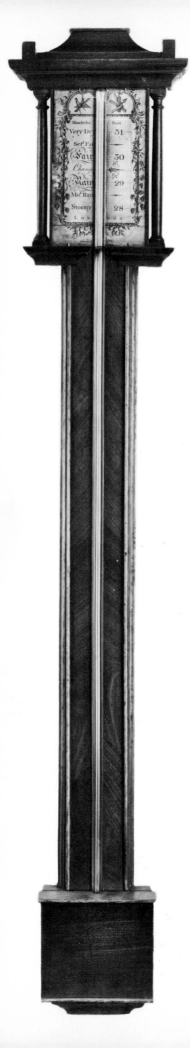

DOMINICK MANTICHA
fl 1805

11 Ely Court, Holborn

DESCRIBED as a barometer maker in the Directory for 1805, Manticha was one of the many Italians established in London at the beginning of the nineteenth century. Like J.M. Ronketti, James Gatty and Lione Somalvico and Co. he sold barometers of better than average quality. Unfortunately he has proved almost as difficult to trace as Gatty and the 1805 entry in the Directory, which is the only one I have found, did its best to escape by mis-spelling his name 'Monticha'.

A number of barometers survive signed 'Manticha' which can be attributed to him with reasonable confidence. Plate 96 illustrates a straight-tube instrument[1] set in a mahogany veneered frame of a design which several of the early Italian makers favoured. Similar barometers survive, for example by J.M. Ronketti, and it is not inconceivable that the two makers employed the same cabinet-maker. The pillared hood maintains the architectural tradition but there is a touch of Chinese influence in the pediment which was contracted no doubt from the rash of Chinese furniture designs earlier in the eighteenth century. The finials which once surmounted the hood are missing. The weather indications and scale are printed on paper and decorated with entwined leaves and fruit and masonic symbols; they coincide in form with the scales and states commonly engraved on brass plates, the elaborate Gothic lettering of 'Fair' and 'Rain' being in deliberate contrast to the lettering of the other states (cf. Plate 128). The barometric inches are divided into decimals but no vernier is fitted since it would be impractical. The paper plates are protected by glass which is laid flush against them: this was a common precaution. In this example the glass is cut and the tube slightly recessed but in other examples the tube is often set in front of the glass which, like the printed plates, is uncut. The siphon tube is an early one and the pierced bulb cistern, which is protected by the square hinged cover, is pear-shaped.

Another barometer in the Science Museum, London[2] which can be attributed to Manticha, this time with more certainty, is a double barometer of the type shown in Plate 41:

[1] Science Museum, London, Inventory No. 1918–191.

[2] Inventory No. 1954–257.

PLATE 96
Manticha, London
37·5″ × 6·9″
By courtesy of the Director
of the Science Museum, London

unlike the example illustrated it has varnished paper scales and is given the express title of 'Double Barometer'. This barometer is dated 1781 and if it was in fact sold by Dominick Manticha it proves that he was active for at least twenty-five years at the close of the eighteenth century.

Manticha also sold wheel barometers and a conspicuous example is shown in Plate 97. The case is of standard design but not the decoration: the surface is painted black with a white border and the floral and foliate designs are gilt. The paintwork is not in pristine condition but the effect is still most elegant. The 8″ silvered dial is framed behind the usual flat glass and the standard of the engraving rivals the paintwork of the case. The fact that this barometer was intended primarily as a piece of furniture, albeit with a degree of utility, is further demonstrated by the division of the scale not into hundredths of an inch but into twentieths: the same relatively imprecise division has already been noted in the case of the decorative barometer by James Gatty (Plate 81). The hands are very simple, the main hand being steel: and the recording hand, which is adjusted by the knob which passes through the glass, is brass. As in so many barometers of this period the tube has been replaced but the brass pulley wheel is original.

A wheel barometer of the same shape and dimensions signed by 'Manticha and Co.', with a rounded top but otherwise similar to the mahogany barometer of Plate 126, recently passed through the London salerooms. The dial was engraved with masonic symbols (cf. Plate 96). The conjunction of the name and this form of decoration make it consistent to attribute this barometer also to Manticha.

PLATE 97
D. Manticha, 11 Ely Court, Holborn, London
36·3″ × 9·5″
Norman Adams Ltd.

BENJAMIN MARTIN b. 1714 –d. 1782

1. Hadleys Quadrant and Visual Glasses, near Crane Court, Fleet Street
2. Newtons Head, 171 Fleet Street

BORN IN Chichester, Martin worked there until 1740 when he came to London and worked for a while as assistant to the lecturer and scientist J. T. Desaguliers. Martin presumably set up on his own when Desaguliers died in 1744. During subsequent years he became a noted optical, mathematical and physical instrument-maker with a shop in Fleet Street opposite the establishment of George Adams. In *c.* 1776 he took his son Joshua Lovell Martin into partnership, an event which was shortly followed by the firm's bankruptcy. Martin had probably himself retired from active business beforehand.

Martin was a self-taught mathematician. While still at Chichester he ran a school and published a *Philosophical Grammar* (1738). During his later life in London he published over thirty books on subjects which included optics and microscopes (1740), geography, navigation and globes (1758), astronomy (1759), horology (1762), surveying (1766) etc. He also gave lectures, at Reading in 1747 and in London from 1764 onwards, on a wide range of scientific subjects. In 1769 Jean Bernoulli, the astronomer to the King of Prussia, visited Martin's workshop and said in his letters—'son magasin est un des mieux fournis: et on fréquente avec empressement ses leçons, dans les quelles il traite ordinairement des sujets de méchanique, de physique expérimentale, et d'astronomie, et que ses beaux instrumens rendent doublement intéressantes'.[1] In a footnote he added that these 'beaux instrumens' were Martin's advantage over the more eminent scientific lecturer James Ferguson who gave similar lectures 'avec de moins beaux instrumens, mais il faut le dire, avec plus de clarté'. Martin also published a *General Magazine of the Arts and Sciences* and in a 1763 directory he is described as its 'author'. It was offered in fourteen volumes on W. and S. Jones' booklist of 1793.

[1] *Lettres Astronomiques* pp. 72–3.

PLATE 98
Martin, London
39·5″ × 6·3″
M. Harris and Sons

In an undated *Catalogue of Philosopical* [*sic*], *Optical and Mathematical Instruments*[1] which was issued when Martin was working at the Sign of Hadleys Quadrant and Visual Glasses he advertised

						£	s.	d.
Best sort of barometer	..	..	..	..	..	1	11	6
Fahrenheit's thermometer	..	..	..	..	..	1	16	0
Pocket ditto	..	..	..	..	..	1	1	0
Hydrometers in ivory	..	..	..	..	..		5	6
Barometer, thermometer and hydrometer all in one frame	..	2	12	6

The use of the word hydrometer, which is an instrument for measuring the specific gravities of liquids, must have been a printer's error.

I have seen a number of cistern-tube barometers by Martin but so far none of any other type. His 'best sort of barometer' was not, judging from the price, anything very special and by inference did not boast either a thermometer or a hygrometer. It is reasonable to identify it with the simple cistern-tube barometers which he sold in cases similar to Plate 18. An example in a lighter coloured mahogany case with a brass door and fuller weather indications can be seen in the Whipple Science Museum at Cambridge but it has been severely doctored and now has the wrong cistern cover and the wrong type of tube. Another example, similar in style but with an exposed tube and some rather amateur foliate carving on the cistern cover and hood, is in the Museum of the History of Science at Oxford.

There is nothing simple or amateur about the barometer of Plate 98. Unlike the two examples mentioned so far this is not signed 'B. Martin, Fleet Street', but only 'Martin, London'. There is no doubt however about its authorship: not only is there no other recorded Martin who was making barometers at this period (a fact which is not alone conclusive) but also an unusual carved mahogany barometer survives with almost identical register plates signed 'B. Martin'.[2] The case of the barometer illustrated is veneered with rich mahogany and the trunk is of serpentine section. The finial is brass and the pillars and the mouldings below the hood are decorated with ivory: the gadrooned cistern cover is most elegantly executed and the spindle columns are alternately made of ivory and ebonized wood. The silvered register plates (Plate 99) which are protected by a glazed brass door are equally well designed and executed. It could be argued that the effect is fussy but the engraver was required to compress a great deal of information into a small space and by the skilful use of 'wheat-ear' borders he has avoided confusion. The titling of each instrument should be compared with the work of

[1] Science Museum, London.   [2] Private collection.

other makers, notably Balthazar Knie and John Russell (Plates 95, 128). The tube, which was originally of the usual leather-based cistern type, has been replaced by an incongruous siphon tube with a bulb cistern, and the hole through which the portable screw once passed has been blocked with wood. The hygrometer is unusual. It employs gut and the method of its operation can be seen in Plate 100. The arbor of the indicating hand is fixed to a cog which is moved by a rack: attached to the rack is a wheel to which is fitted a short length of catgut fixed at its other end to a pin. The rack is held under tension by a small spring and the relaxing and tautening of the catgut are thus transmitted to the indicating hand. The gut is too short to be very efficient but although other makers tried to use longer pieces they found the design

PLATE 99
Detail of Plate 98

of the case a limiting factor: and at least catgut generally lasted longer than an oatbeard.

Another of Martin's barometers, this time of completely different design, is illustrated in Plate 18. I have chosen to illustrate it in Chapter Four because it represents one of the typical designs of its period—a portable bayonet tube encased in a mahogany case and fronted by a thermometer which is itself set against a silvered brass scale. It is of good but not exceptional quality and the engraving of the signature in a pennant should be compared to the barometer by George Adams of Plate 20. It is a feature also of the instruments at Cambridge and Oxford mentioned above. Neither the barometer nor the thermometer tube is original.

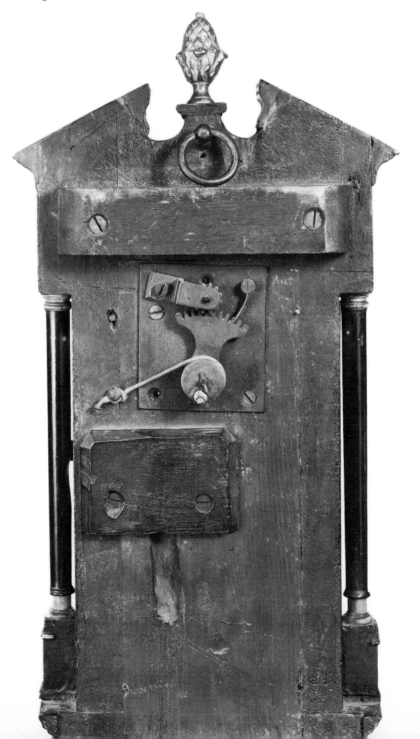

PLATE 100
Detail of Plate 98
showing gut hygrometer

NAIRNE AND BLUNT fl 1774–1805

20–2 Cornhill

THE PARTNERSHIP of Edward Nairne and his former apprentice Thomas Blunt. Nairne seems to have retired to Chelsea by 1805 and died in 1806 but according to Professor Taylor[1] the style of the firm was maintained until Blunt's death in 1822. This cannot have been exclusive practice since Blunt appears in many directories under his own name. The business enjoyed a high reputation for the quality of its optical, mathematical and physical instruments. J. H. de Magellan called their work excellent and they made instruments to his designs: he commended especially their marine barometers.[2]

An example of their work, similar in many respects to the barometer signed 'Nairne' which is described on pp. 169–70. is in the Whipple Science Museum, Cambridge (Plate 101). The case is of mahogany and other common features include the hemispherical cistern cover and the rounded top. There is no hygrometer but the thermometer plate, which is set on the trunk of the case, and the barometer plate are decorated in closely similar fashion. The weather indications also coincide. The pierced brass cover fitted to the thermometer bulb is also similar but more elaborate. The tube, as in the previous example, is of bayonet form and is portable.

In the London Science Museum[3] can be seen a barometer which falls outside the scope of the present study but which is of great interest to the historian of science. Described on the display placard as a 'travelling barometer' it is in fact modelled on a portable barometer used by de Luc in his experiments and described in detail in his *Recherches sur les modifications de l'Atmosphere* (1772)[4].

[1] Taylor *Mathematical Practitioners of Hanoverian England* (manuscript).
[2] *Description et Usages des Nouvaux Baromètres* p. 142 *et passim.*
It is likely that, as Middleton suggests in his *History of the Barometer* p. 104, Magellan learnt more from Nairne and Blunt than vice versa.
[3] Inventory No. 1924–51.

[4] Part 3, Chapter 1.
For a full discussion of de Luc's design see Middleton *History of the Barometer* p. 135 *et seq.* The same author on p. 451 mentions an apparently domestic barometer by Nairne and Blunt which hangs in the office of the Director of the Museo di Storia della Scienza, Florence: I have not yet seen this.

PLATE 101
Nairne and Blunt, London
36″ × 5″
Whipple Science Museum,
Cambridge

E D W A R D   N A I R N E   b. 1726 – d. 1806

20 Cornhill, opposite the Royal Exchange

AN 'OPTICAL, philosophical and mathematical instrument-maker', Nairne published various booklets on astronomical, navigational and pneumatic instruments, etc. He was apprenticed in 1741 to Matthew Loft and became free of the Spectaclemakers' Company in 1748 when Loft died. He was elected F.R.S. in 1776 and is described in an 1801 directory as 'mathematical instrument maker to His Majesty'. He was Master of the Spectaclemakers' Company in 1797. He enjoyed a wide contemporary reputation and his telescopes received the approval of the Prussian astronomer Jean Bernoulli, who visited his workshop in 1769.[1] Abraham Rees called him an 'ingenious artist of London' in 1788.[2] A trade card, written in both English and French, survives in Cambridge[3] and a similar trade card can be seen in the Science Museum, London. In 1774 Nairne took his former apprentice Thomas Blunt into partnership and they worked together (although appearing separately in several directories) until Nairne's apparent retirement in 1805. At one time Nairne's workmen also included Jesse Ramsden.

According to his trade cards Nairne made 'diagonal, standard or portable' barometers. He also made marine barometers. According to Charles Hutton[4] he invented a new type with a constricted bore in the bottom two feet of the tube which stopped the vibration of the mercury. The instrument was mounted on gimbals.

Since Nairne and Blunt appear from the directories to have continued to work under their own names while they were simultaneously selling instruments under their joint names it is not easy to date individual instruments. Barometers survive for example signed 'Nairne, London' which should logically be dated before 1774 but this perforce cannot be done with confidence. In the Museo di Storia della Scienza at Florence there is a portable cistern barometer with a bayonet tube bearing this signature and in this case a date of manufacture before 1774 could be defended on stylistic grounds. Regrettably I have not yet studied this barometer: my only contact with it has been through a photograph and I cannot therefore speak about it with much authority. The mahogany case sports a hemispherical cistern

[1] *Lettres Astronomiques* p. 70.
[2] *Cyclopaedia* (1788), a revision of Ephraim Chambers' *Cyclopaedia*, *s.v.* 'Barometer'.
[3] See p. 53.
[4] *Mathematical and Philosophical Dictionary s.v.* 'Barometer'.

cover and a rounded hood: it is surmounted by a finial and at the top is set a standard glazed oatbeard hygrometer. The trunk is panelled with a silvered brass thermometer plate (*cf.* Plate 101) on which is fixed an alcohol Fahrenheit thermometer whose bulb is protected by a brass cover pierced with diagonal slots. The thermometer plate is bordered with formal engraving. The silvered barometer plate continues the panelling of the case from the top of the thermometer plate and carries some formal engraving at the base but no border. At the top it is shaped to conform to the circular surround of the hygrometer. The scale consists of the usual barometric inches divided into decimals and a manual vernier is fitted. The weather indications read normally enough 'Very Dry, Set Fair, Fair, Change, Rain, Mh Rain, Stormy' and are engraved in Roman Script. The signature appears above the scales but below the top of the tube which is protected by a brass cover.

I have seen an almost identical barometer signed by J. Somalvico which poses a problem. It is possible that Somalvico was an important maker of barometers for the trade in the last quarter of the eighteenth century (in which case Nairne could have bought stock from him) but I have so far been unable to verify this. There appear to have been Somalvicos in this country from early in the eighteenth century but no Somalvico is mentioned in the directories before the appearance of the firm of Lione, Somalvico and Co. in 1805. If the second partner of this firm was the Joseph Somalvico who was probably born in 1759 the same man could not have made Nairne's barometer before 1774 when he would have been fifteen. It is not unlikely that Somalvico repaired the barometer on which his signature appears: it was not uncommon for a repairer to substitute his own name for the signature of the original maker and it was not difficult to do. I have seen photographs of barometers probably made by Charles Orme and by one of the Watkins family similarly treated by later 'makers'.

Like other leading makers Nairne produced cheap stock instruments and many survive. The examples noted in my records are all cistern-tube instruments, most of them in simple round-topped mahogany cases, some panelled with glazed doors but others with exposed tubes.

PLATE 102
Title page of
Negretti and Zambra's
Catalogue 1859

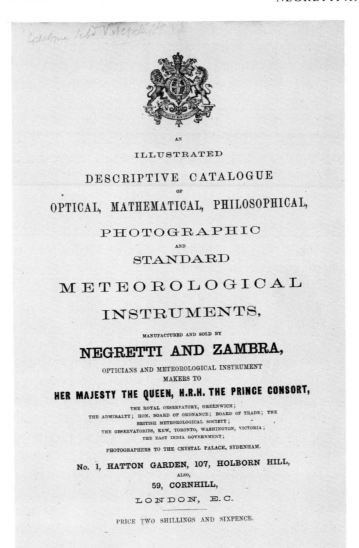

PLATE 102
Title page of
Negretti and Zambra's
Catalogue 1859

N E G R E T T I   A N D   Z A M B R A   fl 1850–

1. 11 Hatton Garden (1850–9)
2.   1 Hatton Garden (1859–   )
3. 107 Holborn Hill (1859–60)

Branches:

1. 120 Crystal Palace (1852–   )
2. 68 Cornhill (1857–8)
3. 59 Cornhill (1858–60)
4. 45 Cornhill (1859–   )

ORIGINALLY the partnership of Henry Negretti (1818–79) and J.W. Zambra (b. 1822) this firm became a public company in 1948 and still carries on a flourishing business in scientific instruments, etc. Enrico Angelo Ludovico Negretti came to England in 1830 and was apprenticed in 1838 to F. A. Pizzala. An 1839 directory mentions a barometer maker called H. Negratti at 2 Dorrington Street but although this very probably refers to Negretti there is no other trace of him at this address. In 1840 he was established at 20 Greville Street as a glass-blower: in 1841 he was working for the widow of Valentino Pizzi at 19 Leather Lane as a glass-blower and barometer maker. By 1845 Pizzi's widow seems to have died and in 1849 Negretti was working as a philosophical instrument-maker at 9 Hatton Garden. The partnership with Joseph Warren Zambra, who was born at Saffron Walden, was formed in 1850.

The partnership was most successful and the firm rapidly became established as the leading manufacturer of meteorological instruments. At the Great Exhibition of 1851 they gained the Prize Medal for these, while also exhibiting other physical, musical, surgical instruments, etc: they also took an important interest in photography and were notable opticians. In 1859 they published an *Illustrated Descriptive Catalogue* of their wide range of wares which ran to 181 pages and advertised 2,134 separate items (Plate 102): considering the brief nine years during which the firm had been in existence the list is impressive and the various official appointments emphasize the story of success.

It is clear from this catalogue, of which over 10,000 copies were sold at 2s. 6d. by 1864 when an enlarged edition appeared, that the firm enjoyed a prominent position among barometer manufacturers. Besides domestic instruments they offered the whole range of standard mercurial barometers, including Gay-Lussac and Fortin instruments, mountain, marine, agricultural barometers, etc.; also sympiesometers and aneroid barometers, including a watch-sized pocket instrument which was claimed to be a remarkable achievement of design. Their later catalogues reflect the growing importance of the firm whose most successful years fall outside the scope of this study.

In the City of Gloucester Museum there is a rosewood marine barometer inlaid with mother-of-pearl by 'Negretti and Co., 19 Leather Lane' which is interesting because it can be dated fairly precisely between 1845 and 1848, i.e. after the death of Pizzi's widow and before Negretti's move to Hatton Garden. The firm was still advertising this type of barometer in 1859 and a similar example is illustrated in the catalogue.

I do not illustrate any example of this firm's domestic instruments because, as can be seen from their catalogue which is quoted on pp. 85 and 99–100, their range was comprehensive and their volume of production prolific. The illustrations from the catalogue are reproduced in Plates 39 and 52 and give as basic a guide as any to the variety of their work.

CHARLES ORME b.1688 –d.1747

Ashby de la Zouch, Leicestershire

VERY FEW records of Charles Orme are available. He seems to have died before 1750 since no Charles Orme appears in the Leicestershire probate records after that date. A brass plaque has been recorded in the Ashby church bearing the inscription 'C. Orme, died Jan. 20 1747 aged 59'.[1] Orme was a fairly common name in Leicestershire in the eighteenth century but it seems fair to surmise that, since extant work by Orme bears dates from 1731 to 1742,[2] the plaque referred to him. If so he was born in 1688 and was probably the son of Thomas Orme, Rector of Garesden in Wiltshire, who died in 1715 aged sixty-one and on whose tombstone in Ashby churchyard the names of his seven children were given: Charles was the sixth.[3] A second plaque in the church recorded the death of Charles' eight-year-old son Charles in 1737.

Orme owes his eminence to his successful exploitation of the angle tube principle. Several angle barometers signed by him survive and I have yet to see any other type bearing his signature. Some of these angle instruments have only one tube while others have two or even three giving of course a more extended scale. The Portuguese scientist J. H. de Magellan said that he had found among the elder George Adams' papers, which had been lent to him by the younger Adams, this proposal of Orme's to shorten the tube and add two more, using the same reservoir (Plate 103). By doing this 'Mr. Horme, gentilhomme Anglois de Ashby en Lancastre, rendit bien plus commode cette espece du barometre'.[4] Magellan thought that J. T. Desaguliers had been wrong to suggest in his lectures[5] that Orme's improvement of the angle barometer had been in the preparation of the mercury: it was rather in the greater accuracy brought about by the use of three tubes. Desaguliers' statement was founded on a paper submitted to the Royal Society by a certain Henry Beighton in 1738.[6] Beighton appears to have been on friendly terms with Orme: in fact he attended while Orme

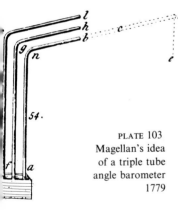

PLATE 103
Magellan's idea
of a triple tube
angle barometer
1779

[1] John Nichols *Antiquities in Leicestershire* (*Bibliotheca Topographica Britannica* Vol. 8) (1790) p. 1241.
[2] A brass ruler signed 'Made by Cha Orme of Ashby-de-la-Zouch 1731' is in the City of Leicester Museum: and various barometers are dated 1738–42.
[3] Nichols *Antiquities in Leicestershire* p. 1240.
[4] *Description et Usages des Nouvaux Baromètres* (1779) p. 152.

[5] *Experimental Philosophy* Lesson 10 p. 263.
[6] *The Imperfections of the common Barometers, and the Improvement made in them, by Mr. Cha. Orme of Ashby-de-la-Zouch in Leicestershire where they are perfected and rectified.* (*Philosophical Transactions* Vol. 40 p. 248 *et seq.*) Beighton says (p. 255) that Desaguliers was acquainted with Orme 'and his glasses' but according to Desaguliers *Experimental Philosophy* the acquaintance was second-hand.

filled and boiled a tube on 20 January 1735[1] and there is no reason to doubt his account. Magellan had probably never read it: indeed if he had he would not have said that Ashby was in Lancashire. He was probably so pleased with his own discovery in George Adams' papers that he could not resist the unscholarly urge to correct what he considered to be a previous writer's error.

Beighton's account suggests that Orme was responsible for introducing to England the practice of distilling and boiling mercury in order to rid it of imperfections. Distillation was a preliminary operation and the mercury was of course boiled in the tube. In addition to these innovations Orme should also be given credit on Magellan's evidence for originating the use of multiple tubes in angle barometers. John Nichols says in a footnote: 'of this family is Dr. David Orme, a celebrated physician and man-midwife, and a no less ingenious mechanick having been the inventor of the double-tubed barometer'.[2] I can neither deny nor confirm this statement: it is possible that Charles Orme only gave physical expression to his relation's ideas but the existence of George Adams' papers suggests that Nichols' account, which was written many years later, depended on hearsay.

The rare triple tube instrument[3] illustrated in Plate 104 differs from Magellan's account in that it has a separate cistern for each tube. This suggests that Magellan had not in fact seen an example of the instrument which he was describing. The ponderous shape of the case is dictated by the triple tubes. This does not make for an elegant piece of furniture but instead of trying to design a symmetrical frame on the lines attempted by John Patrick and Francis Watkins (Plates 108 and 152) the maker has chosen to interest the eye with the contrast between the finely figured walnut veneers and the polished brass border and inlays, some of which have recently been restored. The casework is finely executed. The silvered plates (Plate 105) are protected by glass which is bevelled at the edges and the engraving is precise and of good quality. The scale covers the usual barometric 28"–31", each tube representing one inch which is divided into hundredths. Since the mercury can move over 20" for each 1" of the scale its potential 'rise and fall' has been extended from the usual 3" to 60". The original tubes have not survived but the boxwood cisterns (Plate 106) are original and measure 2·3" square and 1·4" high. Each one is fitted with a wooden sleeve which is cemented to the tube: there is a sleeve of

---

[1] *Philosophical Transactions* Vol. 40 p. 251.
[2] *Antiquities in Leicestershire* p. 1241.
[3] According to Beighton, *Philosophical Transactions* Vol. 40 p. 251, four hours were required for boiling each tube.

PLATE 104
Charles Orme,
Ashby-de-la-Zouch 1741
41·7″ × 31·8″
Author's collection

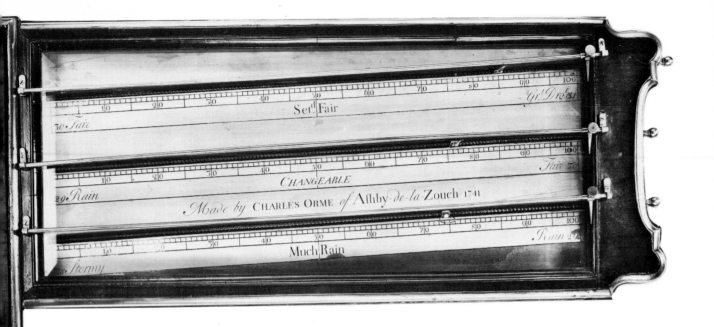

Ser.ᵈ Fair

30 Fair

CHANGEABLE

29 Rain

Made by CHARLES ORME of Aſhby-de-la-Zouch 1741

Much Rain

Gr.ᵗ Dro.ᵗʰ

Fair 30

Rain 29

Stormy

PLATE 105
Detail of Plate 104

similar diameter beneath each cistern which is plugged and sealed but can be used for draining and inserting the mercury; this avoids the necessity of splitting the glued lid off the box. There is a small plugged aperture in the top of each box through which mercury can be added. The cisterns are not level with each other but tiered: their positions are carefully gauged however to ensure that each tube gives the required barometric measurement. In front of the glass are three manually operated pointers which slide on brass rods. Because of their distance from the tubes these cannot be very accurately adjusted and they may be a later addition. Each tube is also fitted with a ring pointer: these are operated by wormed rods which are turned by the three brass knobs visible at the righthand extremity of the case. The tubes had not been replaced when the photographs were taken.

There is a barometer in a very similar case but with two tubes instead of three in the City of Gloucester Museum. The case is not bordered with brass and many of its line inlays and some of the woodwork need, and are undergoing, restoration. The scale and weather indications are identical but because there are only two tubes the total 'rise and fall' is reduced: 29·5″ ('Changeable') is at the right-hand end of the lower tube and the lefthand end of the upper tube, the repetition echoing the design of the instrument illustrated. The original tubes have been replaced by siphon tubes with bulb cisterns. The barometer is dated 1742.

PLATE 106
Detail of Plate 104
showing cisterns

Another instrument with two tubes in a similar case was illustrated in the *Dictionary of English Furniture*[1] and was dated 1742 in the subtitle to the illustration in which unfortunately the date is not clear: when it was sold in London in 1954 the sale catalogue stated that it carried the date 1740. I have not studied this barometer but from the illustration it is extremely similar to the Gloucester barometer. The inlaid brass lines lack the fleur-de-lis motifs which the Gloucester

[1] 2nd edition (1954) *s.v.* 'Barometers' Fig. 18.

PLATE 107
Cha Orme,
Ashby-de-la-Zouch
1738
33″ × 27·3″
*Arthur S. Vernay Inc.,
New York*

barometer shares with the barometer of Plate 104 and the modelling of the right-hand end of the casework is different.

Descending *ad profundum* down the numerical scale, Plate 107 shows a barometer with only one tube. This is earlier than the previous examples, being dated 1738. The case is veneered with walnut and inlaid with ebony and boxwood lines. The silvered plates are left exposed and carry a conventional 28″–31″ scale divided into fortieths: the weather indications conform to Plate 104. The pointer which would have been attached to a brass wire rod above the tube is missing. Because this barometer is in America I have not seen it and cannot give an opinion on what has happened to the end of the case: possibly the plates were cut short by a later repairer but other cases survive in an equally unfinished state. Nor can I say whether the cistern, which the illustration suggests is of the usual portable type, is correct. An undated single tube barometer by Orme in a lacquered case which is in the Fitzwilliam Museum, Cambridge, also has a hole for a screw but contains one of Orme's usual square cisterns (*cf.* Plate 106). Perhaps the answer is that Orme bought his cases from a cabinet-maker who was used to providing for the conventional screw-type cistern.

I have seen a photograph of a barometer strikingly similar to Plate 107 signed by 'A. Amadio, Ashby-de-la-Zouch' which was dated 1736. There is no trace of an Amadio working at Ashby at this date and this seems to be an example of a later repairer substituting his own name, oddly enough not his address, for that of the original maker.

JOHN PATRICK   fl 1686 –1720 (?)

1. Jewin Street
2. Ship Court, Old Bailey

PATRICK appears to have been the first instrument-maker to specialize in the manufacture of barometers. Judging from contemporary references to him he enjoyed a considerable reputation: in the *Lexicon Technicum* of 1704 he was called the 'Torricellian Operator' and the writer said, 'I think myself obliged in justice to tell the world, that I have never seen better weather-glasses of all kinds made any where than by Mr. Patrick'. He was well known enough to be visited in 1710 by the German traveller von Uffenbach who called him 'an optico and weather-glass maker'.[1]

In spite of contemporary evidence little is known about his life. He appears to have been apprenticed as a joiner in 1786[2] but to have been making barometers at least as early as 1695 when he assisted the Master and Wardens of the Clockmakers' Company in their resistance to Daniel Quare's patent for a portable weather-glass (p. 30 *et seq.*). At this time his shop does not seem to have been in Old Bailey: a penned comment facing the title page of an extant copy of John Smith's *Compleat Discourse* (1688)[3] gives an illegible address in Jewin Street. Clay and Court furthermore quote a rough trade bill of Patrick's which gives his address as 'against Bull Head Court in Jewin Street, near Cripplegate Church':[4] and the penned address can with some imagination be construed as the same. He had however moved to Ship Court, Old Bailey, by 1704 at the latest. In 1712 he became a member of the Clockmakers' Company. Although he probably joined the Company because of his work as an instrument-maker his association with clock and watchmakers was fairly close: apart from the help given to the Company in 1695 he claimed that his barometers were sold 'at most eminent watchmakers in London'. According to Clay and Court they were sold by Marshall, Quare and Graham and he was evidently the leading maker of barometers for the trade at the time.[5] The date of his death is not known but in 1720 Edmund Halley spoke in a paper of 'Mr. Patrick, who stiles himself the Torricellian Operator'[6]: the use of the present tense suggests that he may have

[1] Quarrell and Mare *London in 1710* p. 145.
[2] Joiner's Company *Admissions Register* 6 July 1686—'John Patrick appd. to Wm. Tompson . . . for 7 years'.
[3] British Museum copy.
[4] *History of the Microscope* p. 251: these authors spell his name Pathrick, but their next entry records a John Patrick.
[5] *Ibid.*
[6] *Philosophical Transactions* Vol. 31 (1720) p. 116.

still been alive. He certainly died before 1738.[1]

Patrick published two pamphlets. The first, *Reflections upon a New Account of the Alterations of Wind and Weather* (1700), was a refutation of weather forecasts made by a certain Gustavus Parker who made extravagant claims for a type of balance barometer: Patrick disproved Parker's forecasts by keeping a daily record of the weather and of the barometric level for September 1700 from which it was clear that his rival had 'mist the wind and weather more days than he has hit right'.

The second pamphlet, *A New Improvement of the Quicksilver Barometer*, is undated, but was published before 1704 since part of it was quoted verbatim in the first volume of the *Lexicon Technicum*. It advertised a number of barometers—pendant, 'common', diagonal, marine and portable—and was accompanied by an illustrated advertisement (Plate 7). This, together with a later more accurate advertisement (Plate 8), is discussed in detail in Chapter Three. A contemporary description of some of Patrick's instruments also survives in the journal of the German traveller von Uffenbach who visited his workshop on 15 October 1710. The relevant text of this journal is quoted in full on pp. 36–7 and discussed in conjunction with the advertisements mentioned above throughout the rest of Chapter Three. Rather than repeat this extensive discussion here I must refer the reader to it if he wishes to gain a comprehensive view of Patrick's work.

Patrick could well have been the inventor of, or at any rate the first maker to apply, the portable screw and leather bag to the cistern barometer (Chapter Three): but his claims are not strong and the literary evidence, which consists of Abraham Rees's *Cyclopaedia* (1788) and Charles Hutton's *Philosophical and Mathematical Dictionary* (1795), is too late to deserve unqualified confidence.

Examples of his cistern-tube and angle barometers survive although not in the numbers which, considering his contemporary eminence, one would expect. An angle barometer of the design advertised by Patrick in Plate 8 Fig. 4 is illustrated in the *Dictionary of English Furniture*[2] but the photograph does not reveal much detail and the frame has sustained considerable damage: it is however of great interest and it is a pity that its present whereabouts is unknown. The frame is veneered with walnut and the only notable variation from the design of Plate 8 Fig. 4 is the squat cylindrical shape of the cistern covers, which in fact look as if they have been replaced.

---

[1] *Ibid.* Vol. 40 (1738) p. 249 where Henry Beighton calls him the 'late curious operator'.

[2] See p. 42 No. 1.

Plate 108 shows an angle barometer of the greatest interest because, with only slight differences, it is a replica of Patrick's advertisement of Plate 8 Fig. 1. The walnut veneers are richly figured and the carcase is of

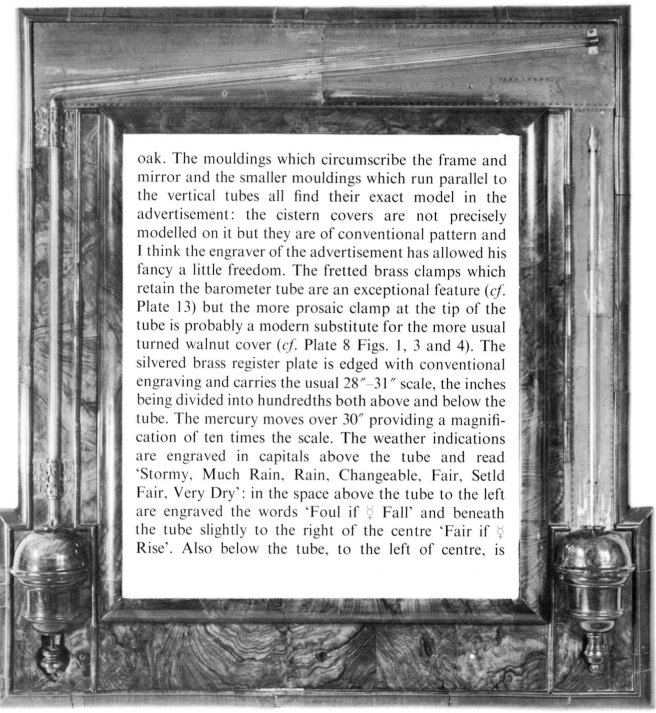

oak. The mouldings which circumscribe the frame and mirror and the smaller mouldings which run parallel to the vertical tubes all find their exact model in the advertisement: the cistern covers are not precisely modelled on it but they are of conventional pattern and I think the engraver of the advertisement has allowed his fancy a little freedom. The fretted brass clamps which retain the barometer tube are an exceptional feature (*cf.* Plate 13) but the more prosaic clamp at the tip of the tube is probably a modern substitute for the more usual turned walnut cover (*cf.* Plate 8 Figs. 1, 3 and 4). The silvered brass register plate is edged with conventional engraving and carries the usual 28″–31″ scale, the inches being divided into hundredths both above and below the tube. The mercury moves over 30″ providing a magnification of ten times the scale. The weather indications are engraved in capitals above the tube and read 'Stormy, Much Rain, Rain, Changeable, Fair, Setld Fair, Very Dry': in the space above the tube to the left are engraved the words 'Foul if ☿ Fall' and beneath the tube slightly to the right of the centre 'Fair if ☿ Rise'. Also below the tube, to the left of centre, is

PLATE 108
John Patrick in the Old Baily, Londini
41·5″ × 39·8″
Collection of
Irwin Untermyer

engraved '☿ Altitude': this is presumably an interpretation of the scale for the sake of the uninitiated purchaser. The signature 'John Patrick in the Old Baily Londini Fecit' appears to the right of the plate in a little engraved frame of its own which is flanked on either side by engraved scrolls. No pointer is fitted—this again is in accordance with the advertisements of Plate 8. The tube is fitted with a closed cistern which is portable and the adjusting screw is recessed in the frame (cf. Plate 8 Fig. 1). The spirit thermometer, using the Royal Society scale, is mounted on a silvered brass plate which is engraved in a style similar to the barometer plate.

An ordinary portable barometer by Patrick is illustrated in Plate 109. Again the walnut veneers are applied to an oak carcase and the cistern covers, hanging hole, hood pillars and curved pediment are modelled on the advertisements of Plate 8 Figs. 6 and 9. Unlike Fig. 9 however the case is panelled and unlike Fig. 6 there is no thermometer mounted on it. There was originally a finial, and possibly three (cf. Plate 8 Figs. 6 and 9 again), but these are lost. The brass plates also reflect the design of the two illustrations of the advertisement: they are adjustable and the weather indications broadly coincide. The 3″ scale is divided in decimals. Neither the tube nor the cistern is original: and the brass pointer is also modern. This barometer is of great interest since it is an example of Patrick's ordinary stock portable barometers. There is nothing pretentious about it, no superfluous decoration and no attempt to improve its accuracy beyond the capabilities of contemporary materials.

An almost exact replica of Plate 8 Fig. 6 survives in the National Maritime Museum, Greenwich.[1] The carcase is of oak and pine, the veneers of walnut. The pediment is curved but has a cornice above the plates as in Plate 109. The ball finials are of gilt brass. The pillars are of turned walnut and are not gilded or embellished with brass: there are inverted gilt 'acorns' beneath them however as in the advertisement. The trunk has moulded edges and the cistern cover is similar to Plate 109. The case measures 40·5″ high and 6·25″ wide. The silvered brass plates which are not adjustable are coarsely engraved but decorated with a 'wheat-ear' border

[1] Gabb Collection, Catalogue No. 0.1: in store in 1964 and in need of restoration.

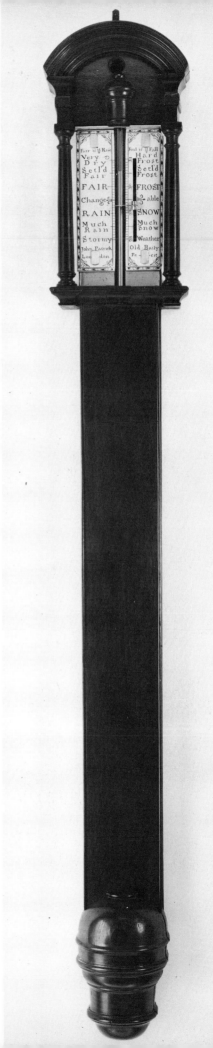

PLATE 109
John Patrick, Old Baily, London
38″ × 5·5″
Garner and Marney Ltd.

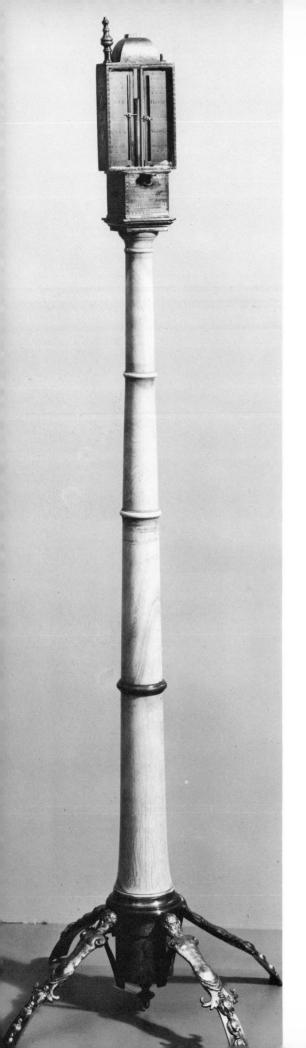

and foliate motifs in the corners. The scale is 28″–31″ divided in decimals and the weather indications are for summer and winter as in Plate 109. The signature 'I. Patrick, London' appears at the base of the plates and there is a manual crescent-shaped pointer which slides in a groove on the right-hand plate. The tube is slightly crimped below the plates but does not seem to be original: the portable cistern is now of the leather-based type. The alcohol thermometer has varnished paper plates carrying the Royal Society scale as in Plate 8 Fig. 6; and its bulb is housed in the cistern cover, the tube being bent just above the bulb to allow this. The original pointer is missing.

An example of a 'Barometer in a pillar' is shown in Plate 110. The case is assembled from sections of turned ivory—a favourite design of Daniel Quare (Plate 124). The overall design of the hood (Plate 111), which consists of brass castings, covered with conventional floral and foliate engraving, is also comparable to Quare's work (Plates 117, 119) as are the finials, two of which are missing. The chased brass decoration of the feet (*cf.* Plate 120) finally suggests either that Patrick and Quare bought their components from the same sources or that one of them made barometers for the other. The feet, as in Plate 120, are attached to steel springs and can be folded against the bottom of the case (*cf.* Plate 121) so that the barometer may be hung from the wall. The brass housing of the portable cistern is finely engraved with formal acanthus motifs. The glazed hood, as in much of Quare's work, can be viewed from both sides.

PLATE 110
John Patrick in ye Old Baily, London
35″ × 2·7″
By courtesy of the
Trustees of the British Museum

Plate 111 shows the French side. The 28″–31″ scale engraved on each of the two silvered brass plates is divided into twentieths; this again is a common feature of Quare's pillar barometers, but the weather indications do not coincide with Quare's designs. They are more conventionally inscribed against the half-inch divisions of the scale. The English side (Plate 110) of which I do not illustrate a detail is equally conventional and reads

Fair if ☿ Rising	Foul if ☿ Falling
Very Dry	Hard Frost
Setld Fair	Setld Frost
Fair	Frost
Change	able
Rain	Snow
Much Rain	Much Snow
Stormy	Weather

These are identical to the states of the weather provided on the barometer of Plate 109. The signature, which is engraved as in examples by Quare below the hood, is in English on both sides. The two pointers are operated by wormed rods and adjusted by the two outer finials. The tube and cistern have been replaced: the original cistern was either of the leather bag type described in Chapter Three (possibly encased in ivory) or of the commoner leather-based boxwood design.

This barometer does not coincide entirely with Patrick's advertisement of a pillar barometer (Plate 8 Fig. 7), but it shares certain features such as the glazed hood, dual pointers and portable cistern. The advertised example furthermore was made only to hang from the wall.

Considering his importance Patrick's work is poorly represented in public collections in this country. As far as I know the only two barometers by him in public collections are those described above and neither of these is, at the time of writing, on show.

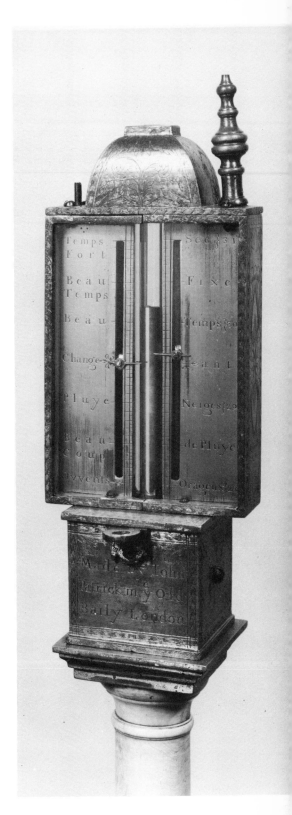

PLATE 111
Detail of Plate 110

HENRY PYEFINCH fl 1739–90

Golden Quadrant Sun and Spectacles, 67 Cornhill

APPRENTICED in 1753 to Francis Watkins the elder, Pyefinch became a member of the Spectaclemakers' Company in 1763. He was a well-known optical and mathematical instrument-maker. The Prussian astronomer Jean Bernoulli visited his workshop in 1769 and described it as 'un magasin très bien fourni'.[1] Bernoulli also quoted the prices of Pyefinch's astronomical instruments, globes and other instruments including:

	£	s.	d.
Le meilleur barometre	1	11	6
Barometre avec thermometre	2	12	6
Le meilleur thermometre de Fahrenheit	1	11	6[2]

A trade card, which survives in the Science Museum, London, gives a slightly longer list:

	£	s.	d.
Best barometer	1	11	6
Ditto	2	2	0
Barometer with thermometer	2	12	6
The same with thermometer and hygrometer	3	3	0
Best sort	4	4	0

In 1765 Pyefinch, described as an optician, secured a patent jointly with the Portuguese scientists J. H. de Magellan[3] for 'A new constructed instrument by which is shewn the true effect of the weight of the atmosphere, with the variation which is caused by the heat and cold, and likewise the quantity of that variation'. The invention, such as it was, consisted of a siphon tube which was rendered 'true' not by any technical innovation but by the graduation of both limbs of the tube, taking into account the measurement of bore and capacity, and by observation of the changes caused to the bulk of the mercury by alterations of temperature.

As in the case of Benjamin Martin, Pyefinch's advertisement suggests that his so-called 'best' barometer did not incorporate either a thermometer or a hygrometer: and judging from its price it was

[1] *Lettres Astronomiques* p. 70.
[2] *Ibid.* p. 71.
[3] The author of *Descripion et Usages des Nouvaux Baromètres* which is referred to elsewhere.

probably housed in an unadorned case. Twentieth-century advertisements were not the first to misuse epithets. Barometers signed by Pyefinch seem to be rare but the barometer illustrated in Plate 112[1] answers the description 'the same with thermometer and hygrometer' and incontrovertibly justifies the category 'best sort'. Several makers were selling portable bayonet-tube barometers of this type—with a thermometer on the trunk and a hygrometer at the top—during the last quarter of the eighteenth century including Martin, Nairne and Watkins, but few of them have the same elegance. The highly carved case is of mahogany and the traditional diminishing husks on each side of the hood are especially well executed. The shallow carving in relief round the hygrometer is almost certainly not contemporary: and the inconsistent quality of the large finial suggests that this could also be a later addition. The engraving on the silvered plates is, in contrast to the casework, no more than ordinary and lacks decoration of any sort. The barometer plate is a standard example of the type used by practically all the makers of the period (cf. Plates 18, 20, 71) with the usual weather indications, a decimal scale which is extended down to 27″ and a manual vernier. The rounded cover at the top of the tube is ivory. The tube is not original and the cistern is of the usual leather-based cylindrical type. The oatbeard hygrometer is encased in a glazed brass box of a type found (like the scales) on barometers by many makers. The alcohol Fahrenheit thermometer has been replaced by a modern enamelled tube: the perforated brass cover which protects its bulb is also found on other contemporary instruments.

[1] Victoria and Albert Museum, Inventory No. W. 17–1957

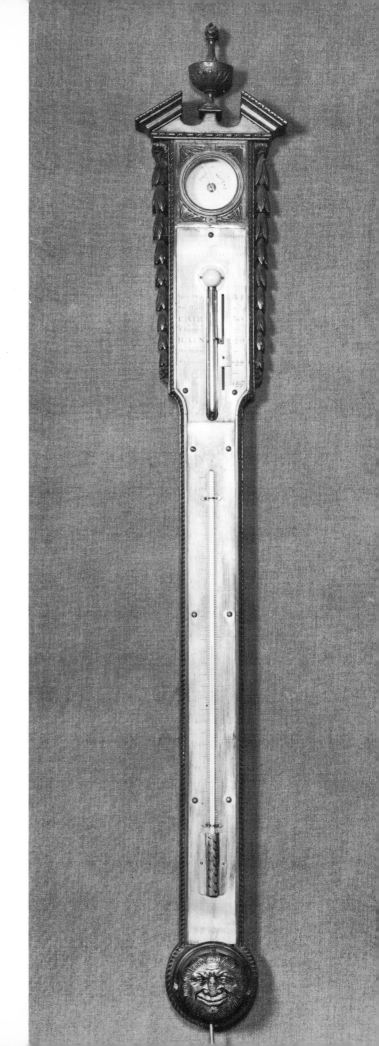

PLATE 112
H. Pyefinch, London
45·8″ × 7·2″
*Victoria and Albert Museum,
London:
Crown copyright*

DANIEL QUARE   b. 1649 –d. 1724

Kings Arms, Exchange Alley

ONE of the most eminent watch and clockmakers of his day, Quare also made mathematical instruments and barometers. He became a member of the Clockmakers' Company in 1671 and was Master in 1708. Many of his watches and clocks are described by F. J. Britten[1] and he has a special place in the history of watchwork owing to his invention of a repeating watch. Quare was a Quaker and apparently an astute and successful businessman: he also had many rich customers, including William III. In his *Chronicles and Characters of the Stock Exchange* (1849)[2] John Francis reported that in 1715 'one Quare, a Quaker and celebrated watchmaker in 'Change Alley, having successfully speculated in the shares and funds with which it abounded, was of sufficient importance to invite to the marriage feast of his daughter, Sarah Jennings, Duchess of Marlborough, and the Princess of Wales, who, with three hundred guests of distinction, graced the wedding entertainment'.

In 1695 Quare obtained a patent for a portable barometer in spite of opposition from the Clockmakers' Company who traditionally disapproved of monopolies. John Patrick, not himself a member at the time, assisted the Court of the Company. The patent is quoted and discussed in Chapter Three (p. 30 *et seq.*). Previous writers have almost invariably said, without evidence, that it consisted of the screw and leather-based cistern which is described in the same chapter (p. 29): but there is a great deal of evidence against this assumption. As I have argued it probably involved merely the constriction of the bore of the tube at the top. This reduced the risk of breakage when the mercury surged and as will be seen later Quare seems to have lengthened the tube to reduce the risk further. He may also, as I have said in Chapter Three, have cemented a leather cover over the top of the cistern to prevent the spilling of the mercury or used a leather bag to contain it and the second of these alternatives seems more likely. Whether or not Quare's invention was his own idea is questionable: Huygens[3] thought that he was inspired by Joachim d'Alencé's description of a portable barometer which was published in Holland in 1688[4] and Hooke

[1] *Old Clocks and Watches* p. 291 *et seq.*
[2] p. 46.
[3] See p. 32.
[4] *Traittez des Baromètres.*

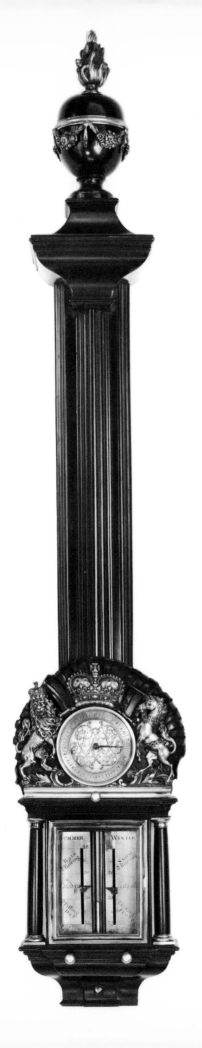

considered that Tompion deserved precedence.[1] Quare certainly does not seem to have had a monopoly even in 1695 since the *Minutes* of the Clockmakers' Company for 30 September 1695 include the remark that 'there may be suits of law or trouble to some members that make or sell those weatherglasses'. John Patrick for one was doubtless in the field. William Derham, a Fellow of the Royal Society who was actively interested in the barometer, used one of Quare's 'best portable barometers' for experiments on the measurement of heights at the Monument in September 1696: it was apparently unsatisfactory since in November 1697 he tried the experiment 'again, more nicely', using this time an instrument of his own devising and construction.[2]

It is possible that some of Quare's barometers were made by John Patrick who was apparently a prolific maker for the trade in the early years of the eighteenth century: but this is conjectural.[3] A large number of barometers signed by Quare survive and he is one of the very few makers whose work is adequately represented in public collections in this country.[4] I have studied nearly forty, most of them in person but some, for geographical reasons, with the aid of photographs and helpful correspondents. They are all, with only one exception, barometers of the pillar type.[5] It is therefore convenient to describe the exception before proceeding to general remarks about Quare's more normal genre.

It is an exceptional exception (Plate 113). The elaborate royal monogram which is applied to the centre of the calendar dial demonstrates that it was made for William III. It thus forms part of a royal collection — Tompion's two wheel barometers (Plates 143 and 146), his siphon-tube barometer (Plate 140), and Quare's angle barometer and ivory barometer (Plates 125, 120)—all of which were

---

[1] Royal Society *Journal Book* 31 January, 1695: see p. 32.
[2] *Philosophical Transactions* Vol. 20 (1698) p. 2.
[3] See p. 178.
[4] Because Quare's pillar barometers are popular with collectors he is also one of the few makers to have attracted forgery. I have seen four forgeries, two of them skilful: collectors can only hope to detect deceit if they have studied as many genuine examples in detail as possible.
[5] I include the angle barometer at Hampton Court (Plate 125) in this category.

PLATE 113
D. Quare, Lond.
38″ × 6·4″
Collection of Leslie Godden

PLATE 114
Detail of Plate 113

probably made before the King's death in 1702. Its remarkable similarity to Tompion's siphon-tube barometer (Plate 140) suggests that they were both made for Hampton Court and that they were commissioned at more or less the same time. They were both design-ed to reveal all the 'sensible rising and falling of the mercury' in the short limb of the siphon tube;[1] and to achieve this a bulb, or 'bolt-head' as Robert Hooke called it, had to be fitted at the top of the long limb of the tube to act as a cistern.[2] This was concealed in each case by the decorative finial. Tompion was making barometers for Hooke as early as 1675–6[3] and the principles embodied in his royal barometers probably derived from discussion with Hooke: it is tempt-ing to suggest liaison between Tompion and Quare on the evid-ence of these two barometers.

The oak frame is veneered with ebonized fruitwood but the carved shell which frames the royal arms (Plate 114) is made of ebonized walnut. Some minor restorations have been necessary, including the left-hand pillar and small pieces of the veneer at the base, but these have been well executed and the casework is other-wise in excellent condition. The

[1] See p. 8:
Hooke's proposal was for a wheel barometer.
[2] Recent repairs by craftsmen who did not understand the principles involved have ensured that neither instrument is now fitted with the correct tube.
[3] See p. 229.

decorative mounts are exquisitely made. They are all silver, except the tip of the flame finial (Plate 115) which is of gilt brass, and the deliberate contrast between them and the black frame is typical of the work of some of the finest clock-case makers of the day. It was a formula used later by the maker of the frame of Daniel Delander's barometer which is illustrated in Plate 69. The register plates are also silver and are protected by a bevelled glass which is itself set in a silver frame. The scale and weather indications are inverted because observations are taken from the short open limb of the tube in which the mercury falls as the pressure rises. Simple weather indications are given for summer and winter and they are engraved in boxes: this, as will be seen shortly, is a peculiar and common feature of Quare's work. The left-hand plate is similar to that of the Tompion baro-meter (Plate 141) but Tompion's right-hand plate gives a conventional list of summer indica-tions. As on the Tompion barometer the 3″ scale, which is divided into twentieths of an inch, is engraved on both plates and the signature 'D. Quare, Lond. Fecit' is engraved at the bottom. Quare's two pointers, which are operated by rackwork and adjusted by the two brass knobs beneath the plates, are set in grooves. The glazed calendar dial has a brass bezel, a mat brass centre to which the silver monogram of William III is applied and a silver chapter ring: the steel hand is adjusted by the brass knob beneath the dial.

Some of the features of this barometer—not-ably the scale, the dual pointers and the design but not the detail of the weather indications—reappear in Quare's characteristic pillar baro-meters. The calendar dial also reappears but only on the two instruments at Hampton Court (Plates 120, 125). Before passing on to describe these however there are certain general observations about Quare's pillar barometers which can usefully be made. So many of these survive and they embody so many slight variations of design that I cannot hope to give

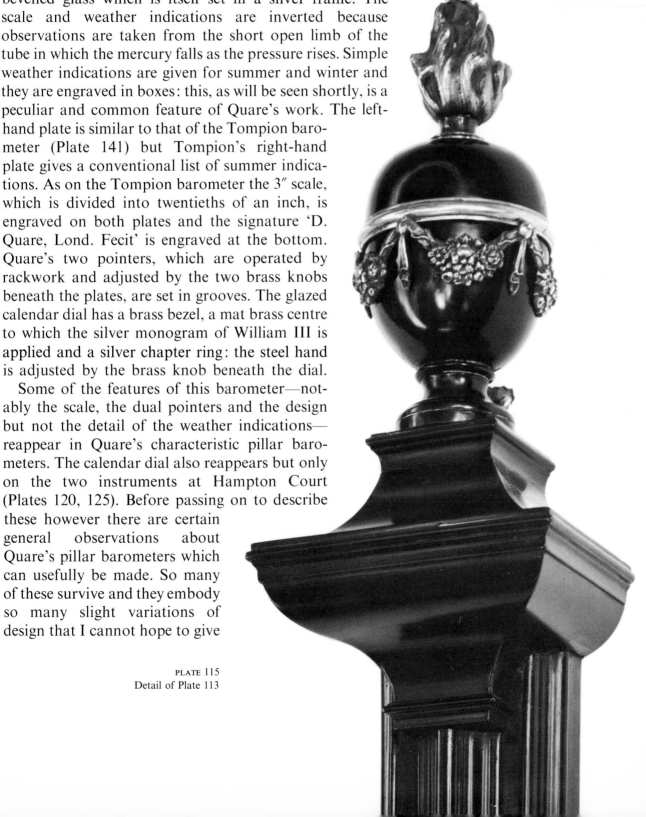

PLATE 115
Detail of Plate 113

a comprehensive account within the scope of the present study. Quare's work needs a separate study on its own. I hope therefore that readers will be satisfied with some valid general comments followed by descriptions of particular examples which have been selected because they demonstrate as many typical aspects of his work as possible.

There are three important ways of classifying nearly all Quare's pillar barometers. Firstly, while some of them are of the finest quality others were made for less affluent customers and the calibre of their casework and engraving leaves much to be desired. This variation of quality needs to be emphasized since it may not be generally appreciated by the less rational devotees of the 'great age of English clockmaking'. Tompion sold some inferior clocks and Quare sold some inferior barometers: but the high prices achieved by such works in the salerooms suggest that many dealers and collectors are still blinded by a famous signature.

Secondly, nearly all of them are framed in cases made of either walnut or ivory. I have records at the moment of only three exceptions. One is not really an exception at all since it combines an ivory stem with an ebonized wooden pedestal (Plate 118). Another is a rare barometer framed in a metal case which is covered with black shagreen.[1] It is a decorative object but the photographs which I have of it are regrettably not good enough for reproduction: it is unusual in having French weather indications on one side and German on the other. The third is an example of dubious parentage whose case has been painted with a modern simulation of Chinese lacquer. There are no doubt other exceptions and I hope they will come to light.

The barometer itself, i.e. the tube and cistern, provides the third means of classification. Some of Quare's extant barometers were made before the general application of the screw-type portable cistern while others are fitted with it. The latter survive in greater numbers and hence arose the hitherto widespread misunderstanding of the nature of Quare's patent of 1695. Since Quare could have been actively producing barometers for about twenty-two years after the introduction of the screw-type cistern and for only about twelve years or so before this event (during which period demand for barometers was not great) the predominance of the later type is scarcely surprising. Furthermore some of his earlier barometers seem to have been converted soon after they were made, possibly even in Quare's own workshop. This confusion has been further aggravated by subsequent repairers of his earlier barometers: unaware no doubt of any portable

[1] Department of Collections, Colonial Williamsburg: formerly in the collections of Percival Griffiths and J. S. Sykes. Illustrated in R. W. Symonds' *Masterpieces of English Furniture and Clocks* (1940) Figs. 124, 127 and in the same author's *English Furniture from Charles II to George II* (1929) Fig. 255.

device other than the very common leather-based cistern and screw—for its precursors were not in vogue for long—and rightly convinced of its efficiency they have consistently fitted Quare's earlier barometers with the wrong tubes. Extant examples are now found either (a) fitted with a leather-based cistern but with neither a screw nor a pinched head or (b) fitted with a leather-based cistern and with a screw, to accommodate which the case has been drilled at the bottom. His later barometers have also generally suffered at the hands of repairers and most of those which I have studied have been fitted with more modern leather-based cisterns. I have to emphasize that in scarcely any eighteenth-century barometers do the original cisterns or tubes survive. This makes discussion of Quare's barometers, to say the least, difficult.

Apart from these three chief methods of classifying Quare's pillar barometers there are a number of other common features which deserve general comment. The stem of a walnut case, not including the cistern housing, is usually constructed in two parts, the lower half twisted and the upper half fluted and reeded (Plate 116): but I have seen seven examples in which the upper half was plain. If hinged feet are attached the pedestal of the column, which houses the cistern, is invariably squared (Plates 116, 118): if on the other hand a walnut barometer was designed to be pendant only (and these are often the ones which were not originally fitted with the portable screw device) the base is frequently shaped as in Plate 125.[1] An ivory case is almost always constructed in four parts and plainly turned (Plates 120, 124); Plate 118 is, as I have said above, exceptional.[2]

[1] There is an example in the Philadelphia Museum of Art; previously in the Garvan Collection.
[2] A curious ivory pillar barometer is illustrated in R. W. Symonds' *English Furniture from Charles II to George II* (1929) Fig. 258 and again in the same author's *Masterpieces of English Furniture and Clocks* (1940) Fig. 123. It is like Quare's walnut barometers in design but there are many suspicious features about it.

PLATE 116
Danl Quare, London
36″ × 2·6″
Private collection

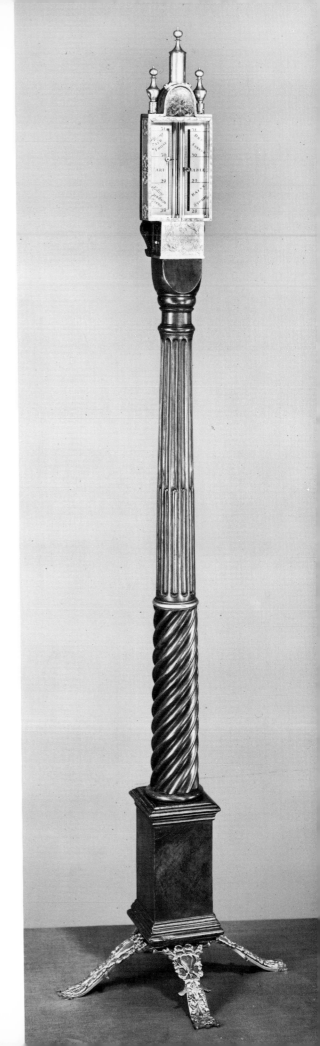

Mounts are invariably of brass which was, in the case of finer examples, originally gilt. The brass feet attached to walnut examples are fitted to a square brass plate by ordinary hinges so that they hang downwards when the barometer is suspended from the wall: they vary greatly in quality, some being cut from plain brass sheet (Plate 118) and others being decorated with a finely chased moulding of formal foliate design (Plate 116). Standing ivory barometers are more often than not fitted with more elegant feet whose design frequently represents an armless and legless figure who is generally given the description 'triton' because of his beard and the slightly fishy look of his loins: this design was also used by Patrick (Plate 110). These feet are usually attached to an engraved brass sleeve at the bottom of the case (Plate 120); by pressing in the steel spring each foot can be retracted so that the barometer can be hung from the wall (Plate 121). There are as usual exceptions to this design.[1]

The cast brass housing at the top of walnut examples most frequently follows the pattern of Plate 118 although this is not itself a walnut barometer. It consists of eight separate pieces—the hollow squared piece on which the signature is engraved, two castings which are each screwed to this and form the housing of the register plates, a piece which holds these together at the top and forms a decorative arch, an engraved piece set into this arch and three finials. In most examples the central finial is hollow (Plate 116). This suggests that Quare's original tubes extended well above the plates or there would be no need for a hollow finial of this ponderous shape. It is

[1] An example which I have not seen is illustrated in J. Gloag and Y. Hackenbroch *English Furniture. The Collection of Irwin Untermyer* (1958) Plate 18 Fig. 31. This has three plain brass feet of unusual shape, each fitted with what looks like a levelling screw. There are other unusual features about this barometer including a window in the cistern housing and weather indications in German on the obverse side of the hood.

PLATE 117
Detail of Plate 116

tempting to conclude that he lengthened his tubes by two inches or so at the same time as constricting the bore, the effect being to considerably reduce the force of the mercury as it surged on movement. It is also logical to assume that if this was so he continued to use an extended and constricted tube even after adopting the screw device: many of his barometers fitted with the screw device also have hollow finials. The largest extant finial is fitted to the ivory barometer which is shown in Plate 124: the tube could have been over 37″ long. Usually most of the available space on the hood is decorated with engraving and, while its quality differs widely, the engraving regularly consists of various forms of the popular acanthus motif. On several ivory examples the hood is made in an identical fashion but the more elaborate barometers have dual scales and register plates (Plates 124, 120). These are fitted with a hanging device beneath the register plate housing which can be swivelled so that the barometer can be hung either way round at choice (Plates 123, 124). Usually the states of the weather were given in English on one side and in French on the reverse but German examples are also recorded.[1] The assembly of a typical hood is demonstrated in Plate 124.

In four recorded examples a hollow domed type of casting similar to the Patrick barometer of Plate 110 takes the place of the customary arch beneath the centre finial. I have only studied one of these: it was not of Quare's finer workmanship but since this style was certainly used by contemporary makers the use of it does not necessarily throw doubt upon a barometer's authenticity.

Some of Quare's barometers are engraved with a number at the base of the right-hand

[1] See p. 190 and p. 192 Note 1.

PLATE 118
Danl Quare, London
36·5″ × 2·6″
Victoria and Albert Museum, London:
Crown copyright

PLATE 119
Detail of Plate 118

face of the square signature casting. My records include only ten numbered barometers, the highest number being 148. It seems to have been a spasmodic habit and no logical pattern can be detected: further research is needed before Quare's motive for numbering some products but not others of identical design, and presumably date, can be deduced. Numbers are also found on other parts of the hood and case: typical places are the wooden piece behind the hood or, on ivory examples, the underside of the swivel device (Plate 124) and the ivory block beneath the signature casing.

Quare' scales invariably cover the inches 28–31 which are subdivided into twentieths: they are engraved on silvered brass plates on both sides of the tube (Plate 117). The inch digits themselves are engraved most frequently as in Plate 117 but in several extant examples they appear at the outer edges of the plates. His weather indications, instead of being more traditionally arranged in a list so that they coincide with the half-inch divisions of the scale, are mostly engraved at a slant in imprecise fashion and boxed in as it were by the extended lines of the inch divisions: 'Variable' is however set at the traditional 29·5″ line. Plate 117 shows Quare's standard wording:

☿ Rising	Dry
Fair or Frost	Serene
Vari	able
☿ Falling	Rainy
Rain Snow	Stormy
or Winds	

Except in the unusual barometer of Plate 113 and the angle barometer of Plate 125 I have never seen a variant of this wording. Similarly his French wording (Plate 122) invariably reads

☿ Montant	Sec
Beau-Temps	Serein
ou Gelees	
Vari	able
☿ Descendant	Pluvieux
Pluies Neiges	Orageux
ou Vents	

although in at least two examples 'Orageux' is spelt 'Oragoux'. A comparison of Plates 117 and 119 will demonstrate the variety of the style of Quare's engraving. Readers will find equal variety in the engraving of the signature plate which is sometimes richly decorated and at other times left almost plain: the signature usually takes the form of 'Invented and Made by Danl Quare London' (Plates 117, 119) but it is frequently simpler.

The register plates are slotted to allow the operation of the two recording pointers (Plate 119). These consist of brass or steel pins attached to small brass blocks: these are moved by double wormed rods attached to the flanking finials and, in the case of the simpler walnut barometers, the rods can be easily inspected by removing the wooden backing to the hood. An inspection of the thread of these rods can often help to detect a forgery. Plate 124 shows the methods of assembly and operation.

These somewhat sketchy generalizations make it unnecessary to describe the examples in great detail. Plate 116 shows a typical walnut barometer of above average quality although the body of the central finial and the ring at the base of the twisted column have been replaced. It shows practically all the common features of Quare's work although the hood-castings are assembled differently. Numbered 36 in the usual place it also has 56 in larger digits engraved more

PLATE 120
Daniel Quare, Lond.
37″ × 2·6″
Hampton Court:
reproduced by gracious permission
of Her Majesty the Queen

roughly at the top of the same face of the signature block and this is repeated on the inside of the back of the hood. I cannot explain this second number. The decorative engraving (Plate 117) is remarkably like that of the very fine ivory example in the City of Gloucester Museum (Plate 124) which is numbered 79. The characteristic 'Q' of the signature, which was not always used, should be noted. The base is fitted with a portable screw and is assembled as usual but the tube and cistern have been clumsily renewed.

Several similar walnut pillar barometers can be seen in public collections. One survives for example in the Science Museum, London.[1] There are two examples, with unadorned feet and plain stems above the twisted section, in the Museo di Storia della Scienza, Florence.[2] Another, very similar to these but with weather indications in English, is in the Philadelphia Museum of Art: and the same Museum owns an interesting walnut barometer with a twisted, fluted and reeded stem and a cistern housing similar to Plate 125 but without the calendar dial. This I consider to be one of Quare's earliest barometers of the pillar style. Another example of this type, numbered 25, survives at the Meteorological Office, Bracknell:[3] it is housed in a similar case but the cistern housing is cruder, each face being oval in shape with no attempt at turned mouldings. A portable screw has been subsequently fitted. I have studied an ivory barometer of similar style in a private collection. Finally, several from private collections have been illustrated in the books mentioned in the footnotes to these pages.

[1] Inventory No. 1948–227.
[2] Inventory Nos. 1135 and 1136.
One of them has French weather indications, the other has a central finial as in Plate 118 and weather indications which might be French but I cannot interpret the photograph in my possession.
[3] Inventory No. 1.

PLATE 121
Detail of Plate 120
Reproduced by gracious permission of Her Majesty the Queen

Plate 118 shows an unusual ivory baro-meter[1] which has already been referred to as exemplifying the normal assembly of the hood. Like Quare's typical walnut baro-meters it has a square wooden pedestal and a wooden backing to the hood (Plate 119): both are ebonized. The feet are unadorned but hinged to a square brass plate in the usual way. It is numbered 148 at the top of the right-hand face of the signature block and has lost its original tube and cistern. Whether the cistern consisted of a bag or was leather-based is impossible to say.

The barometer of Plate 120 was one of the many made for William III, and it hangs at Hampton Court.[2] It is unique although its stem and feet are typical of Quare's finer ivory barometers (cf. Plate 124): so too is the dual scale with French on one side and English on the other. The feet can be seen in their folded position in Plate 121 and it will be noticed in the same illustration to what extent the use of engraving was taken: what cannot be seen is the face of the brass plate beneath the base which is also decoratively engraved and which carries the letters E and F (standing perhaps for English and French). The gilt brass hood (Plate 122) is positively covered with exquisitely fine engraving which has spread even to the swivel ring by which the barometer is hung to the wall. The sides of the hood (Plate 123) have unfortunately been worn by constant handling but the royal monogram Я W R can just be detected on each side. There is nothing unusual about the scales or the weather indications on either side except the numbering of the subdivisions

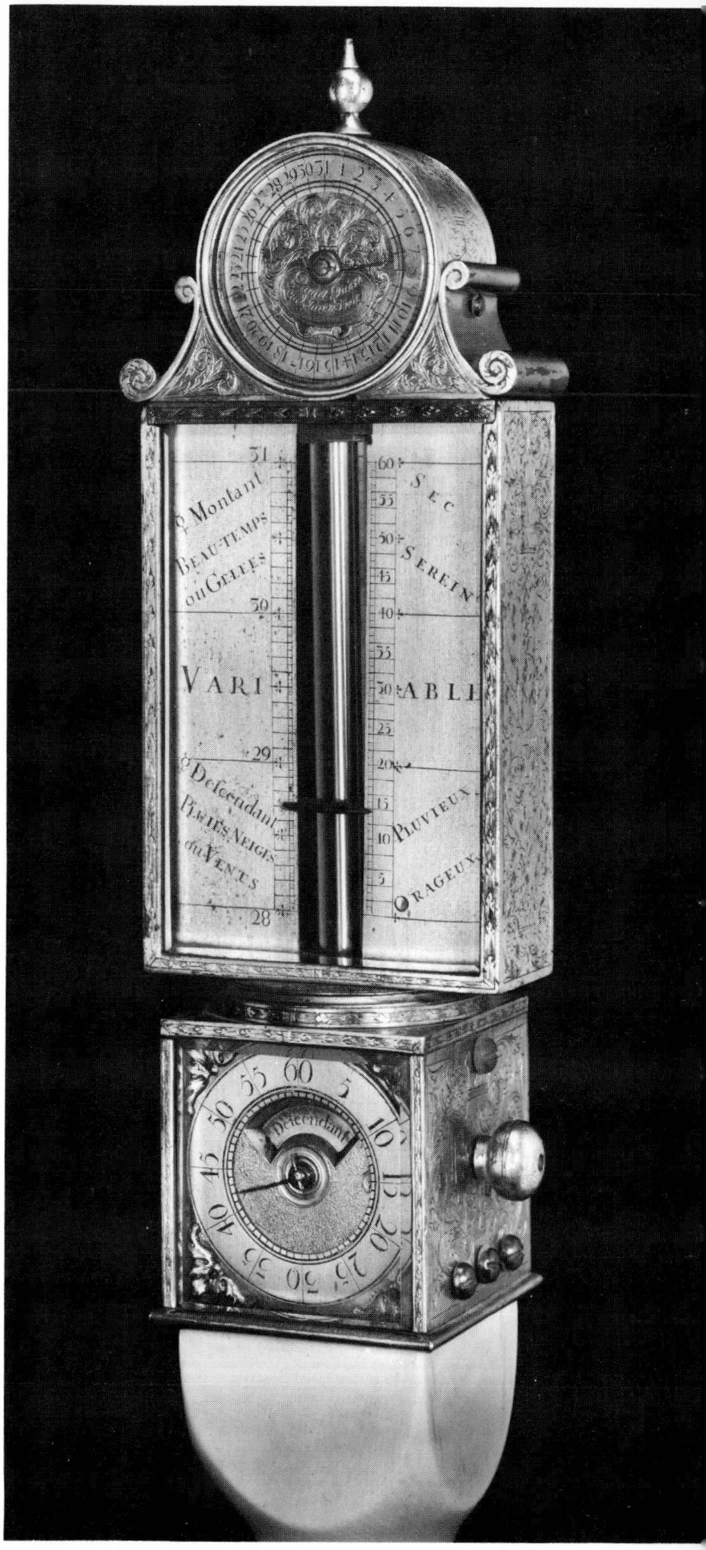

PLATE 122
Detail of Plate 120
Reproduced by gracious permission of Her Majesty the Queen

---

[1] Victoria and Albert Museum, Inventory No. W.64–1926.
[2] King William III's Bedroom.

to accord with the recording dial: the silvered plates on the English side have become pitted by corrosion over the years and are not altogether legible in Plate 120, but they conform to those of Plate 117. The tube has been replaced but the original ivory cistern survives: this now has leather cemented to its base but it could have originally housed a leather bag. Assuming this barometer was completed before William III's death in 1702 it must be one of the earliest surviving examples of a screw-type portable cistern. The recording ring which encircles the tube (Plate 122) is unusual, Quare's normal habit being to fit two pointers with slots in the plates (Plate 119). This ring is operated through a wormed rod by the knob seen on the right of the signature mount in Plate 120: the same knob operates the 'Montant/ Descendant' disc which is visible in the aperture of the recording dial (Plate 122). This dial has a silvered chapter ring which is engraved with sixty divisions corresponding to the divisions on the main scale. It is glazed for protection and has a mat brass centre and brass spandrels like a clock in minature. Its steel hand is turned by the knob of Plate 122. Above the plates is set a glazed calendar dial: the dates of the month are engraved on a silvered chapter ring and the hand is set by the knob at the top. These dials are exactly reproduced on the reverse side of the hood where the weather indications are in English and the recording hands are moved simultaneously. The only difference is linguistic—'Rising/Falling' in the aperture of the lower dial. The signature 'Daniel Quare Inv & Fecit' is engraved in English in the centre of the calendar dial on both sides.

The ivory barometer of Plate 124 to which I have already drawn frequent attention is a more usual example of Quare's very best work. Its hood is similar in decoration to the walnut barometer of Plate 116 and since it is numbered 79 it was presumably made soon afterwards: it has however dual scales in English and French with a reversible hanging device as in Plate 120. The cistern and tube are lost and the portable screw does not appear to be original but the casework is basically in fine condition and is currently being restored to its former glory.

There appear to be no ivory barometers by Quare in public collections apart from those which I have

PLATE 123
Detail of Plate 120
Reproduced by gracious permission of
Her Majesty the Queen

opposite: PLATE 124
Daniel Quare, London (Dan Quare, Londres)
38·7″ × 2·6″
City of Gloucester Museum:
from the collection of S. Marling

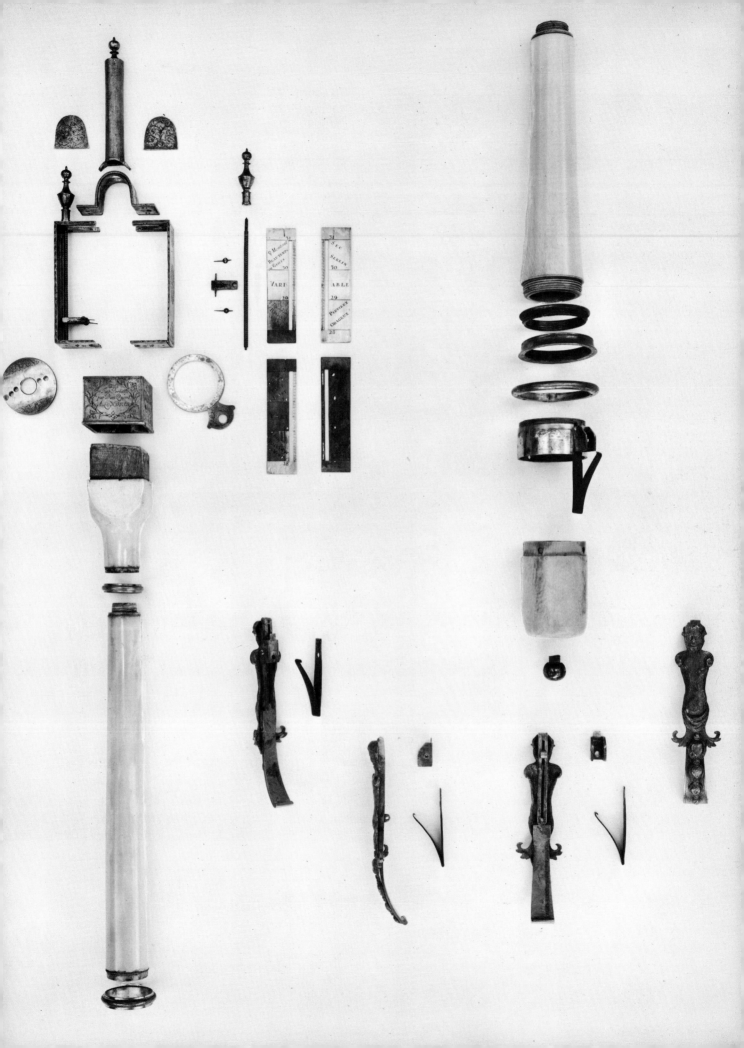

illustrated but several which remain in private hands are recorded.[1]

The final illustration shows one of the earliest English angle baro-meters (Plate 125). It is again of the highest workmanship and is yet another of the remarkable collection of barometers at Hampton Court.[2] The stem conforms to the standard pattern of Quare's walnut pillar barometers: the back of it can however be removed to enable the tube to be extracted. All the dials are protected by glass and the various bezels and mounts are of brass. The silvered brass register plates are engraved with more consistent quality than is usual on Quare's baro-meters: the scale covers 28·5″ to 30·5″ and is divided into twentieths. The mercury can move over 19·5″ between these points providing a magnification of just under ten times. The inexactness of this calcula-tion is surprising. Except for 'Changable' (sic) the usual states of the weather are not given: I have been unable to trace the origin of the rare (I believe unique) wording used by Quare: '☿Rising Presages Fair or Cleer Air & often ye wind coming to some pt North' and '☿ Falling Stormy or Moist Aire & comonly yᵉ Wind coming some pt So'. What-ever the origin the engraver did not plan his work carefully beforehand. In the centre of the lower plate is an aperture in which the words 'Rising' and 'Falling' are adjusted by the lower of the two brass knobs to the left of the plates. This knob also operates the lower of the two little steel arrow-head pointers (cf. the pillar barometer of Plate 120): I am unable to say whether or not this is correct, not having dismantled this part of the instrument. I suspect not; and it is certainly not working properly. The upper knob operates the pointer above the tube. The tube is modern and is now fitted with a leather-based boxwood cistern. The portable screw is also used for clamping the barometer to the wall like the brass fittings above the elbow and beneath the extremity of the arm. Whether or not this barometer was originally fitted with a portable screw is open to doubt. The dial at the top of the pillar has a silvered chapter ring on which the hours of the day are engraved in Roman numerals (I to XII for morning and afternoon): and the words 'Fore-noon' and 'Afternoon' are engraved on the polished brass centre. The steel hand can be set by the brass knob beneath the dial to which it is connected by two ivory pulley wheels. The dial at the base gives the days of the month in Arabic numerals (1 to 31) and its polished brass centre is signed 'Daniel Quare London'. The hand is operated in similar fashion.

---

[1] A very fine example, with dual scales and numbered 95 beneath the swivel device and on the ivory beneath the signature block, is illustrated in R. W. Symonds' *English Furniture from Charles II to George II* (1929) Fig. 257 and in the same author's *Masterpieces of English Furniture and Clocks* (1940) Figs. 122, 125, 126, also in P. MacQuoid and R. Edwards' *Dictionary of English Furniture* (2nd edition 1954) *s.v.* 'Barometer' Fig. 10.
[2] King's Drawing-room.

PLATE 125
Daniel Quare, London
36″ × 33″
Hampton Court:
reproduced by gracious permission
of Her Majesty the Queen

JESSE RAMSDEN   b.1731 –d.1800

1. Haymarket (1768–9)
2. 199 Piccadilly (1772–1800)

RAMSDEN was an optical instrument-maker of international repute and his workshop, in which he is said to have employed over fifty workmen, was one of the largest of its sort in London. Bernoulli, who gave his address as Haymarket,[1] said that he often made frames and scales for his brother-in-law Peter Dollond's optical instruments and preferred Ramsden's more solid frames.[2] Ramsden's reputation for accurate scale division was high and he invented a machine for the purpose in 1771. He was born in Halifax and started work as an apprentice to a clothier in London. In 1758 however he was working for an instrument-maker named Burton for whom, according to Maurice Daumas,[3] his task was engraving the maker's name on the instruments. Further experience was gained in the workshops of Sisson, Adams, Nairne and Dollond and he married Dollond's sister in 1766. Between 1771 and 1791 he published various works on astronomical and mathematical instruments and dividing machines and in 1786 he was elected F.R.S. After his death his substantial business was carried on by Matthew Berge. Barometers survive signed 'Berge late Ramsden'.

Barometers formed only a minor part of Ramsden's business: unfortunately Bernoulli does not mention any. His workshop however produced several instruments for scientific work and, according to Professor Taylor,[4] Henry Kater used an 'excellent mountain barometer by Ramsden' in 1818. Hutton[5] mentions that Ramsden made portable barometers incorporating improvements suggested by Sir G. Shuckburgh and William Roy, who described a portable barometer made by Ramsden in a paper submitted to the Royal Society in 1777.[6] Maurice Daumas[7] suggests that Ramsden invented the floating gauge discussed on pp. 66–7 but George Adams the elder may have a prior claim; and his son was probably referring to Ramsden when he said that others since his father's time had 'assumed the merit to themselves'.[8]

[1] Bernoulli *Lettres Astronomiques* p. 75.
[2] *Ibid.* p. 69.
[3] *Les Instruments Scientifiques* p. 319.
[4] Taylor *Mathematical Practitioners of Hanoverian England* (manuscript).
[5] Hutton *Mathematical and Philosophical Dictionary s.v.* 'Barometer'.
[6] *Philosophical Transactions* Vol. 67 (1777) p. 653 *et seq.*
[7] *Les Instruments Scientifiques* p. 274.
[8] *A Short Dissertation* p. 8.
The anonymity of 'others' could be due to the fact that Ramsden was still alive. The documentary evidence for Ramsden's claims is assessed by Middleton *History of the Barometer* p. 207.

Two improvements to the barometer should undoubtedly be attributed to Ramsden. Both are more relevant to the scientific history of the barometer since neither was commonly applied to domestic instruments: I shall therefore mention them only briefly. The first concerned the problem of the cistern level. Ramsden proposed an inverted ivory point which was fixed above the cistern level of which the tip represented the zero of the scale: the cistern level could be raised or lowered by turning the usual screw at the base so that it coincided with the tip.[1] This was a rather clumsy precursor of the later portable cistern barometer of Nicolas Fortin (1750–1831) which was first described in 1809 and had a colossal influence on the development of scientific and marine barometers. Ramsden's second improvement was the proposal to place a second pointer behind the tube of the baro-meter:[2] by adjusting the double pointer so that it was at a tangent to the meniscus the observer could eliminate the problem of parallax. In order to make the contact of meniscus and pointer clearer a slot was cut in the frame behind the tube.[3]

In the Science Museum, London, there is a barometer signed by Ramsden[4] which is set in a mahogany case very similar to the Sisson instrument of Plate 135. The tube is of 0·5″ diameter and is widened at the top into a bulb in similar fashion (see pp. 220–1): the open cistern has a diameter of 3·5″, the exceptional size being intended to minimize the cistern level error. The brass plates, which were once silvered, carry the normal weather indications, a scale of 27″–31″ divided into twentieths and a manually operated vernier: the pointer is hinged to the vernier and notched so that readings are taken from the centre of the meniscus. An ivory gauge is fitted to the case to indicate the cistern level but it is fixed and not divided. This barometer is not as refined as Sisson's but it is of great interest because some of Ramsden's experience was gained in Sisson's workshop and it can be assumed that the two makers did not lose touch with each other's designs and techniques. An almost identical instrument signed by 'Bennett, London' incor-porating an ivory scale for judging the cistern level survives in the Whipple Science Museum at Cambridge: this has been discussed on pp.121–2. It is tempting to suggest a connection between this maker and Ramsden: and it was possibly his son who was later among Ramsden's workmen and to whom William Simms was apprenticed in 1807.

Ramsden certainly sold instruments which incorporated the floating

[1] See Middleton *History of the Barometer* p. 207 and Fig. 9.1. p. 198 where this device is discussed and illustrated and the sources given.
[2] George Adams *A Short Dissertation* p. 11 attributes this invention to Ramsden.
[3] This type of pointer could most conveniently be made in the form of a ring encircling the tube providing its lower surface was flat. Middleton in *History of the Barometer* pp. 196–7 in fact suggests that Ramsden's invention was a ring but this is conjectural.
[4] Inventory No. 1893–143.

gauge apparently invented by the elder Adams. I have seen only one, and like many of its type it had been 'repaired': the gauge had been removed, an ordinary leather-based cistern inserted and the hole in the urn-shaped cistern cover blocked up. The bow-fronted, panelled case was veneered with mahogany, the silvered plates being protected by the usual glass, and the hood was as in Plate 21. The vernier was operated, as in George Adams' barometers 'of the best kind', by a key whose hole was placed directly below the plates.

JOHN MERRY RONKETTI   fl 1790–1819

1. 180 Holborn (1790–7)
2. 6 Peter Street, Bloomsbury (1800–19)

ONE OF THE many Italian immigrants who settled in England at the end of the eighteenth century, Ronketti was established in Holborn by 1790 when he is described in a directory as 'J. and M. Ronkett, weather-glass makers'. The 'and' is a mistake and the initials are printed correctly in later editions. By 1800 he had moved to Bloomsbury and the commercial directories continue to be misleading by describing him variously as 'barometer maker' and 'artificial flower and feather manufacturer' and by spelling his name Ronketti, Ronkerti, Ronkitte etc. His firm is also listed as Ronketti & Co. throughout its residence in Bloomsbury. The Ronketti family was extensive. Baptis Roncheti (or Ronchate—both signatures appear on extant barometers) was another early Italian maker and could have been a relation, perhaps J. M. Ronketti's father. Various John Ronkettis appear in the directories after 1820 at addresses in Bloomsbury and Hatton Garden and may be his successors—if indeed they are not all the same man.

Ronketti deserves special mention because his barometers are typical of the best period of the nineteenth century and are of above average quality. Judging from extant examples he seems to have concentrated on siphon-tube stick and wheel barometers.

A correspondent gave me details for instance of a barometer carrying the address at 180 Holborn which was remarkably similar to the

Manticha barometer of Plate 96. A picture of a further example of this type, signed 'J. Merry Roncketi Fecit' without an address, was kindly sent to me by another correspondent. It had a pillared hood similar to the barometer of Plate 96 but was surmounted by three finials: the tube was left exposed on the trunk which was veneered with mahogany arranged in a herring-bone pattern. The hinged cistern cover was square. The paper plates, protected by glass which was fitted flush, were elegantly printed and carried the usual 3″ scale divided into twentieths of an inch and the common weather indications 'Very Dry, Dry, Set Fair, Fair, Change, Rain, Much Rain, Storm'. The tube had a bulb cistern but not having seen it I cannot say whether it was old or not. The case measured about 38″ high (without the central ball finial) and 5·5″ wide. Stylistically this barometer belongs to about 1790–1800 and it can be attributed to Ronketti's sojourn in Holborn.

Plate 126 shows a wheel barometer which carries the Holborn address. The pine carcase is veneered with the lighter mahogany which came into vogue in the late eighteenth century and is inlaid with coloured paterae: these consist of yellow wood—probably holly, the edges of which are singed to simulate shadow—on a stained green background. The engraving of the silvered brass dial is of reasonable quality but does not compare with the standard of for instance Plates 81 and 97. The usual scale is divided into twentieths of an inch. The main hand is steel and the manually operated recording hand of brass. The alcohol thermometer is not detachable. The mechanism of the barometer has been entirely renewed. In Chapter Five I described this instrument as an example of the type which began to appear in *c.* 1795. It can be confidently dated before 1800 because by then Ronketti had moved to 6 Peter Street. Once there he continued to make barometers of this design and almost identical examples carrying the new address are extant. Ronketti's firm was at 6 Peter Street until at least 1819 and it can be assumed that products included most of the designs common in the first two decades of the century. I have not yet seen a wide variety but apart from the types so far mentioned I have also recorded mahogany wheel barometers with 10″ dials and scroll pediments.

PLATE 126
J. M. Ronketti, 180 Holborn, London
38·5″ × 9·8″
Collection of
R. S. C. Abel Smith

J O H N   R U S S E L L   b. *c.* 1745 –d. 1817

Falkirk

ORIGINALLY a wright or blacksmith, Russell became 'by his ingenuity and industry'[1] one of the best-known clock and watchmakers of his day. He settled in Falkirk in about 1770 in a shop opposite the top of Kirk Wynd. Several of his clocks and watches survive and such was the quality of his work that he was appointed Watchmaker to the Prince of Wales, later George IV, the title changing to 'Watchmaker to his Royal Highness the Prince Regent' on the establishment of the Regency in 1811. John Smith quotes an extract from the *Edinburgh Evening Courant* of 6 July 1812 which described an interview which Russell was granted by the Prince Regent at Carlton House during which he presented 'a superb gold chronometer of his making, according to his R.H. gracious order' and studied with the Prince 'a great many curious clocks and watches'.[2] An advertisement in the same newspaper of 12 May 1783 claimed that Russell 'makes and repairs musical clocks, organs, etc.: also makes portable jacks of a new construction, barometers, thermometers, and every kind of machinery in the watch and clock branch'.[3] Another notice in 1792 advertised a lottery organized by Russell in which prizes included a barrel organ, clocks, watches, a microscope, barometers and thermometers, and prints, and stated that he had been in London and other English towns collecting a 'fresh stock of materials'.[4]

I have studied eighteen barometers by Russell in detail and have seen photographs of a further five: all but one of these (the exception was a simple but mauled cistern-tube barometer in a mahogany frame with a broken pediment) belong to one of two distinctive categories. Plate 127 illustrates a fine cistern-tube barometer which was probably made at about the turn of the century, or perhaps (since Russell was advertising barometers as early as 1783) ten or fifteen years earlier. I have seen only three other examples of this type but I am sure that many more survive. Two of these were almost identical but both had lost their protective Corinthian columns, finials and pediment rosettes. One of them was signed beneath the weather indications and its plates had been cut to admit a taller siphon tube the top of which trespassed into the hygrometer. The third was somewhat heavier

[1] *Edinburgh Advertiser* 30 September 1817, quoted by Smith *Old Scottish Clockmakers* p. 333.   [2] Quoted by Smith, pp. 332–3.   [3] *Ibid.* pp. 330–1. [4] *Ibid.* p. 332.

in design with rather primitive carving on the pediment, the cistern cover and the cornice beneath the plates. The plates were very similar in design and execution but again the signature was beneath the weather indications; and the hygrometer which had a dual scale of 0–50 was entitled 'Haygrometr'. It is conceivable that the engraver had never heard the word before and that he wrote down what he heard, in a Scottish accent, when taking his instructions. This fanciful theory suggests, since the same engraver undoubtedly executed the other register plates, that this barometer was one of the earliest examples of Russell's work, which may account for the relative inelegance and primitiveness of the case.

The barometer illustrated in Plate 127 is an almost perfect example of Russell's mature style in this particular genre. The only blemish, apart from some slight damage to about an inch of the inlaid border, is the loss of the finial and of the original ornaments which decorated the scrolls of the pediment. These are unlikely to have been of wood since it would have been more natural to have carved them out of the pediment than to apply them afterwards: they could have been ivory, a material commonly used for this purpose, but this would have been inconsistent with the general design. They would almost undoubtedly have been rosettes (a motif used by many makers including Russell) and gilt brass seems the logical material. Their loss is understandable since they are simply plugged, not screwed, into drilled holes about 0·25″ deep. The carcase of the case is of pine and the veneers of mahogany: the base and capital of the Corinthian column which protects the tube are of gilt brass. The engraving of the silvered plates (Plate 128) is of high quality and the habit of

PLATE 127
Jno Russell, Falkirk
40·1″ × 6″
Author's collection

entitling each instrument has already been noted in the work of Balthazar Knie and Benjamin Martin. The scale is conventional although extended downwards to 27″ but the pointer and vernier cannot be used below 28·07″ since the groove is not extended far enough downwards—a common fault on domestic barometers. The mercurial thermometer is original. The barometer tube is not original but is contemporary. It is of 0·5″ diameter and 0·25″ bore and is cemented to a leather bag which is enclosed in a cylindrical wooden box. This pattern of portable cistern (Fig. v.) appears to have been favoured by a number of Scottish makers well into the nineteenth century: but it may well not have been the type originally fitted to this barometer. A concertina cistern for instance was also favoured by Scottish makers (Plate 24). At some time or other a repairer discarded the original tube and substituted a siphon tube with a bulb cistern, which made it necessary to carve a space for the bulb inside the cistern cover; but his repairs which must have rendered the instrument totally inaccurate, have now been rectified.

Russell is best known for his wheel barometers and specifically for his so-called 'royal' barometers. This epithet should strictly be reserved for barometers such as those by Tompion and Quare (Plates 113, 120, 143) which were expressly made for royal patrons: but Russell's barometers earned it because he gave two of them to George III and the Prince of Wales, who later became George IV. His reputation for these barometers was considerable. H. C. Smith[1] quotes an excerpt from the *Alloa Monthly Advertiser* of 7 February 1845 which announced that William Dobbie of Falkirk 'has just completed two of Russell's splendid and celebrated royal barometers (now scarce), warranted identical with those made by the original constructor. The dial presents two indexes, the one of common range and the other indicating the thousands of an inch in the rise or fall of the mercury'. It is not clear whether Dobbie went so far as to copy Russell's signature, but the text of this announcement suggests that not every extant Russell barometer should be approached in a spirit of unquestioning faith.

Plate 129 illustrates a good example, the only barometer by Russell as far as I know which is on view in a public collection. As in most of his work the mahogany veneers are rich in colour but rather coarse in grain. The *verre eglomisé* panels below and above the dial are delicately executed in gold on a black ground, the lower one representing the thistle which is an almost invariable motif of Russell's and betrays his nationality. The bezel, applied border decorations and the finial, which takes the form of the Prince of Wales feathers, are all of brass. The feathers could be construed as a deliberate part of a general

[1] *Buckingham Palace, Its Furniture, Decoration and History* (1931) p. 267.

PLATE 128
Detail of Plate 127

aim to establish a royal cachet: but they had been a fairly common form of decoration in cabinet-work from about 1780.[1] The dial is typical of Russell's royal barometers. The surface is painted white and there is a painted gold border round the circumference: the bevelled borders of the subsidiary dials are also gilt. The scales, weather indications and inscription are black, the decoration of 'Rain' and 'Fair' displaying great facility. The scale of $28''$–$31''$ is normal and on the main dial each inch is divided into decimals, with the quarter and three-quarter points marked by painted diamonds. The upper of the two subsidiary dials divides each of these decimal divisions into 100 parts, i.e. the subsidiary hand turns a full circle while the main hand moves over $0.1''$, thus permitting readings to $.001''$. This is a degree of accuracy which is hardly justified by the average barometer of the early nineteenth century, still less by the wheel barometer which suffers from the additional disadvantage of transmitting the barometric measurement through materials—float, cord, and arbor wheel—which can suffer from thermal effects and dirt. But Russell was a clockmaker of 'ingenuity and industry' and the mechanism of these barometers is a remarkable attempt to apply the principles of gear reduction to the barometer. It is also well made. Plates 130 and 131 illustrate the mechanisms of two other barometers made to the same design.[2] The gearwork is contained in a box measuring about $1.7''$ by $3.5''$; this has sliding brass sides and a detachable brass plate at the top to protect it from dirt and is constructed like a clock with stout pillars in order to minimize any friction. It is set back from the dial in order to allow the connection of the recording hands, one on the main dial and the other on the lower subsidiary dial, to the wormed rods by which they are manually adjusted (the adjusting knobs can be seen in Plate 129, the right-hand knob operating the hand on the main dial). Inside the box is the usual double-grooved pulley wheel which is attached to the main arbor: the arbor also carries a contrate wheel which transmits the movement to a tapered spindle at the top of which is set a further contrate wheel: this transmits the movement by a further reduction to the arbor of the subsidiary dial. The upper contrate wheel and part of the lower one can be seen in Plate 131. Other notable features of the mechanism are the sealed glass float (Plate 130) which is filled with mercury in order to counteract to some extent the thermal expansion and contraction of the barometric mercury, and the neatly fashioned brass counterbalance. The tube is of $0.5''$ diameter and $0.25''$ bore. The

[1] See Hepplewhite's *Cabinet-Maker and Upholsterer's Guide* (3rd edition 1794) Plate 97 which was engraved in 1787. The motif was probably inspired by the Prince of Wales's lavish expenditure on furniture, etc., for his apartments at Buckingham House, St James's Palace and Windsor in 1780–2 and at Carlton House from 1783.
[2] Both hang in Buckingham Palace, Plate 130 in the Household Corridor, Plate 131 by the Visitors' Door.

PLATE 129
J. Russell, Falkirk
$47.5'' \times 13''$
Victoria and Albert Museum, London:
Crown copyright

PLATE 130
Detail of barometer mechanism
by John Russell
Buckingham Palace:
reproduced by gracious permission of
Her Majesty the Queen

float has a diameter of 0·6″. To return to Plate 129 again the hands are delicately made of pierced steel, the main hand having a tail for the sake of balance. The design of the recording hands is in each case simpler than that of the indicating hands: this seems to have been a common but not invariable feature of Russell's barometers. The mercury thermometer is set on a silvered brass plate on which are engraved no fewer than three scales—Réaumur, Fahrenheit and Royal Society. This again is a normal feature of Russell's royal barometers as is his signature at the bottom right-hand corner of the thermometer plate,

which is similar in style to the signature of his cistern-tube barometers (Plate 128).

Thanks to the maker's eagerness to display his appointments this wheel barometer can be dated between 1811, when the Prince of Wales became the Prince Regent, and 1817 when Russell died. Of the other barometers of almost identical design which I have studied three advertised the appointment to the Prince Regent and can be similarly dated. All are in private collections and they vary only slightly in design, the main differences being the hands and the formal designs of the *verre eglomisé* panels.

Russell made almost identical barometers before 1811 when he held the appointment of 'Watch Maker to His Royal Highness the Prince of Wales'. There is an example in the collection of the National Galleries of Scotland[1] which shares all the features of the barometer of Plate 129 except the pierced hands: in this case the two indicating hands are of stamped and patterned brass with simple arrow heads and ring tails, and the recording hands are of steel. Similar instruments are to be seen in private collections and there is one in Buckingham Palace[2] whose mechanism is illustrated in Plate 130: this barometer unusually lacks the normal feather finial but there are signs that it was originally fitted with one. The barometer of Plate 132 also lacks this feature and was apparently made without it: it also hangs in Buckingham Palace.[3] Another gilt barometer hangs in the Palace[4] and if these were the two instruments which Russell gave to George III and the Prince of Wales, the absence of the feathers seems odd. The only logical supposition is that both instruments are early examples of his work of this type and that the feathers entered the design at a later date. The casework of the barometer in Plate 132 is, for Russell, most unusual: apart however from the use of gilt gesso pinewood and the substitution of carved borders for the applied brass mounts of the other examples it is basically similar in design. The dial is almost identical and the bezel is of brass: the attractive symbols at the inch divisions should be noticed. The hands are of the same pierced design as is evident in Plate 129 but they are made of beaten brass like the simpler hands of both the mahogany barometer at the Palace and the barometer owned by the National Galleries of Scotland. The mechanism and the thermometer are similar to the previous examples. The second giltwood example is similar but has a carved wooden bezel with beading similar to that used for the edges of the case of this example.

I have seen simpler wheel barometers signed by Russell set in mahogany cases of the same shape with *verre églomisé* panels but without the brass decorations: these lacked the dial and mechanism for reading measurements to ·001″ and had plain silvered brass dials. Another difference was a simpler alcohol thermometer using only the Fahrenheit scale. Using an evolutionary argument these instruments could be dated earlier than the more complicated and refined barometers described above.

[1] Now hanging in the office of the Board of Trustees, Portrait Gallery Building.
[2] Household Corridor.
[3] Visitors' Door: its mechanism is illustrated in Plate 131.
[4] Privy Purse Door.

opposite: PLATE 132
J. Russell, Falkirk
42″ × 12·5″
Buckingham Palace:
reproduced by gracious permission of
Her Majesty the Queen

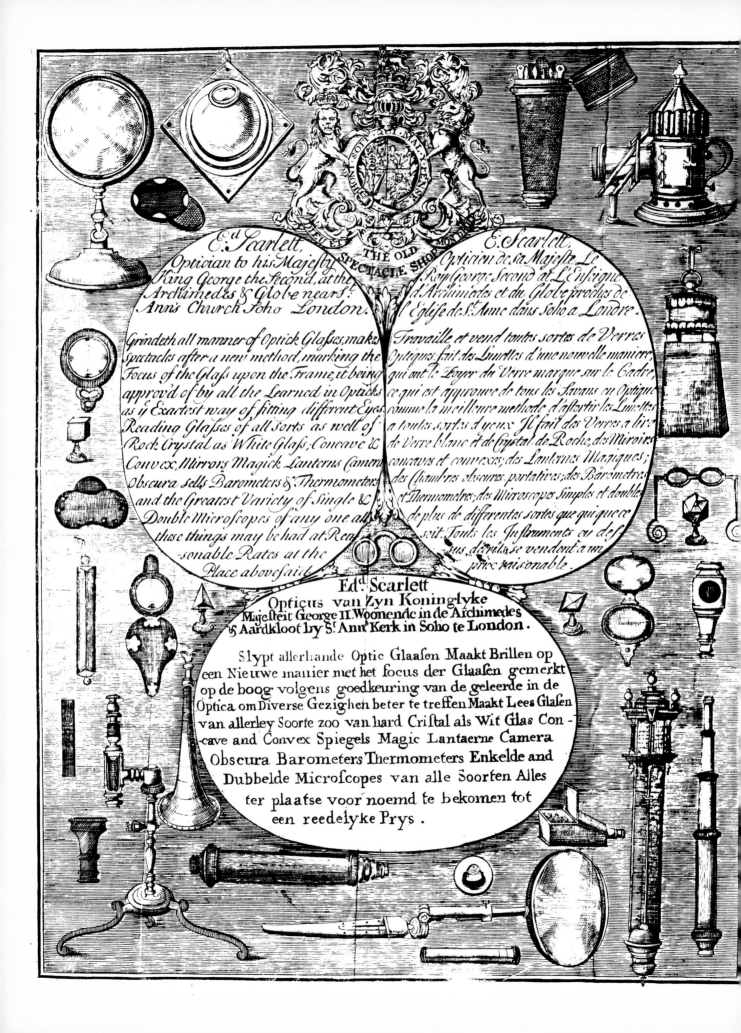

THE OLD SPECTACLE SHOP LONDON

Ed. Scarlett
Optician to his Majesty
King George the Second, at the
Archimedes & Globe near S.t
Ann's Church Soho London.

Grindeth all manner of Optick Glaſses, makes
Spectacles after a new method, marking the
Focus of the Glaſs upon the Frame, it being
approv'd of by all the Learned in Opticks
as ij Exactest way of fitting different Eyes
Reading Glaſses of all sorts as well of
Rock Crystal as White Glaſs, Concave &
Convex Mirrors Magick Lanterns Camera
Obscura sells Barometers & Thermometers
and the Greatest Variety of Single &
Double Microscopes of any one all
these things may be had at Rea-
sonable Rates at the
Place abovesaid.

E. Scarlett
Opticien de sa Majeste Le
Roy George Second at L'Enseigne
d'Archimedes et du Globe proche de
l'Eglise de St Anne dans Soho a Londre.

Travaille et vend toutes sortes de Verres
Optiques fait des Lunettes d'une nouvelle maniere,
qui ont le Foyer du Verre marque sur le Cadre
ce qui est approuve de tous les Savans en Optique
comme la meilleure methode d'aſsortir les Lunettes
a toutes sortes d'yeux Il fait des Verres a lire
de Verre blanc et de Cristal de Roche, des Miroirs
concaves et convexes; des Lanternes Magiques;
des Chambres obscures portatives; des Barometres
et Thermometres; des Microscopes simples et doubles
de plus de differentes sortes que qui que ce
soit. Tous les Instruments ci deſ-
sus decrits se vendent a un
prix raisonable.

Ed. Scarlett
Opticus van Zyn Koninglyke
Majesteit George II. Woonende in de Archimedes
& Aardkloot by S.t Ann. Kerk in Soho te London.

Slypt allerhande Optic Glaaſen Maakt Brillen op
een Nieuwe manier met het focus der Glaaſen gemerkt
op de boog volgens goedkeuring van de geleerde in de
Optica om Diverse Gezighen beter te treffen Maakt Lees Glaſen
van allerley Soorte zoo van hard Criſtal als Wit Glas Concave and Convex Spiegels Magic Lantaerne Camera
Obscura Barometers Thermometers Enkelde and
Dubbelde Microſcopes van alle Soorten Alles
ter plaatſe voor noemd te bekomen tot
een reedelyke Prys.

EDWARD SCARLETT b. *c.*1688 –d. 1743

1. Archimedes and Globe, 9 Macclesfield Street, Soho (1712–43)
2. Archimedes and Globe, near St Ann's Church, Soho

ONE OF THE leading opticians of his day, Scarlett became a member of the Spectaclemakers' Company in 1705 and was Master in 1720–2. He held the appointment of Optician to George II. Among his apprentices were Oliver Combs and his own son, another Edward Scarlett (b. *c.* 1702—d. 1779) who was apprenticed in 1716, became a member of the Spectaclemakers' Company in 1724, was Master 1745–6 and succeeded to his father's business.

The elder Scarlett's trade card, which can be dated between 1727 and 1743, is illustrated in Plate 133. Its design lays emphasis on his chief trade, but besides spectacles and optical glasses he sold a wide variety of wares and found it worth while to advertise in three languages. The barometer which is illustrated in the trade card is closely similar to Desaguliers' illustration of 1744 (Plate 17) which it precedes. It follows a design which was apparently popular during the approximate period 1720–40 but I have seen no example signed by Scarlett in spite of his advertisement: the same design in fact was used in the advertisements of several different makers.

Plate 134 illustrates the only barometer sold by Scarlett which I have so far been able to trace. It is signed 'E.S—rlet, Lo–don' at the top of the thermometer plate, the intermediate letters being obscured by the tube. While therefore the attribution to one of the Scarletts seems inevitable, it is by no means certain whether the father or the son was responsible: the boldly carved architectural case, which strongly reflects the influence of William Kent and Benjamin Goodison, could stylistically have been made for either of the two, and I am only tempted to prefer the elder man because barometers are expressly advertised in his card.

Unfortunately I have never been able to study this barometer. It is probably now in America and I have only been fortunate enough to trace it at all through the kindness of Mr. Stephen J. Jussel who sent me a very old and precious photograph of it which has been carefully copied. Considering its age the photograph is remarkably clear but many details of the instrument's construction—including for example the type of cistern—are unknown. The frame is however clearly of mahogany and the idea of making the angle tube acceptable by setting

opposite: PLATE 133
Edward Scarlett's trade card
By courtesy of the
Director of the Science Museum, London

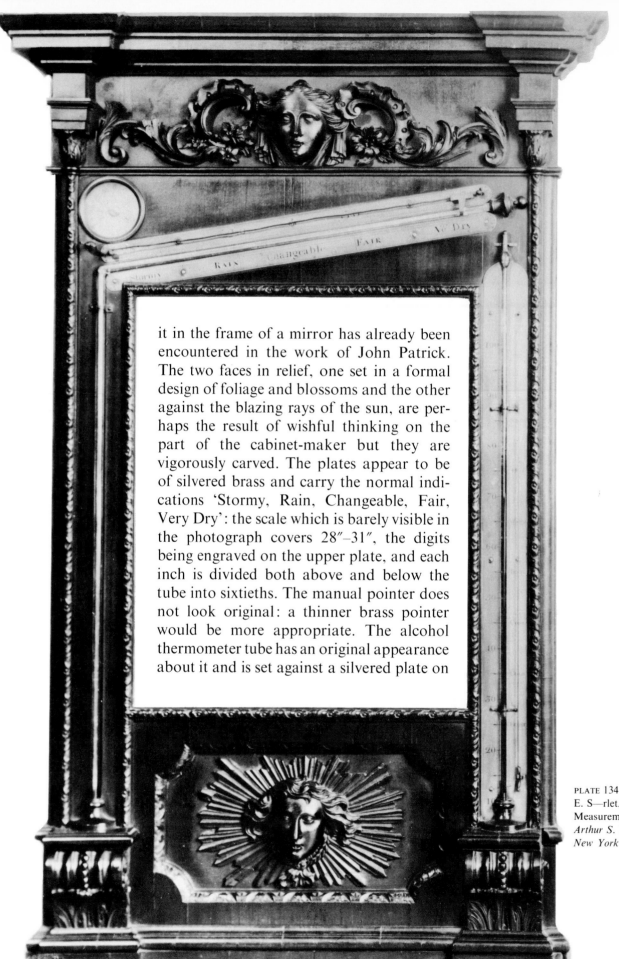

it in the frame of a mirror has already been encountered in the work of John Patrick. The two faces in relief, one set in a formal design of foliage and blossoms and the other against the blazing rays of the sun, are perhaps the result of wishful thinking on the part of the cabinet-maker but they are vigorously carved. The plates appear to be of silvered brass and carry the normal indications 'Stormy, Rain, Changeable, Fair, Very Dry': the scale which is barely visible in the photograph covers 28″–31″, the digits being engraved on the upper plate, and each inch is divided both above and below the tube into sixtieths. The manual pointer does not look original: a thinner brass pointer would be more appropriate. The alcohol thermometer tube has an original appearance about it and is set against a silvered plate on

PLATE 134
E. S—rlet, Lo–don
Measurements unkn
Arthur S. Vernay In
New York

which the usual Fahrenheit scale is engraved. The hygrometer is squeezed rather tightly into its corner.

R. W. Symonds illustrated an almost identical barometer by T. Blunt in *Masterpieces of English Furniture and Clocks* (1940)[1] and in *Furniture-making in 17th and 18th century England* (1955).[2] There were slight differences in the detail of the carving and the tube had been shortened in order to admit an oatbeard hygrometer in the top right-hand corner of the frame: this was mysterious since it meant that the tube ended at about 30·9″ and, owing to its cover (*cf.* Plate 134), was only visible as far as about 30·8″. The hygrometer in fact appears to have been a later and incongruous addition: and it is tempting to suggest that in view of its cramped position the same could be true of the hygrometer in Plate 134.

It is impossible to say who made either or both of these barometers. Scarlett only claimed to sell barometers and thermometers and the assumption must be that he only retailed the one which I illustrate.

[1] Fig. 131: the photograph is indistinct and in the caption the maker is said to be 'unknown'.
[2] Figs. 362, 363 (see p.124).

b. 1793 – d. 1860 WILLIAM SIMMS

136 Fleet Street

THE SON OF a mathematical instrument-maker of the same name who had moved to London from Birmingham in 1793, Simms was working before 1825 with Edward Troughton on astronomical instruments for the East India Company: the two combined their businesses under the name of Troughton and Simms in 1826 and the name continued to be used after Troughton's retirement in 1831. Simms was elected F.R.S. in 1852.

JEREMIAH SISSON fl 1747-70

Corner of Beaufort Buildings, Strand

SISSON carried on business as a mathematical and physical instrument-maker in succession to his father Jonathan Sisson in 1747. He was adjudged bankrupt in 1751 but was able to resume the business. His range was wide and Professor Taylor[1] suggests that he was probably a more notable maker than his father in spite of the elder man's contemporary eminence. Unfortunately both men appear to have signed their instruments 'J. Sisson' and it is therefore impossible, unless instruments are dated or have well defined stylistic characteristics, to say certainly which man made them. There are however several mathematical instruments in the Science Museum, London, by Jeremiah, i.e. bearing dates after Jonathan's death. A logical case can be made for ascribing to Jeremiah the barometer of Plate 135. This is in the George III Collection in the Science Museum, London,[2] although at the time of writing it is not on show. This collection was probably started in his private capacity by S.C.T. Demainbray (1710–83), a friend of J.T. Desaguliers and a fellow Huguenot, some time before he became the tutor of the royal Princes in 1754: most of the collection however was doubtless accumulated after this date and Jonathan Sisson had died in 1747. Another circumstantial reason for ascribing this barometer to Jeremiah is the existence of a similar barometer by Ramsden who was only sixteen when Jonathan Sisson died. Neither of these arguments is conclusive or even very strong.

It is not strictly a domestic barometer and I could be accused of exceeding my brief in illustrating and describing it. This is done deliberately because, as I have said in Chapter Four, in the eighteenth century it was often still difficult to draw a distinguishing line between domestic and scientific barometers. The portable barometers of de Luc and Magellan, Sir Henry Englefield's mountain barometer and the various marine barometers of the period are clearly of little relevance to the subject in hand: but Sisson's barometer shares many of the features of contemporary domestic design and could almost be described as a domestic barometer refined to allow more accurate observation. The frame is constructed of mahogany without any

[1] Taylor *Mathematical Practitioners of Hanoverian England* (manuscript).
[2] Inventory No. 1927–1910.

attempt at embellishment. The top half of the hemispherical cistern cover is detachable in order to allow the observer to see the cistern level. The silvered brass plates carry conventional weather indications but the words 'Fair if ☿ Rise, Foul if ☿ Fall' are added at the foot of the left-hand plate. The scale is from 27″–31″ and is divided into twentieths. The sliding vernier is unusual, being 1·6″ in length instead of the more usual 1·1″ and carrying a scale numbered from 0 to 50. Attached to it is a small low-power microscope through which the observer can see the mercury meniscus. The wide tube is of 0·6″ diameter and has a bulb at the top which is protected by a brass cover and is designed to dilute the effects of any vapours which may affect the vacuum. The cistern is made of iron and is open: its diameter is 4·75″, the width being designed to minimize the variation of the cistern level. Above the cistern an ivory scale measuring 1″ is attached to the frame: against it slides an ivory vernier of 1·1″, the lower end of which extends downwards so that it can be adjusted to the level of the mercury in the cistern. Both the scale and vernier are divided into twentieths. By this means the rise or fall of the cistern level from its mean can be computed to the nearest ·005″ and an adjustment made to the reading.

This barometer is of great interest since it incorporates one of the earliest methods of compensating for the cistern error. A similar instrument by Bennett has been mentioned on pp.121–2 and other makers used wide open cisterns but without the vernier to compute the changes of the mercury level. Other examples of low-power microscopes also survive and I have seen a standing barometer by an anonymous maker in the form of a Corinthian column which incorporated this device. The earliest maker to propose and use a microscope for this purpose was the amateur instrument-maker Stephen Gray (fl 1694–1701).[1]

[1] *Philosophical Transactions* Vol. 20 (1698) pp. 176–8. Although a vernier was not applied he claimed to achieve readings to ·001″. See Taylor
The Mathematical Practitioners of Tudor and Stuart England p. 290,
A. Wolf *A History of Science, Technology and Philosophy in the 16th and 17th Centuries* (2nd edition 1950) pp. 97–8 and Fig. 57, and
Middleton *History of the Barometer* pp. 201–2 and Fig. 9. 3.

PLATE 135
J. Sisson, London
38·3″ × 7·3″
By courtesy of the Director of the Science Museum, London

A much simpler barometer signed 'J. Sisson, London' which can also be ascribed to Jeremiah is in the Whipple Science Museum at Cambridge.[1] The case is similar to Plate 135 but the instrument has incurred a certain amount of damage. The original tube probably had a bulb at its upper extremity: both the tube and the brass bulb cover have been replaced, the latter by an incongruous brass plate, and the cistern also has been altered. The hemispherical cistern cover is of a shape and size which suggest that there was originally an open cistern but this has at some time been replaced by a closed portable cistern and a screw device has been fitted. The scale on the silvered plates covers 27″–31″ but is only divided into decimals. A vernier is fitted.

[1] Inventory No. 281.

JONATHAN SISSON b. 1690 –d. 1747

The Sphere, corner of Beaufort Buildings, Strand (1735)

A MATHEMATICAL instrument-maker of eminence, Sisson was born in Lincolnshire. He was established in a workshop in the Strand by 1722 by which time he had already achieved a reputation for good workmanship. In the *Weekly Journal* of 5 April 1729 was reported his appointment as Instrument Maker to the Prince of Wales. He was especially known for his accurate division of scales and he executed the division of the standard yard which George Graham presented to the Royal Society in 1742. His association with Graham seems to have been close and he was probably to begin with one of Graham's workmen. Among his own workmen was Jesse Ramsden. He died in 1747 and was succeeded by his son Jeremiah.

Although very few survive, Sisson probably made several types of barometer. J. H. de Magellan,[1] writing in 1779, said that he had seen a static barometer started by Sisson (one of the only two such instruments in Europe at the time, the other being made by George Adams the elder). He called him an 'artiste celèbre de London'. Edward Saul, whose book was published in 1735,[2] ends his exposition with the

[1] *Description et Usages des Nouvaux Baromètres* p. 156.
[2] *An Historical and Philosophical Account:* although this was substantially written in about 1710 the paragraph referring to Sisson was probably added nearer the date of publication.

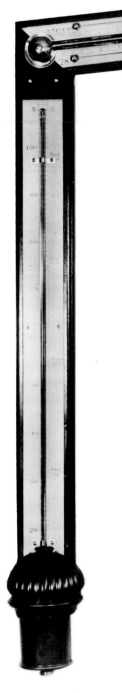

paragraph 'I shall only add by way of advertisement. That it may perhaps, be an inducement to some of the gentlemen of Lincolnshire, to deal with Mr. Jonathan Sisson, mathematical instrument maker, at the corner of Beaufort Buildings, in the Strand, London; that he is their countryman, and eminent for his great skill, accuracy and fidelity, both in the construction of his barometers, and in whatever other works he undertakes, or delivers out of his hands.'[1]

Since both father and son signed their instruments 'J. Sisson' attribution is difficult. In the interests of equity however it seems reasonable to ascribe to Jonathan the angle barometer of Plate 136, although stylistically this could have been sold by either man. The case is veneered with mahogany: the only attempt at embellishment is the gadrooned cistern cover which appears in the work of other makers (*cf.* Plates 153, 155). The silvered barometer scale extends from 28″–31″ over a distance of 30″, i.e. giving the movement a magnification of ten times. It is divided both above and below the tube into decimals and subdivided into hundredths. The weather indications cater for both summer and winter; since the photograph is regrettably a poor one, it is worth quoting the engraving:

Stormy	Much Rain	Rain	Changeable	Fair	Setled Fair	Very Dry
28	Much Snow	29	J. Sisson London	30	Setled Frost	31

Two sickle-shaped pointers slide along wires above and below the tube. The tube is not original but follows the original design, being crimped at the corner of the angle in order to descend behind the panel on which the thermometer is mounted: it was of course common to crimp the tube of a 'stick' barometer for this purpose (Plates 18, 101) but I do not recall seeing another example of this in an angle barometer. The cistern is a standard closed boxwood cistern with a leather base and portable screw. The alcohol Fahrenheit thermometer is set against a silvered plate on the case, the bulb being concealed by the cistern cover.

This barometer shares many features with the angle barometers of Francis Watkins—the shape of the cistern cover, the sickle-shaped pointers, the weather indications and scale, the brass covers which shield the corner and extremity of the tube—but there is no attempt to compromise over the design. Yet in spite of an unusually extended scale it enjoys a certain elegance which is achieved by the slim lines of the case.

[1] *Ibid.* p. 107.

PLATE 136
J. Sisson, London
32·5″ × 35·3″
Private Collection.

ADDISON SMITH fl 1750–89

1. St Martins Lane, Charing Cross
2. 5 Charing Cross (1763–74)
3. 481 Strand (1779)
4. Charlotte Street, Rathbone Place (1783)

SMITH was a mathematical instrument-maker and examples of his surveying instruments survive. He was apprenticed to Francis Watkins and became a member of the Spectaclemakers' Company in 1763. In 1763 he also became Watkins' partner and the firm of Watkins and Smith flourished until 1774. After this Watkins seems to have been on his own at 5 Charing Cross and Smith to have moved to the Strand.

Very few barometers appear to survive bearing Smith's sole name but there are several extant signed by Watkins and Smith (p. 253). It seems reasonable to conclude that Smith was not himself a prolific maker of barometers, an assumption which is if anything supported by the fact that the firm's barometers showed no apparent changes in design after Smith became a partner. I have seen only one cistern-tube barometer signed solely by 'Addison Smith, London'. It conformed closely to a design used by Watkins. The case was 42″ high and veneered with mahogany, both the trunk and the silvered plates having a border of chequered woods inlaid in a geometrical pattern. The cistern cover was hemispherical. The pediment was missing but was probably of the broken classical type. The weather indications and scale (27″–31″ in twentieths) were conventional and a manual vernier and alcohol Fahrenheit thermometer were fitted to the plates. An oatbeard hygrometer was fitted above the plates. Unfortunately some later restorer had added to the damage by substituting a siphon tube with a bulb cistern for the original closed portable cistern and, owing to the greater length of the former, had found it necessary to lengthen the groove cut in the register plates.

JOHN SMITH fl 1674–94

St Augustine

A MEMBER of the Clockmakers' Company, to which he was elected in 1674, Smith is best known as the author of what is thought to be the first book in English on watch and clockwork, his *Horological Dialogues* (1675). Britten suggests that he was originally a tool-maker from Lancashire and that he died before 1730 when his books were advertised exclusively by one Mary Smith, possibly his widow.[1] He also wrote on painting, theology and other subjects.

In 1688 he published *A Compleat Discourse of the Nature, Use, and Right Managing of that Wonderful Instrument, the Baroscope or Quicksilver Weather-Glass*, a popular summary of the subject containing a description of the simple cistern-tube instrument in use at the time together with instructions and advice on its assembly and suspension. This was followed in 1694 by *The best Rules for the Ordering and Use of the Quick-silver and Spirit Weather-Glass* which was appended to his well-known *Horological Disquisitions*. This booklet covers roughly the same ground as its predecessor but contains one or two interesting divergences. It was extensively plagiarised by the polymath Richard Neve in his *Baroscopologia* (1708). I have referred a great deal to these two books of Smith's in Chapter Two because they represent important evidence of the type of instrument constructed by both amateurs and instrument-makers of the earliest period. Whether Smith ever sold instruments himself must be open to doubt.

[1] Britten *Old Clocks and Watches* p. 747.

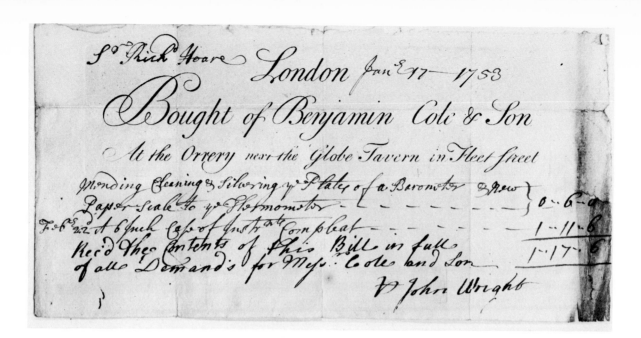

PLATE 137 Bill submitted by Benjamin Cole and Son to Sir Richard Hoare 1753
Heal Collection: by courtesy of the Trustees of the British Museum

JOSHUA   SPRINGER   fl 1759–1808

1. Hadleys Quadrant, St Stephen's Lane, Bristol (1759–60)
2. 2 Clare Street, Bristol (1775–1808)

SPRINGER made and sold optical, mathematical and physical instruments of all sorts. Although a provincial maker he produced instruments of good quality in large numbers and the prosperous port of Bristol must have provided a demanding market for his wares. There was a line of succession too which connected Springer with the eminent London maker Thomas Wright. Wright was succeeded by Benjamin Cole the elder, among whose apprentices was John Wright. One of Cole's bills dated 17 January and 22 February 1753 survives (Plate 137).[1] It reads

	£	s.	d.
Mending cleaning and silvering ye plates of a barometer and new paper scale to ye thermometer	0	6	0
A 6 inch case of instrnts compleat ..	1	11	6

and is receipted by Wright. By 1756 Wright had settled in Bristol and set up shop at the Sphere and Hadleys Quadrant, near St Stephen's Church: in this year he was advertising an extensive list of instruments including 'barometers, either standard, diagonal, or portable, with or without thermometers.'[2] By 1759 he had been succeeded by Springer

[1] Heal Collection, British Museum.   [2] *Felix Farley's Bristol Journal* 20 March 1756.

whose wholesale and retail list of instruments was equally extensive and included 'barometers and thermometers of all sorts'.[1] The same claim was made on his trade card, a copy of which dated 1760 survives in the Banks Collection.[2]

I have seen an angle barometer signed by 'Springer, Bristol' which presumably came from his workshop. The tube was exposed over its whole length, the upright section of the case being veneered with mahogany in herring-bone fashion. The turned cistern cover was of the type shown in Plate 157. The case measured 32″ high and 30·5″ across, the width of the trunk being 3·2″. The silvered plates were engraved above the tube with the usual 28″–31″ scale which was extended over a movement of 26″. The inches were subdivided into eighths and fortieths. The weather indications below the tube read 'Stormy, Much Rain, Rain, Changeable, Fair, Settled Fair, Very Dry' and were engraved in cursive script. A grooved sliding pointer was set below the tube. The most remarkable feature of this barometer was the wooden cistern. This was open with a diameter of 2·5″ and a depth in the centre of 1″.

Plates 138 and 139 illustrate a wheel barometer by Springer. From the style of the case, which is veneered with mahogany and enriched with inlaid paterae and striped banding, it can be dated c. 1795–1805. The veneers are of deep colour and the hinged thermometer frame is also elaborated with a chequered inlay. The brass bezel is unusually deep and this fact, together with the difficulty of avoiding reflections from the glass, accounts for the invisibility of the engraving in Plate 138. The engraving is in fact very faint anyway and Plate 139 shows the silvered dial with the glass removed. It will be noticed immediately that this is an unusual instrument. The usual scale of 28″–31″ is engraved beneath the arbor of the hand and a brass weight which is attached to a wheel on the arbor indicates the height of the mercury as it falls or climbs in front of the

[1] *Ibid.* 29 September 1759.
[2] British Museum.

PLATE 138
J. Springer, Bristol
35·2″ × 10·2″
City of Gloucester Museum:
from the collection of S. Marling

PLATE 139
Detail of Plate 138

scale. Readings are taken level with the top of the weight. The usual weather indications are given against the half-inch graduations of the scale but no further subdivisions are needed since the hand, which revolves once round the dial each time the weight rises or falls over one inch, makes possible readings to ·01″. The crescent-tailed hand is made of steel. The pulley wheel is ivory. The thermometer is not original. I have recorded other examples of this type of wheel barometer but they are rare.

THOMAS TOMPION b.1638 –d.1713

Dial and Three Crowns, Water Lane, Fleet Street

THE MOST famous and one of the best English clockmakers, Tompion was born in Bedfordshire but came to London and set up as a clock-maker when fairly young. He became a member of the Clockmakers' Company in 1671 and was Master in 1704. For details of his life and horological work I cannot do better than refer the reader to R.W. Symonds' book *Thomas Tompion, His Life and Work* (1951) where his clocks are profusely illustrated and the known facts of his life, which are few enough, adequately marshalled. He took George Graham into partnership 1711–13 and was succeeded by him.

Besides clocks Tompion made equally fine mathematical instruments and barometers. He was associated for many years with Robert Hooke and gave concrete expression to many of Hooke's ideas. The relation-ship was not always friendly and Hooke abused Tompion on more than one occasion in his diary,[1] criticizing him for being slow in finish-ing his work. It was however a mutually advantageous relationship and over the years Tompion effected a number of devices to Hooke's designs including watch and clockwork and astronomical instruments. From entries in Hooke's diary for 1675–6 it seems that Tompion made him at least two barometers: these were probably wheel instruments. On 1 September 1675 Robert Boyle also 'desired barometer of Thompion' (*sic*). By 1678 however Hooke was employing Henry Wynne besides of course Harry Hunt, the Operator to the Royal Society.

A bill submitted by Tompion to the Hon. Robert Harley, covering the years 1695–1705, survives and includes, among various clocks and watches, the items:

1701 August 23	And for a spirit glass	01: 07: 06
	And a portable weather glass	04: 06: 00
1704 July 4	For mending a portable weather glass	01: 05: 00[2]

This portable barometer could have been of the type discussed in Chapter Three with a leather bag[3] cemented to the base of the tube: it could even have been one of the earliest barometers

---

[1] *Diary* 1672–80
(edited by H. W. Robinson and W. Adams 1935).
[2] In the possession of
His Grace the Duke of Portland: reproduced in

Symonds' *Thomas Tompion* p. 175.
[3] That Tompion used such a device is
suggested by the extract of the Royal Society
Journal Book quoted on p. 32.

to incorporate a screw device. It was expensive—Clement Forster charged only from 12s. to 50s. for weather-glasses about ten years earlier—but was doubtless of high quality.

Extant instruments by Tompion are rare. The only genuine examples which I have studied are the three which survive in the Royal Collections (Plates 140, 143 and 146). All three are of exquisite workmanship. The two wheel barometers were specifically made for William III: one of them (Plate 143) carries his royal cipher and the other probably used to. The siphon-tube barometer of Plate 140 hangs at Hampton Court[1] but carries no sign of royal patronage: but its close similarity to the superb barometer by Daniel Quare (Plate 113) which also bears the cipher suggests that it was made for William III but possibly not delivered until after his death in 1702. The oak carcase is richly veneered with burr walnut, now attractively faded. The mounts, which reflect architectural motifs of the period, are of ormolu. The two strange brass knobs on the pedestals at each side of the base of the pillar are not original and indeed are out of keeping with the rest of the design. It is probable that these were originally ball or urn finials of the type seen on contemporary clocks and arguable that they were similar to the subsidiary finials of the barometer of Plate 143: they had wider bases than their present imitators since marks of wider diameter can be detected on the wood. It is probable too that originally there were pillars on each side of the register plates (Plate 141): the ledges on which their bases would have stood are not veneered and their restoration would certainly enhance the design (*cf.* Plate 113). One can only surmise that they would have been walnut with

[1] Queen's Gallery.

PLATE 140
Tompion, London
43″ × 6·9″
Hampton Court:
reproduced by gracious permission of
Her Majesty the Queen

PLATE 141
Detail of Plate 140

ormolu bases and capitals. Before describing the plates it is necessary to describe the tube. This would originally have been a siphon tube with a fairly large bulb at the closed end which would have been concealed in the flaming urn finial at the top of the case: the finial is slit at the back to allow the bulb to be inserted. The principle of this tube is that proposed by Robert Hooke (pp. 8–9) for application in his wheel barometer; the bulb, or 'bolt-head' as he called it, acts as a cistern and permits the mercury in the short limb of the siphon tube to show the actual extent of the movement. The scale on the silvered brass plates is thus engraved in precise inches and all would be well if the original tube had not been replaced by a modern one of the wrong design. The barometer cannot at the time of writing function intelligibly. The plates (Plate 141) are protected by glass set in a brass frame and bear a slight resemblance to those of Quare. The plate to the left of the tube in fact repeats the wording of Plate 114 but Tompion did not apparently favour Quare's rather imprecise weather indications even though they tried to cater for both seasons: he therefore reverted on the right-hand plate to the usual weather indications which are inscribed conventionally against the half-inch gradations. The scale, which is engraved on both sides of the tube, is divided, as almost invariably in stick barometers of this period, into twentieths. It is inverted because of course observations are made of the short open limb of the tube and the visible mercury rises with a fall in air pressure. There are two small steel pointers which are operated by the brass knobs beneath the plates to which they are connected by rackwork (Plate 142). Finally a manual calendar is set at the base (Plate 141). The date is set to the indicating arrow at

PLATE 142
Detail of Plate 140 showing rackwork of pointers
*Reproduced by gracious permission
of Her Majesty the Queen*

twelve o'clock by turning the central knob, and the month ring is turned with the aid of four raised thumb knobs: both rings are made of silver and the setting is brass. This barometer, which has been illustrated in several previous books on furniture and clocks but never correctly explained, is of the greatest interest as one of the few surviving examples of the practical application of Hooke's 'bolt-head' tube: its elegance and its colour are also causes for enthusiasm even though the case is incomplete.

The wheel barometer of Plate 143 is also at Hampton Court[1] and has probably been there ever since it was made for William III. The German traveller von Uffenbach visited Hampton Court on 24 October 1710 and 'observed a special kind of barometer and thermometer in the form of a clock, which are made by Tomson'.[2] Allowing for his poor spelling, which is reminiscent of Hooke's, and his inaccurate cataloguing, which is widely imitated today, it can be assumed that he was referring to this barometer. The case is flamboyant, the richly figured veneer combining with the applied ormolu mounts to give a magnificent impression of opulence. The carcase is made of oak and pine and the horizontal mouldings are of either walnut or kingwood, the colour suggesting the latter, but it is difficult to be categorical. There is considerable doubt about the wood used for the veneers. One school of thought supports a theory that it is stained burr maple and another that it is mulberry. It is a pity not to be able to advance yet another theory but I cannot: from my all too meagre study of the various woods employed by cabinet-makers I favour the mulberry faction. The ormolu decorations were

[1] Communication Gallery.
[2] Quarrell and Mare *London in 1710* p. 154.

Falling
Raine

Change-
:able.

Rifing
Faire

Raine.

Faire.

Much
Raine.

Clear.

Stormy.

Tho: Tompion fe

Londini

Settled
Faire.

opposite: PLATE 143
Tho Tompion, Londini
44″ × 11·5″
Hampton Court

right: PLATE 144
Detail of Plate 143
*Reproduced by
gracious permission of
Her Majesty the Queen*

badly restored when the instrument was last repaired but in form they
are strikingly similar to Plate 140: and the decoration of the royal
cipher should be compared to Plate 146. The dial (Plate 144), which is
protected by a glass set in a brass bezel, is handsomely executed and
displays many of the features of contemporary clock design—a matted

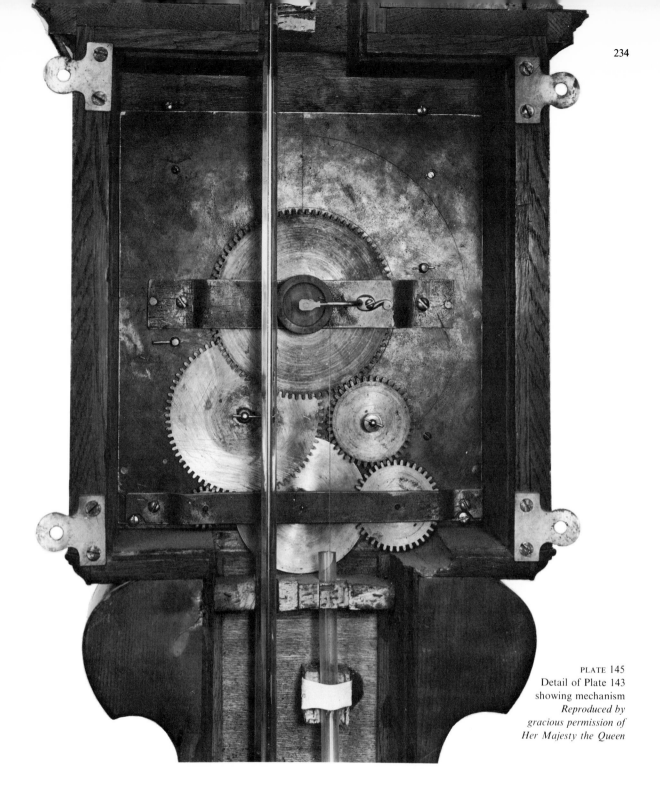

brass dial plate, a silvered brass chapter ring, chased brass spandrels and finely pierced steel hands. The engraving is of high quality, the encirclement of each state of the weather being an elegant feature. The actual states are not unusual although, as can be seen by comparing the three illustrated examples of his work, Tompion does not seem to have stuck rigidly to the same detailed form. No inches are engraved on the scale but since there are 300 divisions the scale represents the usual three inches divided into hundredths. This compares with Hooke's scale of 200 divisions with which Tompion was probably familiar.[1] The hands are superbly fashioned: the recording hand assumes the shape of a not very typical hour hand and is operated by the left-hand knob beneath the dial to which it is connected by three brass gears (Plate 145). The central knob operates—indeed is attached to the centre of—a silvered dial which indicates the month in the aperture at the bottom of the chapter ring: and the right-hand knob operates the brass gearwheel, on the front of which are engraved the dates of the month which are seen in the aperture cut through the dial above the signature (Plate 144). As in the case of the previous barometer the urn finial is cut away at the back. The tube has, as before, been recently renewed and it seems inevitable that this barometer was also originally fitted with a tube of Hooke's design.

There is similarly a strong case for believing the same about the barometer of Plate 146. This time the repairer has made no concessions and has fitted an aneroid mechanism which accounts for the two incongruous screws in the centre of the dial.[2] This barometer was probably made for Kensington Palace where the ubiquitous von Uffenbach saw it in 1710, recording in his diary on 25 October that it had a 'round disc as a clock'.[3] It was still there in 1819 when it was depicted in J. B. Pyne's *Royal Residences* hanging over the chimney-piece in the Queen's bedroom.[4] George IV moved it to Carlton House where, in 1826, it was catalogued as 'A wheel barometer by Tompion in a rosewood case, ornamented with figures in ormolu':[5] and when Carlton House was pulled down it moved to Buckingham Palace with the King. It was presumably in company with whichever of John Russell's wheel barometers the maker gave to George IV before he succeeded to the throne.

The barometer is thus one of the best-documented instruments in existence and it has been frequently illustrated in books about furniture etc.[6] There can be no doubt whatever that it deserves the praise which so many writers have bestowed on it. The walnut veneers have a pleasing figure and the carving of the ball finial, the circumference of

[1] Hooke *Micrographia* (1665), Preface: see pp. 8–9
[2] H. C. Smith *Buckingham Palace* p. 265 concludes that this was fitted in the nineteenth century.
[3] Quarrell and Mare *London in 1710* p. 157.
[4] Vol. 2 facing p. 83: the picture is not an accurate representation of the barometer but the general shape is correct. I am grateful to Mr Geoffrey de Bellaigue who confirms that Pyne cannot be wholly trusted on points of detail.
[5] Quoted by H. C. Smith *Buckingham Palace* p. 265.
[6] e.g. H. C. Smith *Buckingham Palace* Plate 349, Symonds *Thomas Tompion* Figs. 262–3, MacQuoid and Edwards *Dictionary of English Furniture* s.v. 'Barometer' Fig. 8, *et al.*

the dial and the scrolls on each side of the base (Plate 147) is finely executed. The gilded brass mounts are also of high quality. The two almost nude figures are each holding and gazing at a blazing sun (wishful thinking perhaps) and between them is applied a decorative frame composed of a crown, palm leaves and a cherub. This decoration can also be seen on the wheel barometer of Plate 143 on which Tompion used it for framing the royal cipher. The intention was clearly the same in this case and we must conclude either that the cipher has been subsequently neatly removed (signs of it can be seen on the palm leaves) or that the barometer was not delivered until after William III had died in 1702. The dial (Plate 148), which is protected by a glass set in a brass bezel, is of superb quality. It shares many of the features of the barometer of Plate 143 but because it is larger (13″ diameter against 8″) and is set in a round frame it seems less crowded with detail and so achieves a greater degree of elegance. The centre is of matted brass and the silvered chapter ring is finely engraved. As in Plate 143 the scale is divided into 300 divisions and no inch digits are engraved. The weather indications almost correspond: 'Dry' is substituted for 'Clear', 'Falling Raine' and 'Rising Faire' are abbreviated to 'Falling' and 'Rising', the final 'e' is omitted from the words 'Raine' and 'Faire', the 'e' is even expelled from 'Changeable' and 'Much' and 'Settled' are abbreviated. The treatment of them is decidedly more decorative. In the aperture above the signature the words 'Rising' or 'Falling' can be set by turning the left-hand of the two brass knobs beneath the dial. Unfortunately I have not seen the mechanism of this (it was anyway inoperative in 1963) or of the recording hand which is operated by the right-hand knob. The steel hands themselves are of passing elegance, the pierced hour-hand type of decoration being placed at the half-way mark in order to avoid confusion with the chapter ring. Beneath the dial is set a manually operated calendar similar to the calendar of Plate 140. It is however operated not by direct adjustment but by the two brass knobs placed beneath it and is protected by a glass framed in a brass bezel. The centre of the dial is again of matted brass and the calendar rings are silvered: the inner ring, operated by the right-hand knob, can be set so that the day of the month is indicated by the fixed pointer at the top, and the outer ring, which can be similarly set by the left-hand knob, gives the month, the number of days in the month (Roman figures) and the appropriate zodiacal sign.

There are probably other barometers by Tompion in existence and it can only be hoped that they will come to light. As in the case of Daniel Quare Tompion's eminence has attracted forgers. Careless collectors can often be persuaded to buy a piece of doubtful origin

when the opportunity is rare: and barometers by Tompion have the same attraction as religious pictures by Vermeer in that collectors believe, logically enough, that the great artist must have created some. Van Meegeren proved how powerful this belief can be. I have seen two forgeries purporting to be by Tompion—one of them a very poor effort which passed through the London sale rooms in 1962[1]—but fortunately neither was made by a craftsman of van Meegeren's calibre.

[1] Sold for £480: see *Country Life* 10 May 1962 p. 1096, where incidentally a cataloguing error is faithfully reproduced.

PLATE 147 Detail of Plate 146
*Reproduced by gracious permission of
Her Majesty the Queen*

EDWARD TROUGHTON b. 1753 –d. 1831

1. Surrey Street, Strand

2. The Orrery, 136 Fleet Street (from 1782)

EDWARD was apprenticed to his eldest brother John Troughton and in 1770 became his partner in the firm of J. and E. Troughton which later enjoyed a high reputation as optical and mathematical instrument-makers. The rival business of Benjamin Cole in Fleet Street was absorbed in 1782 and after his brother's death Edward expanded the business considerably. He was well known for his astronomical instruments and writings and was elected F.R.S. in 1810. He appears on his own in the 1817 directories and in 1826 the firm became Troughton and Simms when William Simms was taken into partnership.

Although from the early nineteenth century the firm concentrated on barometers more for scientific than domestic use, there are several more decorative barometers of typical style extant which can be dated to the period between John Troughton's death and the partnership with William Simms. Like George Adams the younger Troughton also made barometers for export and Dr Middleton reports one with a dual scale in English and French inches in the Museo Copernico, Rome.[1]

[1] Middleton *History of the Barometer* p. 174.

J. AND E. TROUGHTON fl 1770–84

1. Surrey Street, Strand

2. The Orrery, 136 Fleet Street (from 1782)

THE PARTNERSHIP of John and his brother Edward Troughton: although John appears to have retired or died in 1784 the joint name was continued and the firm became under Edward's auspices one of the leading instrument-makers of the early nineteenth century.

JOHN TROUGHTON fl 1752–84

1. Standgate Lane, Lambeth (1752)

2. Surrey Street, Strand

3. The Orrery, 136 Fleet Street (from 1782)

AN OPTICAL and mathematical instrument-maker, Troughton joined his uncle Edward Troughton senior in Surrey Street in about 1760. Between 1764 and 1770 he was in partnership with a younger brother named Joseph—the firm being called J. and J. Troughton—and he then took into partnership another brother Edward who was then seventeen and who was later mainly responsible for the considerable reputation of the resultant firm J. and E. Troughton. Professor Taylor reports that, according to Edward, John had a reputation for scale divisions as high as that of Jesse Ramsden.[1]

In 1782 the Troughtons took over the business of Benjamin Cole at 136 Fleet Street. With this business came the sponsorship of Joseph Harris's *Description and Use of the*

[1] Taylor *Mathematical Practitioners of Hanoverian England* (manuscript).

Globes and the Orrery and the twelfth edition of this popular book of 1783 contains a catalogue of Troughton's instruments. Among these are found:

	£	s.	d.	£	s.	d.
Barometers .. .. *from*	1	1	0 *to* 1	16	0	
Ditto and thermometer, in one frame .. .. .. *from*	1	11	6 *to* 2	12	6	
Barometer, thermometer, and hydrometer, all in one frame *from*	2	12	6 *to* 3	13	6	

As in the case of Benjamin Martin's advertisement (p. 165) the word 'hydrometer' is a misprint for 'hygrometer'.

There is a barometer in the Museum of the History of Science at Oxford which should I think be attributed to approximately this period. It bears a number of resemblances to instruments by Bennett, Ramsden and Sisson which I have already mentioned. The case, which is veneered with mahogany, is not similar but is of traditional design, having a hemispherical cistern cover, a broken pediment and an exposed tube: it is not unfortunately in good enough condition to illustrate. The engraving of the silvered brass plates suggests that Troughton bought his components from a source common to many of his eminent contemporaries (*cf*. Plates 18, 20, 71). The interesting features of this barometer belong to the tube and cistern. The top of the tube is widened to a bulb in order to dilute the damaging effect on the vacuum of any vapours: and the cistern is open with a diameter of 3·25″. In order to gauge the movement of the level of the mercury in the cistern an ivory guide is fitted. This barometer is not quite domestic, but as his advertisement suggests Troughton's firm sold domestic instruments and there was nothing unusual about the range offered. The most expensive, consisting of a barometer, thermometer and hygrometer in one frame, was probably of the type illustrated in Plate 91 with a bayonet tube but not necessarily in a case of identical design.

TROUGHTON AND SIMMS fl 1826–60

136 Fleet Street

THE PARTNERSHIP between Edward Troughton and William Simms: Troughton retired in 1831 but the name was carried on and survived until recently when Cooke Troughton and Simms Ltd. became Vickers Instruments Ltd.

The firm produced a large number of barometers, many of them standard instruments of the Gay-Lussac and Fortin types which do not fall within the scope of this book. Domestic instruments are found carrying their signature however and judging from descriptions kindly sent to me by correspondents their range appears to be very similar to that of their eminent rivals Watkins and Hill. The only three which I have had an opportunity to study were almost identical. The frame of each was bow-fronted with mahogany veneers and had the traditional scroll pediment and urn-shaped cistern cover (*cf*. Plate 33). The finial was ivory and ivory rosettes were applied to the scrolls of the pediment. The silvered plates were protected by the usual bow-fronted glass and carried a mercury Fahrenheit thermometer on the left and a rack-operated vernier: the scale was in decimals and the weather indications were the usual seven. One of the barometers had an ivory float of the type discussed on pp. 66–7 but this had been removed from the other two. In no case was the tube original.

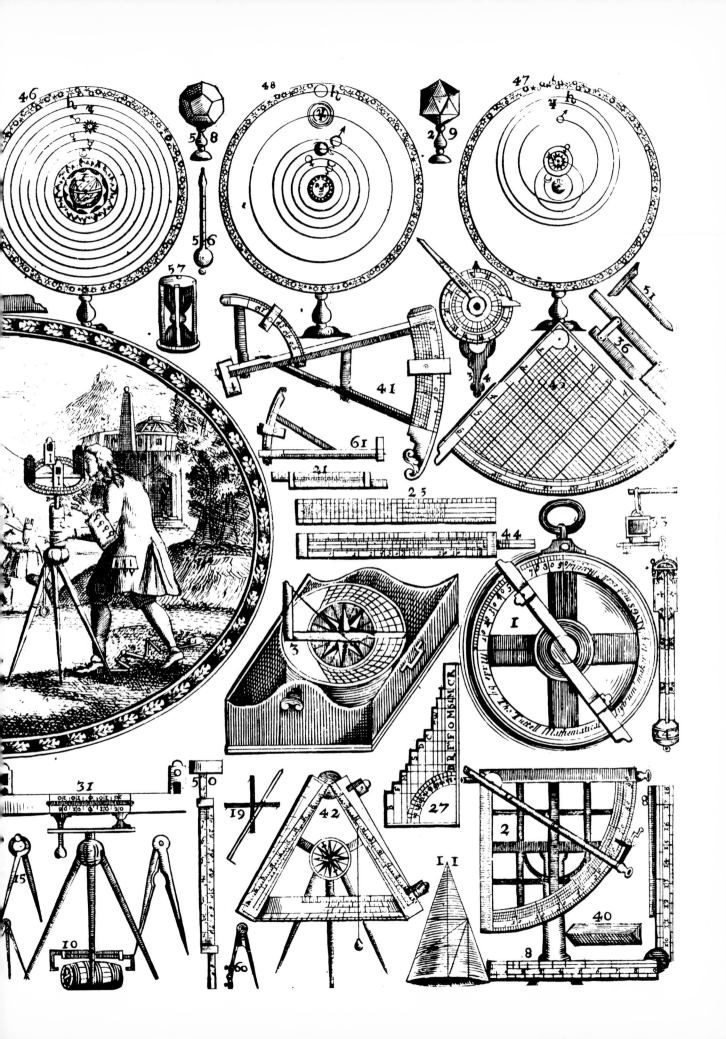

THOMAS TUTTELL fl 1688 –d. 1702

1. Kings Arms and Globe, Charing Cross (1695–1702)
2. Royal Exchange (1695–1702)

TUTTELL was probably born in about 1674 since he was apprenticed to Henry Wynne, who was the first instrument-maker to indulge in the commercial production of barometers on any scale, in 1688. He was therefore only about twenty-eight when he was drowned on a marine survey early in 1702.[1] He became a member of the Clockmakers' Company in 1695 and held the appointment of Mathematical Instrument Maker to William III from 1700 to 1702. He was an eminent maker, and was somewhat unusual in having two shops. Several fine examples of his work survive.

His trade card (Plate 149) advertised a wide selection of astronomical, navigational and surveying instruments besides stock mathematical instruments and globes. The barometer, which is squeezed in on the right of the card, does not take pride of place but is of great interest. Firstly it shows that Tuttell assumed his former master's practice of selling barometers and did so simultaneously, since Wynne lived until 1709. Secondly it displays many of the features—the architectural hood and three ball finials, arched plates and weather indications for both summer and winter—which were typical of the period (cf. Plates 8, 9). Thirdly, and most important, this appears to be the earliest extant illustration of a portable cistern-tube barometer of the screw type. The card is unlikely to have been printed before 1700 since Tuttell was probably appointed Mathematical Instrument Maker to William III in 1700 and the appointment is cited on the astrolabe immediately to the left of the barometer: nor can it have been printed after January 1702 since Tuttell died before 3 February. It can therefore be dated in either 1700 or 1701 and I have argued in Chapter Three that the screw device was introduced at about this time. I do not know of any extant barometers which carry Tuttell's signature; like his former master Wynne he may not have signed them.

[1] *Post Boy* 3 February 1702.

previous page:
PLATE 149
Thomas Tuttell's
trade card
*By courtesy
of the Director of
the Science Museum,
London*

FRANCIS WATKINS b. *c.*1723 –d. 1784 (?)

1. Sir Isaac Newton's Head, 415 Charing Cross
2. 5 Charing Cross (1747–84)

WATKINS was another of the leading instrument-makers of the second half of the eighteenth century. The son of one Jeremy Watkins of New Church, Radnor, he founded a business which remained pre-eminent under several variations of the name until 1856 (Watkins and Smith, J. and W. Watkins, Watkins and Hill). He was apprenticed in 1737 to Nathaniel Adams, who in turn had been an apprentice of the elder Edward Scarlett, and became free of the Spectaclemakers' Company in 1746. He appears to have worked for Scarlett himself at some juncture since in the *Daily Advertiser* of 4 March 1747 he announced that 'Francis Watkins, Optician, late from Mr. Scarlet's, has open'd the shop kept by the late Mr. Nathaniel Adams, at Sir Isaac Newton's head, Charing Cross'. This was probably the younger Scarlett since his father had died in 1743. In 1763 Watkins took his own apprentice Addison Smith into a partnership which lasted until 1774, and among his other apprentices was Henry Pyefinch.

The name of Watkins is associated chiefly with a type of angle barometer which is set in a frame also containing a thermometer and, in the centre, a 'Perpetual Regulation of Time' (Plate 150). Besides tables giving the dates of Easter from 1753 until 1852, the movable feasts and the dates of the Kings of England, these Perpetual Calendars incorporate a series of movable dials which can be set by keys operating through gear-work (Plate 151) and which show the time of high water at London Bridge, the times of sunrise and sunset, the length of the day, the days of the month, the zodiacal signs, etc. They were presumably inspired by the adoption in Britain of the Gregorian Calendar in 1752 but similar and earlier calendars survive. It is most unlikely that Watkins designed them and he probably bought several of them at once, planning to use them gradually. It is certainly wrong to assume that every barometer which incorporates one of these calendars was made in 1753 as most writers, cataloguists and dealers have assumed in the past. Examples are extant by Watkins & Smith, a partnership which is not recorded before 1763, and by William

A Perpetual Regulation of Time

Easter Day

Year	Easter Day
1753	April 22
1754	14
1755	March 30
1756	April 18
1757	10
1758	March 26
1759	April 15
1760	6
1761	March 22
1762	April 11
1763	3
1764	22
1765	7
1766	March 30
1767	April 19
1768	3
1769	March 26
1770	April 15
1771	31
1772	April 19
1773	11
1774	3
1775	16
1776	April 7
1777	March 30
1778	April 19
1779	4
1780	March 26
1781	April 15
1782	March 31
1783	20
1784	11
1785	March 27
1786	April 16
1787	8
1788	March 23
1789	April 12
1790	4
1791	24
1792	April 8
1793	March 31
1794	April 20
1795	5
1796	March 27
1797	April 16
1798	8
1799	March 24
1800	April 13
1801	5
1802	18
1803	10
1804	1
1805	14
1806	6
1807	March 29
1808	April 17
1809	2
1810	22
1811	14
1812	March 29
1813	April 18
1814	10
1815	March 26
1816	April 14
1817	6
1818	March 22
1819	April 11
1820	2
1821	22
1822	7
1823	March 30
1824	April 18
1825	3
1826	March 26
1827	April 15
1828	6
1829	19
1830	11
1831	3
1832	22
1833	7
1834	March 30
1835	April 19
1836	3
1837	March 26
1838	April 15
1839	March 31
1840	April 19
1841	11
1842	March 27
1843	April 16
1844	7
1845	March 23
1846	April 12
1847	4
1848	23
1849	8
1850	March 31
1851	April 20
1852	11

High Water at London Bridge

Moveable Feasts

The Fixed Feasts

September XXX Days

2. London burnt. 1666.
21. S.t Matthew
Days & Nights equal
29. S.t Michael

Sun at 5h. 45m. Rises
The 15.th
Sun at 6h. 14m. Sets

Days 12 h. 29 m. Length
The 15.th
Break of Day at 3h. 42 m.

The Zodiack Signs

Suns Declination
Suns Place
Day of the Month

After February in every Leap Year the Suns Place will be one Degree forwarder than the Table shews it

A Regal Table

Kings & Queens Names	Began to Reign	Reign'd	Buried at
The Norman Line			
William I	1066 Oct. 14	20 10	Caen Norm.
William II	1087 Sep. 9	12 10	Winchester
Henry I	1100 Aug. 2	35 4	Reading
Stephen	1135 Dec. 1	18 10	Feversham
The Saxon Line Restored			
Henry II	1154 Oct. 25	34 8	Funtev.
Richard I	1189 Sep. 6	9 9	Funtev.
John	1199 Apr. 6	17 6	Worcester
Henry III	1216 Oct. 19	56 0	Westminst.
Edward I	1272 Nov. 16	34 7	Westminst.
Edward II	1307 Jul. 7	19 6	Glocester
Edward III	1327 Jan. 25	50 5	Westminst.
Richard II	1377 Jun. 21	22 3	Westminst.
The House of Lancaster			
Henry IV	1399 Sep. 29	13 5	Canterbury
Henry V	1412 Mar. 20	9 5	Westminst.
Henry VI	1422 Aug. 31	38 6	Windsor
The House of York			
Edward IV	1460 Mar. 4	22 1	Winchester
Edward V	1483 Apr. 9	2 0	Unknown
Richard III	1483 Jun. 22	2 2	Leicester
The House of Tudor			
Henry VII	1485 Aug. 22	23 8	Westminst.
Henry VIII	1509 Apr. 22	37 9	Windsor
Edward VI	1546 Jan. 28	6 5	Westminst.
Mary	1553 Jul. 6	5 4	Westminst.
Elizabeth	1558 Nov. 17	44 4	Westminst.
The House of Stuart			
James I	1602 Mar. 24	22 0	Westminst.
Charles I	1625 Mar. 27	23 10	Windsor
Charles II	1648 Jan. 30	36 0	Westminst.
James II	1684 Feb. 6	3 10	
Mary	1688 Feb. 13	10 13	Westminst.
William III	1688 Feb. 13	13 0	Westminst.
The House of Hanover			
Anne	1701 Mar. 8	12 4	Westminst.
George I	1714 Aug. 1	12 10	Hanover
George II	1727 Jun. 11		neart Rex

Years of our Lord / Dom Letter

Year	Epact	Dom Letter
1753	25	G F
1754	6	E
1755	17	D
1756	28	C B
1757	9	A
1758	20	G
1759	1	F
1760	12	E D
1761	23	C
1762	4	B
1763	15	A
1764	26	G F
1765	7	E
1766	18	D
1767	29	C
1768	11	B A
1769	22	G
1770	3	F
1771	14	E
1772	25	D C
1773	6	B
1774	17	A
1775	28	G
1776	9	F E
1777	20	D
1778	1	C
1779	12	B
1780	23	A G
1781	4	F
1782	15	E
1783	26	D
1784	7	C B
1785	18	A
1786	0	G
1787	11	F
1788	22	E D
1789	3	C
1790	14	B
1791	25	A
1792	6	G F
1793	17	E
1794	28	D
1795	9	C
1796	20	B A
1797	1	G
1798	12	F
1799	23	E
1800	4	D
1801	15	C
1802	26	B
1803	7	A
1804	18	G F
1805	29	E
1806	11	D
1807	22	C
1808	3	B A

Year		Dom Letter
1809	14	G
1810	25	F
1811	6	E
1812	17	D C
1813	28	B
1814	9	A
1815	20	G
1816	1	F E
1817	12	D
1818	23	C
1819	4	B
1820	15	A G
1821	26	F
1822	7	E
1823	18	D
1824	29	C B
1825	11	A
1826	22	G
1827	3	F
1828	14	E D
1829	25	C
1830	6	B
1831	17	A
1832	28	G F
1833	9	E
1834	20	D
1835	1	C
1836	12	B A
1837	23	G
1838	4	F
1839	15	E
1840	26	D C
1841	7	B
1842	18	A
1843	29	G
1844	11	F E
1845	22	D
1846	3	C
1847	14	B
1848	25	A G
1849	6	F
1850	17	E
1851	28	D
1852	9	C B

Days of the Month

Equation of Days

Explanation

The First Table shews the Moons Age as Increase and Decrease & how many hours & Minutes it Shines. Likewise the time of high Water at London Bridge in the Cross Columns directly facing each day of the Week. The 1.st Column from 1 to 29 denotes the Moon so many days old the 2.d & 3.d how many Hours & Minutes it Shines and the last Column shews the time of High Water. This Table must be mov'd off seven days on every Sunday & whereas the Moon does not always last 29 days this Table must be regulated the first day of every Month, according to the Moons Age which is found by adding to the Epact the day of the Month & the Figure standing under the Title of the Month. Example what is the Moons Age August 1770 I find the Epact for 1770 to be 3 add to that 1 for the 1.st day of the Month & 6 w.ch is the Number for the Month of August the Amount will be 10 so many days old the Moon is. Note that when such additions exceed 30 then 30 must be substracted from the Amount & what remains will be the Moons Age, by the same Rule the Moons Age may be found any day in the Year.

The 1.st Opening on the Middle Table shews the Fixed Feasts & Remarkable Days & under them the Number abovemention'd to find out if Moons Age the 2.d Opening shews the Suns Rising & the 3.d Suns Setting the 4.th Days Length the 5.th Break of Day for every 15.th day of the Month the 6.th

Opening shews the Zodiack Sign the 7.th of Suns Declination in Degrees and Minutes whether to the North or South the letter N for North & S for South and likewise its Place in Degrees & Minutes for every 1.3.5.7.9.11.13.15.17.19. 21.23.25.27.& 29 day of each Month in the Cross Columns directly facing each of these days The 8.th Opening to y.e left is a Table of Equation of Days in Minutes & Seconds for every 1.3.5.7.9. 11.13.15.17.19.21.23.25.27.& 29 day of each Month in y.e Cross Columns directly facing each of these days w.ch shews how much Faster or Slower a well regulated Clock or Watch goes than a true Sun Dial the letter F for Faster & S for Slower This Table is mov'd off the 1.st day of every Month.

The Opening to the Right shews the day of Month for every day in the Week & is mov'd off Seven days on every Sunday.

The Tables on the outside are easily understood they being Calculated for 100 Years to come and by that of Easter, any of the other Moveable Feasts are easily found. Example On what day falls Whitsunday 1755. I find Easter Day 1755 to be the 18.th of April then I look in the Table of Moveable Feasts in the Column of Easter Days for April the 18. and even with it in the Column on Whit Sunday I find it to be the 6 of June. By the same Rule any other of the Moveable Feasts is easily found.

Each Feasts as fall in Jan.r or Feb.r are every Leap year one day later. Advent Sunday is the nearest Sunday to S.t Andrews above or on or after.

Sunday
Monday
Tuesday
Wednesday
Thursday
Friday
Saturday

Solis
Lunæ
Martis
Mercurii
Jovis
Veneris
Sabbati

PLATE 151
Reverse of
typical Watkins
angle barometer
Hotspur Ltd.

opposite:
PLATE 150
Detail of Plate 155,
showing Perpetual Calendar

Watkins who is not recorded before 1784.

There is a barometer of this type by Francis Watkins in the Museum of the History of Science at Oxford (Plate 152). The plates have lost their silvering and the 'Perpetual Regulation of Time' which is protected by glass has been yellowed by sunlight: the photograph is not therefore very clear. The mahogany case is a little more elegant in conception if plainer in execution than later examples (Plates 155, 156). The shaping of the base and the almost ogee carving in the centre of

PLATE 152
F. Watkins, London
38·8″ × 22·8″
*Museum of the
History of Science,
Oxford*

the pediment break up the uncompromising lines of the later examples. The cistern covers however are plain and the only attempt at decoration is a finial, now missing. As in later examples the plates carry the scale 28″–31″ below the tube and each inch is divided into hundredths above and below: the weather indications are also very similar and read above the tube

Stormy   Much Rain   Rain   Changeable   Fair   Set Fair   Very Dry

and below the tube

Much Snow   Set Frost

The signature 'F. Watkins London' is engraved in the centre of the lower plate. The tube is not old and is fitted with a portable cistern but the screw for compressing the mercury is missing. The mercury can rise and fall over 18″, i.e. a magnification of six. There was once a manual pointer which could be slid along a wire rod beneath the tube (*cf.* Plates 155, 156) but this is also missing: the holes for the ends of the rod can be seen on the lower plate. The alcohol Fahrenheit thermometer is set against a silvered brass plate which is pleasantly decorated with an engraved border: the oatbeard hygrometer, which is adjusted by a key or knob inserted in the right hand of the two 'winding' holes, is of conventional pattern. The method of adjustment can be seen in Plate 4 which illustrates a hygrometer from another Watkins instrument. The other winding holes are used for adjusting the various dials of the calendar. I have seen another very similar barometer by Francis Watkins with a ball finial, a hygrometer above the plates and a spirit level in the centre of the base.

These barometers continued to be made by the firm after Watkins had taken Smith into partnership. Plates 155 and 156 show instruments by Watkins and Smith which must be dated between 1763 and 1774. I have a photograph of a barometer signed 'F. Watkins London' which is almost identical to Plate 155, the only detectable differences being the positioning of the flanking finials, which as in Plate 156 are nearer the centre, and the dimensions of the case. This is taller and allows more space for the diagonal plates which, unlike the example of Plate 155, are not cut short to conform with the right-hand end of the pediment. Another photograph records an instrument by Francis Watkins which is again similar but has ball finials.

Watkins also made portable cistern-tube barometers and there is one in the Science Museum, London.[1] The exposed tube is set in a round-topped mahogany frame with a hemispherical cistern cover. The brass plates carry a scale of 27″–31″ divided in decimals and

[1] Inventory No. 1920–54.

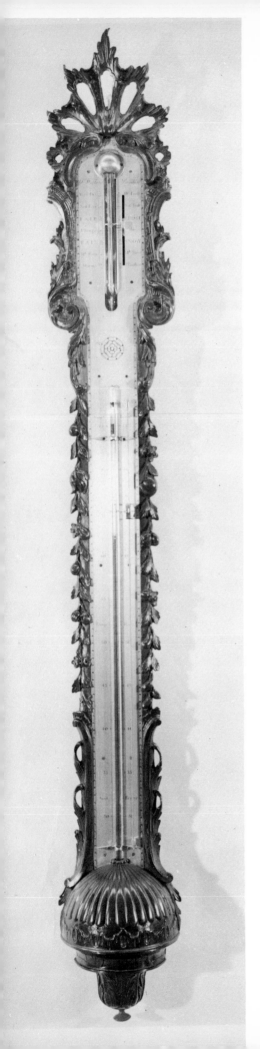

engraved on the inside edge of the right-hand plate so that readings are taken from the edge of the meniscus. The weather indications are conventional although the advice 'Fair if ☿ Rise, Foul if ☿ Fall' is added. A manual pointer is fitted but no vernier. The original tube probably had a bulb at the top but its cover is now missing. Another barometer by Watkins which I have studied consisted of a portable bayonet tube set in a mahogany frame with a band of geometric inlay similar to the instrument by Addison Smith which is described on p. 224. A thermometer was mounted on the register plates and a hygrometer above them.

Like many of his important contemporaries (Plates 18, 101) Watkins seems to have favoured the bayonet tube and Plate 153 shows a conspicuously fine example. Again I must apologise for the quality of the photograph and express regret that as yet I have not had an opportunity to study the instrument in person. With the barometer of Plate 82 and the Quare barometer mentioned on p. 190 it forms part of the fine collection of English furniture at Colonial Williamsburg.[1] The carved mahogany frame is clearly of exceptional quality, in keeping with the finest carved mahogany furniture of its period. Otherwise the instrument is very similar to the work of other makers. The silvered plates are decorated with an engraved border and a stylised rose and the scale of 28″–31″ is engraved and divided in decimals on both sides of the tube. For readers with poor eyesight it might help to give the weather indications which are

Very Dry	Hd Frost
Set Fair	Set Frost
Fair	Frost
Change	able
Rain	Snow
Mʰ Rain	Mʰ Snow
Stormy	Weather

The signature 'F. Watkins London' is engraved above them. The alcohol thermometer uses the common Fahrenheit scale. A very similar but damaged barometer is illustrated in the *Dictionary of English Furniture*[2] but no maker's name is quoted: nor is the picture clear enough to detect whether or not Watkins's signature is on it.

[1] Inventory No. 56–505.
[2] 2nd edition 1954 *s.v.* 'Barometer' Fig. 21 (Mulliner Collection).

PLATE 153
F. Watkins, London
41·8″ × 5·5″
Department of Collections, Colonial Williamsburg, Virginia, U.S.A.

WATKINS AND HILL fl 1819–56

5 Charing Cross

AFTER BEING IN charge of the business for many years Jeremiah Watkins took a Hill into partnership in 1819. Another Francis Watkins (fl 1828–35) later came into the business. This man was an instrument-maker of some repute, writing papers on electricity for the *Philosophical Magazine*. Professor Taylor[1] records an undated *Descriptive Catalogue of Optical Mathematical Philosophical and Chemical Instruments and Apparatus constructed by Watkins and Hill, Curators of Philosophical Apparatus in the University of London*. By 1857 the firm had been absorbed by Elliott Brothers.

The firm's output of domestic barometers was enormous. A rather decorative cistern-tube barometer dressed up in a carved gilt morass of fruit, flowers, ribbons etc. passed through the London sale rooms in 1962 but the firm does not seem to have indulged in many such flights of fancy. Most of its products were solid dependable instruments made with their functional purpose in mind.

Plate 154 shows an early example. In general design it is typical of its period. The ebonized urn-shaped cistern cover and the inlays on the bevelled sides of the base contrast well with the figure of the mahogany veneers. The weather indications follow the simpler version suggested by George Adams in 1790 but the scale covers 5″ although the 26″ digits are not engraved: it is an unnecessarily long scale for the normal variation. The style of the engraving is conspicuously later in date than the engraving of Plates 32 and 33, both of which use the traditional Roman script. The rack vernier, giving readings to ·01″, is operated by the ivory knob set traditionally beneath the hood. The leather-based cistern is of conventional type but is not original. The screw incidentally is operated by the detachable vernier key. The mercury thermometer, framed in its own bow-fronted case, uses both the Fahrenheit and Réaumur scales.

[1] Taylor *Mathematical Practitioners of Hanoverian England* (manuscript).

PLATE 154
Watkins and Hill, Charing Cross, London
37″ × 5″
Collection of Gordon F. C. Cole

I have seen several barometers of this pattern by Watkins and Hill and several more in which a scroll pediment surmounted the head (*cf.* Plate 33). An ivory finial and ivory rosettes applied to the scrolls of the pediment seem to have been strongly favoured: there is not always a thermometer on the front of the case but I have not yet seen an example of a thermometer which did not have the dual scale.

Later in the nineteenth century the firm still produced bow-fronted mahogany barometers but they inevitably became heavier in design. I do not know of any in public collections but I have received details of several from correspondents and seen some in private hands. Two particular examples are worthy of mention since they are identical and seem to have been part of the regular stock. Measuring about 42″ by 4″, each mahogany frame was plain except for some shallow carving beneath the crest which was a flatter version of Plate 154. The cistern was variable and portable and incorporated a version of the ivory float discussed on pp. 66–7. The shape of the cistern case echoed the bow-fronted shape of the hood, the urn motif having by now been discarded. The plates, protected by the usual convex glass, carried a 26″–31″ scale on each side of the tube divided into decimals and two verniers which made possible readings to ·01″ were fitted: at the foot of the plates were engraved the notes 'Yesterday 10 a.m. Today 10 a.m.' which became popular in the Victorian period. The barometers must have belonged to gentlemen who were not obliged to leave the house early each day. As in earlier examples a mercury thermometer with a dual scale was fitted to the case.

JEREMIAH AND WALTER WATKINS

5 Charing Cross   fl 1785–98

FRANCIS WATKINS the elder was succeeded after his death or retirement in 1784 by two nephews. The new partners carried on business as optical, mathematical, and philosophical instrument-makers and continued to employ the bill headings used by their uncle. An extant bill of 1793 describes them as instrument-makers to the Duke and Duchess of York and to the Duke of Clarence.[1] By 1799 Jeremiah was on his own and in 1819 the firm became Watkins and Hill.

[1] Heal Collection, British Museum.

J. and W. Watkins continued to advertise 'all sorts of barometers and thermometers'. It might be expected that they would have sold angle barometers of the traditional family type but I have not seen any examples. Perhaps the stock of calendars was exhausted: or perhaps the remaining stock, such as it was, was removed by their relation William Watkins when he set up on his own in St James.

There are extant barometers similar to Plate 20 signed 'Watkins, London' which can be attributed, not with entire confidence, to the firm: and I have recorded a barometer like Plate 36 but with a hemispherical cistern cover, a hygrometer at the top and an unusually narrow trunk. Barometers are also found signed 'J. Watkins' which should be dated after 1799: one portable example which I have seen recently was set in a round-topped mahogany frame, the tube left exposed and the cistern cover turned as in Plate 32.

WATKINS AND SMITH

5 Charing Cross

THE PARTNERSHIP of Francis Watkins the elder and Addison Smith who was Watkins' former apprentice: by 1775 Watkins was issuing invoices in his own name again and Smith appears to have set up on his own in the Strand: it is not clear why the partnership was dissolved. The firm used the bill heading which was employed earlier by Francis Watkins and later in identical form by Jeremiah and Walter Watkins. It advertised in English and French a wide variety of instruments including 'all sorts of barometers, thermometers' etc.

As I have said on pp. 245–7 the firm continued to sell the peculiar type of angle barometer with which the name of Watkins is associated. Plate 155 shows an example which, since it is almost identical to other extant examples sold under Francis Watkins' sole name, was probably made soon after 1763.[1] The mahogany veneers are of good figure and mellow colour; and the frame, while restrained in design, is as usual carefully made. The gadrooned cistern covers are typical of the period c. 1750–65 (cf. Plate 136). The calendar is protected as usual by glass: its details are discussed on p. 245. The shape of the brass finials is typical of Watkins. The register plates need to be resilvered and cannot be seen clearly but, as in the work of Francis Watkins, they carry a scale of 28″–31″ divided into hundredths which is engraved both below

[1] Science Museum, London, Inventory No. 1876-814.

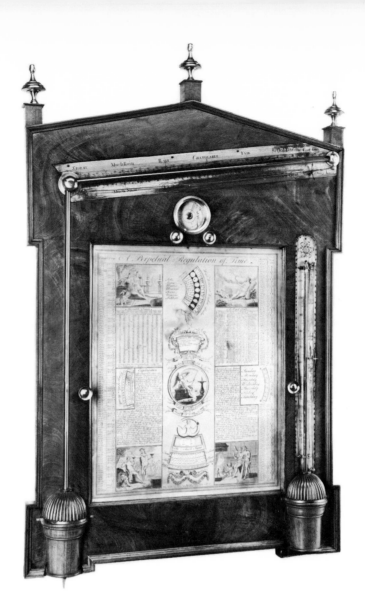

and above the tube: and the weather indications only differ from those of Plate 152 in the use of the word 'Setled' instead of 'Set'. The scale is extended over 21″ and is thus magnified seven times whereas the barometer of Plate 152 provided a magnification of only six. The case is therefore taller and wider by a few inches. In spite of the larger size however the maker, in order to achieve a precise magnification of seven, has been obliged to prune the upper register plate to conform with the cornice of the frame: and the words 'Very Dry' have had to be compressed into an undignified corner. The signature 'Watkins and Smith London' is engraved in the centre of the lower plate. The manual pointer which slides along a brass wire is itself of brass and its extremity is crescent shaped so that it conforms to the arc of the tube: other

contemporary makers used this pattern frequently. The tube is fitted with a conventional portable cistern. The thermometer uses the normal Fahrenheit scale and has a similar pointer. The oatbeard hygrometer is of a type sold in large numbers to barometer makers and, as in Plate 152, is adjusted by the right hand brass knob.

Plate 156 shows another of these barometers by Watkins and Smith. It may seem excessive to illustrate yet another variation on the same theme but the decoration of this example is worth comparing with Plate 155. The carving of the cistern covers and the carved and gilt borders make it a rare piece: otherwise it shares most of the features of the previous example, including details of scale and weather indications, but it is slightly taller and thus, in spite of a scale magnification of seven times, the register plates do not have to be pruned.

The firm also continued to make ordinary cistern-tube barometers. There is an example at Audley End House set in a pale mahogany case with a border of geometrical inlays. This is similar to the barometers signed by Smith and Watkins individually and mentioned on pp. 224 and 250 but the tube is not of the bayonet type and there is no thermometer.

WILLIAM WATKINS   fl 1784–1809

1. 22 St James (1784–99)
2. 70 St James (1800–9)

PRESUMABLY a cousin or brother of Jeremiah and Walter Watkins, this optical instrument-maker went into business on his own in St James, probably after the death of the elder Francis Watkins. It can only be surmised that the three younger men did not see eye to eye. At least one angle barometer of the distinctive Watkins style signed 'Watkins, St Ja.s St' is extant, incorporating the usual Perpetual Calendar of 1753. I do not know where this is now and have not therefore studied it in person: but from a comparative measurement of the calendar and scale in the photograph in my files it is clear that the 3″ scale is extended over 18″. The frame is basically the same shape as in Plate 155 but it is crowned with heavy flaming urn finials and decorated in the recesses of the sides with carved fruits and flowers: there are also inlaid borders of chequered woods round the calendar and the frame itself. In contrast the only surviving cistern cover is plain. There appear otherwise to be few significant differences from previous examples.

Watkins also made ordinary cistern-tube barometers. I have seen one in a mahogany frame with a broken pediment and a turned cistern cover; the tube was left exposed. It was fitted with a vernier and apart from its use of a portable rather than a bulb cistern it was typical of early nineteenth-century domestic design. Since it carried the address '70 St James' it cannot have been sold before 1800. Another cistern-tube barometer which I have studied is signed 'W. Watkins, St James's Street, London':[1] it has a broken pediment, pleasant inlays, a hemispherical cistern cover, a hygrometer above the plates and a thermometer on them. It follows a traditional design of the Watkins family (see pp. 224, 250).

[1] Collection of the Earl Spencer, Althorp, Northampton.

JOHN WHITEHURST (1) b. 1713 – d. 1788

1. 22 Irongate, Derby
2. 4 Bolt Court, Fleet Street, London (1776–88)

WHITEHURST was born in Congleton in Cheshire where his father was in business as a clockmaker. He founded his own business in Derby in 1736 and rapidly achieved a wide reputation for his turret and 'tell-tale' clocks. Many of the former survive. In 1762 he became friendly with James Ferguson the astronomer and lecturer and corresponded with him on philosophical topics until Ferguson's death in 1776. In 1775, at the recommendation of the Duke of Newcastle, Whitehurst was appointed to the newly created office of 'Stamper of Money Weights' at the Mint in London; and he moved south to live in Ferguson's lodgings in Bolt Court. His business in Derby was probably carried on at first by his brother James, since his nephew John who eventually succeeded to it was only fourteen in 1775.[1]

He had an inventive and inquiring mind. While in Derby he had taken an active part in learned societies in the Midlands including the famous Lunar Society and the Club of Thirteen. Once in London he published books on geology and time measurement and was elected F.R.S. in 1779. He was also one of the group of so-called Civil Engineers who met frequently to discuss scientific and mechanical problems. Edward Nairne was a member of this group. Whitehurst applied his mind to a wide variety of practical problems including pumps, ventilation and heating equipment.

There is little doubt that Whitehurst's workshop produced barometers before he left Derby, but I attribute the distinctive and handsome wheel instruments, one of which is illustrated in Plate 158, to his nephew. They are all signed 'Whitehurst, Derby' which is not helpful but I recently saw a wind-vane dated 1791 whose metal bezel and dial were of identical design to these barometers.

Barometers survive which can definitely be attributed to him. I have for example recently come across an angle barometer similar to the one illustrated in Plate 157 and dated 1768. Whitehurst presumably devised this design of angle barometer which became almost a proprietary product of his firm after he had gone to live in London. The instrument of Plate 157 is itself dated 1776, i.e. only a year after his departure and I therefore choose to describe it here. It cannot be attributed to

[1] This suggestion was made by W. D. White in a supplement to *Derbyshire Miscellany* (1958) entitled *The Whitehurst Family*.

PLATE 157
Whitehurst, Derby
1776
39″ × 27·8″
Author's collection

Whitehurst's nephew who was fifteen in 1776 and while it should probably be attributed to his brother James his assumption of the firm is only a matter of surmise. The mahogany veneers are richly coloured and well figured. The gadrooned crest is a not uncommon feature of furniture decoration and is carefully carved. An acorn-shaped projection is missing from the top of the cistern cover but otherwise the case is in good condition. The silvered brass plates are protected by glass and carry an arbitrary scale of 0–60 which is in effect a 3″ scale divided into twentieths. The weather indications are normal but the flourishes with which the engraving is decorated are unusual if a little crude. The pointer has been replaced but is operated by the original wormed rod which is turned by the knob at the end of the arm. The tube is not original: nor is the conventional leather-based portable cistern. The shaping of the case suggests that the cistern was originally a closed wooden box about 2·5″ square. The mercury can move over 20·5″ between the extreme points of the scale, providing an effective magnification of not quite seven times.

The 1768 example is identical except that the signature 'Whitehurst, Derby, 1768' is engraved on the left of the lower register plate instead of in the centre.

A similar but undated barometer hangs in the Duke's room at Hardwick Hall: and another angle barometer signed by 'Whitehurst' and dated 1772 used to be in the Salford City Art Museum[1] but it does not appear to be there now and, according to the Director, was probably disposed of some years ago. Its date suggests that it was probably of the same design and its loss is unfortunate.

A wheel barometer signed by 'John Whitehurst, Derby' which was once in the Percival Griffiths Collection,[2] can be seen in the collection of Sir Harold Wernher at Luton Hoo. Stylistically there is no doubt that this came from the elder Whitehurst's workshop. The oak case is veneered with highly figured walnut and bears a strong resemblance

[1] No. 62 in an Inventory drawn up in 1865. It was described then as damaged.
It is also mentioned by Gunther *Early Science in Oxford* Vol. 1 p. 246.
[2] R. W. Symonds *English Furniture from Charles II to George II* (1929) Fig. 215.

to the type of case associated with the name of John Hallifax (Plate 84). It is made to stand on the floor like the Hallifax barometer discussed on p. 149 and is no less than 52·1″ high without its finial. The clock-like base and the trunk are decorated with line inlays both on the front and at the sides: and the hood, with four plain pillars and a glazed arched door, is closely similar to Hallifax's work. The dial is brass, the centre matted, and the chapter ring is silvered: there are no spandrels and the signature appears on a flat disc in the arch of the dial (*cf.* Plate 84). An arbitrary scale of 0–60 is again used as on the angle barometer of Plate 157 and the weather indications are also similar to those used on the angle barometer but 'Much Rain' is substituted for 'Stormy'. The single pierced steel hand moves clock-wise when the pressure is rising. A recording dial is set on the trunk and again reflects the manner of Hallifax with an eight pointed star inlay in the centre; but its circumference does not project from the trunk. These remarkable similarities to the work of Hallifax suggest some sort of contact between the two men. It is possible because both were clockmakers and both were active during the period 1736–50: Barnsley furthermore is only fifty-one miles from Derby. The mechanism, which has been badly restored, provides no clue but it is possible that Whitehurst bought the complete instrument from Hallifax or employed the same cabinet-maker.

PLATE 158
Whitehurst, Derby
43·5″ × 14·5″
Randolph

JOHN WHITEHURST (2) b.1761 –d.1834

22 Irongate, Derby

JOHN WHITEHURST the elder's nephew and heir was only fourteen when his uncle emigrated to London. His father James Whitehurst probably temporarily assumed the business since, although he originally took on his father's clock workshop in Congleton, Cheshire, he married and died in Derby.[1] Under the younger John's direction the firm maintained its reputation for clocks and other instruments. In about 1810 he took his son John into partnership and the firm was styled Whitehurst and Son until the elder man's death in 1834. I have seen a mahogany 'banjo' barometer signed thus which was similar to Plate 126.

To about the period 1780–90 probably belong the fine wheel barometers for which the Whitehurst name is chiefly known. One of these is shown in Plate 158. The dark mahogany frame is of elegant proportions and elaborately carved. Some faithful restoration has been carried out, notably to the bezel, but the woodwork is otherwise in excellent condition and the scrolling acanthus leaves which decorate the base of the column are especially fine. The column, which is of semi-circular section, is hollowed in order to house the tube. The engraving of the silvered dial is restrained and precise, the only concession to decoration being the flourishes adorning the signature. The 3″ scale is subdivided into hundredths. Both hands are of steel, the pierced recording hand being operated by a worm gear adjusted by the brass knob which is visible on the right-hand side of the bezel. The tube is not original but is of the normal type: it is however set in the centre of the column and is therefore bent lower down in order to avoid the arbor.

Several similar barometers are recorded but there do not appear to be any in public collections in this country. I have a photograph of an almost identical example which is now in America, I believe in a

[1] See p. 257 Note 1.

private collection. Another emigrant, again almost identical but with more elaborate acanthus scrolls and slightly different hands, resides in the Irwin Untermyer Collection in New York.[1] Its finial is missing. Finally an elaborately carved barometer of the same style but with a representation of the sun at the top and with a brace, if that is the correct term, of 'Ho-ho' birds standing on each side of a narrower column was sold recently in the Parke-Bernet Galleries, New York.[2]

The Whitehurst firm continued to produce angle barometers following the design of the elder John Whitehurst (Plate 157) and several examples made later in the eighteenth century survive. One can be seen in the Museum of the History of Science, Oxford; it is almost identical in design to Plate 157 but the mahogany veneers on the trunk are paler in colour and coarser in grain. It is signed 'Whitehurst, Derby' and is undated. Another example is owned by the British Museum[3] and this again is of paler mahogany: instead of a pointer operated by a knob and wormed rod this has a manually adjusted pointer which runs along a wire, and there is no glass in front of the register plates. The cistern cover is also different, being oval in shape, but otherwise the variations from the standard design are superficial. Neither instrument is particularly attractive owing to the choice of inferior wood for the casework: this suggests that barometers of this type were standard and fairly inexpensive products of the firm in the last quarter of the eighteenth century.

Judging from the number of extant examples these two models, wheel and angle, appear to have been the commonest barometers of the firm's range in the later years of the century. Other types survive however. I have studied a wheel barometer in a private collection which was encased in a frame veneered with mahogany with a cross-grained border as in Plate 157: the extreme height of the frame was 41·5″ and its width 8·6″. The 6″ dial was glazed and was set at the top of the frame. The squared base projected from the trunk and beneath it the case tapered to a point. Scrolls of the nineteenth-century type were carved beneath each side of the dial. An arbitrary scale of 0–60 was engraved on the silvered dial and the weather indications read 'Stormy, Rain, Changeable, Fair, Set Fair': the hands were of good quality, especially the pierced recording hand.

I have also seen a cistern-tube barometer which was housed in a case consisting of a fluted column with a plain hood surmounted by an urn: but this was in poor condition.

[1] Gloag and Hackenbroch *English Furniture. The Collection of Irwin Untermyer* Plate 20. It was formerly in the Henry Hirsch Collection, London, and was exhibited at the 'Four Georges' Exhibition in London in 1931: it is also illustrated in MacQuoid and Edwards *Dictionary of English Furniture s.v.* 'Barometer' Fig. 24 and in M. Harris and Sons *A Catalogue and Index* Part 3 Fig. 25, 591.

[2] I believe in 1962 but cannot verify the precise date.

[3] In store in 1962.

JOHN WHITEHURST (3)   b. 1788 –d. 1855

1. 22 Irongate, Derby
2. 1 Cherry Street, Derby (from 1843)

UNDER the third Whitehurst the famous firm continued to prosper after his father's death in 1834. As before business was not confined either to clocks or to Derby. Clocks were sold to 'London, Manchester, Liverpool, and most of the large towns in the United Kingdom, in the establishments of many noblemen and gentlemen, in mills, manufactories, wharfs, docks, etc.'[1] Besides clocks and watches of all sorts were advertised weather vanes, mathematical instruments, spirit levels, thermometers, barometers, etc.

[1] Quoted by W. D. White, supplement to *Derbyshire Miscellany* (1958).

THOMAS WRIGHT   b. *c.* 1686 fl 1748

1. Orrery and Globe, Next the Globe and Marlborough Head Tavern, Fleet Street
2. The Orrery, Nr Water Lane (Later 136 Fleet Street)

WRIGHT enjoyed a high reputation as a mathematical instrument-maker and was especially known for his orreries. He was Instrument Maker to the Prince of Wales (later George II). On his retirement in 1748 he was succeeded by Benjamin Cole, whose firm in 1782 was absorbed by J. & E. Troughton. In successive partnerships with various other instrument-makers Wright published Joseph Harris's *Description and Use of the Globes and the Orrery* (First edition 1731) the twelfth edition of which was published by the Troughtons in 1783. Possibly John Wright, who was one of Cole's workmen in 1753 and who emigrated to Bristol and was later succeeded by Joshua Springer, was a relation.

Besides orreries Wright advertised a 'great choice of mathematical instruments ready made; as cases in silver, brass or ivory, surveying-instruments, sun-dials, weather-glasses . . .'[1]

[1] *Use of the Sector, Mathematical and Plain-Scale* (1746): this pamphlet is quoted by R. S. Clay and T. H. Court in an article entitled *English Instrument Making in the Eighteenth Century* (Edgar Allen News Vo. 31 June 1952).

HENRY WYNNE fl 1654 –d. 1709

Near the Sugar Loaf, Chancery Lane

WYNNE, sometimes spelt Wynn and even Win by contemporary writers, was a notable instrument-maker at the end of the seventeenth century. He was apprenticed to Ralph Greatorex who had made a weather-glass for Samuel Pepys in 1663.[1] He became a member of the Clockmakers' Company in 1662 and was Master in 1690. He stocked a wide variety of instruments ('any sort of mathematical instruments whether for sea or land') and Professor Taylor[2] mentions compasses, a microscope, a sector, a quadrant, dividers, weather-glasses etc.: like many makers he also sold explanatory leaflets with his instruments. Among his apprentices was Thomas Tuttell, one of whose extant trade cards illustrates a barometer among a mass of mathematical and surveying instruments (Plate 149).

According to Roger North[3] Wynne was persuaded to make mercurial weather-glasses by Francis North, Baron of Guilford and Charles II's Lord Chancellor, who was concerned that the instruments were 'rare, and confined to the cabinets of the virtuosi'. Guilford had first persuaded Henry Jones, the well-known clockmaker, to make and sell barometers but his interest soon waned because his 'business lay in other operations he was more used to': whereupon Guilford sent for Wynne who 'pursued the manufactory to great perfection, and his own no small advantage'. Wynne was therefore probably the first commercial maker to sell barometers in any numbers. I have argued in Chapter Two that he did this in about 1680.

Robert Hooke often visited Wynne's workshop and commissioned barometers from him. On 2 February 1678 there is an entry in Hooke's *Diary*—'Win about Sir S. Moreland barometer', possibly referring to Moreland's balance barometer which Wynne may have been constructing or would at least have been able to discuss with Hooke. Wynne appears in other *Diary* entries connected with Moreland's invention in 1678; and again on 6 October 1680 when Hooke says— 'Bid Win send Lord Ranalagh weather-glasses'.

[1] Ralph Greatorex (1625–1712) was an eminent instrument-maker at the Sign of Adam and Eve in the Strand. Pepys 'bespoke' a weather-glass of him on 22 September 1662 and records that on 23 March 1663 'This day Greatorex brought me a very pretty weather-glass for heat and cold'. This was clearly a thermometer and not a mercurial barometer: it was probably an air thermometer but the term 'weather-glass' was applied freely at this date to both open and sealed thermometers.

[2] Taylor *Mathematical Practitioners of Tudor and Stuart England* (1954) pp. 242–3.

[3] *Life of the Right Honourable Francis North* p. 295.

PART III

List of
Makers

IN spite of its inadequacies the following list of barometer 'makers' is the longest and most detailed list to have appeared in published sources. I hope it will be of use to collectors, dealers and historians as far as it goes: but it is of course very far from complete and many years of further accumulation and refinement will be needed before I can claim that it is as useful as I would like it to be.

The information comes principally from two sources. Trade and ordinary directories have been extensively consulted. I searched the London directories and several of the provincial ones myself but I am deeply grateful to a large number of local librarians all over the country who most kindly satisfied my importunate requests to search their local records for names which I could not otherwise trace. The second main source has been extant barometers. Most of these are examples which I have encountered in my travels but some belong to correspondents throughout the world who kindly sent me details of them. Other sources include contemporary literary references, advertisements, trade cards, rate records and very occasionally references found in modern secondary sources.

The list is strictly alphabetical. Each entry is composed, if it is available, of the following information:

1. Name of maker. If a name found on a barometer does not coincide precisely with a directory entry it is given separate mention in this list and I have referred to probable and possible correspondences. I had some difficulty with the spelling of some names in directories: where the directory had obviously made a mistake I disregarded the error but where there were clearly various valid ways of spelling a name I have recorded them. I have also recorded the various spelling of names on extant barometers.

2. Dates of the maker's life or activity. In some cases dates are woefully deficient but a few dates, even one, are better than none. In no case should 1860 be taken as a terminal date: several of the makers recorded here were active long after this date which is my own arbitrary choice as a terminal date for the present study.

In several cases I have mentioned that makers are recorded in G.H.Baillie's useful book *Watchmakers and Clockmakers of the World* (3rd edition 1951): Baillie guessed dates for many of them ('early 19c.' etc.) and I have repeated his guesses although the great majority seem to me to

be many years too early. For this reason I have put them in inverted commas.

3. Addresses at which the maker is recorded with the dates when he is known to have worked at them.

4. Occupations of the maker recorded in directories, trade cards, etc.

5. Any other relevant information about the maker.

6. Examples of extant barometers. Details of each instrument include type, size, wood and style of case, material of register plates, ancillary instruments, address of maker, etc. If an example is not one of the readily classifiable types of case I have ventured a brief description of it. If I have records of several extant examples of the same type I have referred only to one: it is pointless trying to assess whether or not a maker was prolific on the basis of present records and more important to indicate the type of work which he produced.

ABBREVIATIONS
The following abbreviations are used:

AB.	angle barometer	
AB(b).	angle barometer, bulb cistern	
app.	apprenticed	
b.	born	
bar.	barometer maker	
bow.	bow-fronted case	*(Plate 33)*
bp.	broken pediment	*(Plate 36)*
c.	circa	
CC.	Clockmakers' Company	
clo.	clockmaker; clock set above dial	*(Plate 45)*
colln.	collection	
d.	died	
DB.	double barometer	
fg.	flat dial glass	*(Plate 126)*
fl.	floruit	
g.	register plates protected by glass or glazed door	*(Plate 35)*
hc.	hemispherical cistern cover	*(Plate 78)*
hy.	hygrometer	
hycen.	hygrometer in centre of case	
hypl.	hygrometer on register plates	
hytop.	hygrometer at top of case	
inl.	wood inlays	
ivpl.	ivory register plates	
m.	mahogany	
math.instr.	mathematical instrument-maker	
MB.	marine barometer	
mi.	mirror set above dial	*(Plate 47)*
mop.	mother-of-pearl inlays	*(Plate 51)*
naut.instr.	nautical instrument-maker	
o.	oak	

opt. optician
opt.instr. optical instrument-maker
pat. case inlaid with paterae of
coloured woods *(Plate 126)*
phil.instr. philosophical instrument-maker
ppl. paper register plates
pt. pointed top *(Plate 50)*
rc. shallow turned cistern cover *(Plate 36)*
rt. rounded top *(Plate 20)*
rw. rosewood
SB. straight-tube or 'stick' barometer
SB(b). straight-tube or 'stick' barometer, bulb cistern
scroll pattern scroll mouldings at borders of case *(Plate 49)*
sp. scroll pediment *(Plate 45)*
sqb. squared base *(Plate 46)*
sqc. squared cistern cover *(Plate 35)*
sqp. square moulded pediment *(Plate 22)*
sw. satinwood
th. thermometer
thca. thermometer on trunk of case
thpl. thermometer on register plates
therm. thermometer maker
urn. urn-shaped cistern cover *(Plate 33)*
v. vernier
2v. two verniers
w. walnut
wa. watchmaker
WB. wheel barometer
WB-8. wheel barometer with 8″ dial
WB-10. wheel barometer with 10″ dial

Apart from these the usual abbreviations are used for makers' addresses (St, Ct, Pl, Gdns, etc.). Multiple addresses are numbered and a figure given in brackets after an example of a maker's work denotes that it was signed with a particular address. With the most common types of barometer I have made certain assumptions for the sake of brevity. Thus

(a) register plates are assumed to be of silvered brass unless otherwise described (ivpl., ppl., etc.)
(b) 'stick' barometers (SB) are assumed
    (i) to have a portable screw-type cistern unless stated otherwise
    (ii) to have a shallow turned cistern cover unless stated otherwise
    (iii) to be fitted with a vernier scale unless made before about 1750

    (iv) to have no thermometer or hygrometer unless stated.
(c) wheel barometers (WB-8., WB-10., etc.) are assumed
    (i) to be fitted in a 'banjo' style case (Plates 44–7 etc.)
    (ii) to have a convex glass unless stated to be 'fg.' or 'pat.'
    (iii) to be fitted in almost all cases with a hygrometer at the top, a thermometer above the dial and a level at the base. If stated to be 'pat.' or 'scroll pattern' only a thermometer can be assumed.

It may help at this stage to refer the reader to some of the Plates for a pictorial demonstration of this shorthand.

Pl. 36=SB(b).m.bp.thpl.   Pl. 126=WB-8.m.bp.pat.
Pl. 32=SB.m.sp.g.thca.hycen.   Pl. 47=WB-8.m.sp.mi.
Pl. 154=SB.m.sqp.urn.bow.g.   Pl. 46=WB-10.rw.sp.sqb.
Pl. 20=SB.m.rt.g.   Pl. 49=WB-10.w.scroll pattern

I have not on the whole used abbreviations for collections. The following however will be found:

Brit.Mus.   British Museum
Mus.   Museum (various)
Mus.Hist.Sc.   Museum of the History of Science, Oxford
Nat.Mar.Mus.   National Maritime Museum, Greenwich
Sc.Mus.   Science Museum, London.

Finally reference will be found to some secondary sources as follows:

Baillie: G. H. Baillie
     Watchmakers and Clockmakers of the World (3rd edition 1951)

Britten: F. J. Britten
     Old Clocks and Watches and their Makers (3rd edition 1911)

Daumas: Maurice Daumas
     Les Instruments Scientifiques aux XVIIe et XVIIIe Siècles (1953)

Middleton: W. E. K. Middleton
     The History of the Barometer (1964)

Taylor: E. G. R. Taylor
     The Mathematical Practitioners of Tudor and Stuart England (1954) or *The Mathematical Practitioners of Hanoverian England* (manuscript)

A

ABATTE, J.
WB-8.m.bp.fg.hycen.
Possibly—

ABATTE, J.
Peterborough
WB-10.m.sp.

ABEL, Thomas fl 1838–41
55 Ray St Clerkenwell London
Bar. therm., painter, glazier

ABRAHAM,
Liverpool
WB-8.rw.sp.sqb. SB.m.sqp.urn.bow.g.
2v.thca.
Probably—

ABRAHAM, Abraham and Co fl 1817–60
(1) 9–10 Lord St Liverpool 1817
(2) 84 Lord St 1837–49
(3) 20 Lord St 1841–60
Opt.math.instr.bar.

ABRAHAM and DANCER fl 1838–43
13 Cross St King St Manchester
*Opt.math.phil.instr.; one of the
partners was John Benjamin Dancer*
SB.m.sqp.urn.bow.g.2v.thca.

ABRAHAM, E.
Exeter
Opt.
SB.m.pt.g.

ABRAHAM, J.
Liskeard
WB-8.m.sp.
*Baillie records a Joseph Abraham, wa.,
Liskeard 'early 19c.'*

ABRAHAM, Jacob fl 1805–41
(1) 1 St Andrews Terrace Bath 1809
(2) 7 Bartlett St Bath 1819
(3) 'adjoining Thompson's Pump
Room' Cheltenham 1833
*Opt.math.instr. to HRH the Duke of
Gloucester and His Grace the
Duke of Wellington*
SB.m.rt.

ADAMS
Fleet St
*Several barometers survive with this
signature and can be attributed to
Dudley or possibly George Adams (2).*

ADAMS, Dudley p 105

ADAMS, G.
Fleet St
One of the George Adams

ADAMS, George (1) p 110

ADAMS, George (2) p 115

ADAMSON
London
SB.m.sqp.urn.bow.g. WB-10.m.bp.inl.
clo.

ADAMSON and Co
London
WB-10.m.sp.mi. WB-10.m.bp.clo.

ADIE, Alexander p 119

ADIE, R.
Bold St Liverpool
SB.m.rt.rc.g.thca.
*Probably Richard Adie
Opt.math.phil.instr.
(1) 26 Bold St Liverpool 1835–7
(2) 55 Bold St 1841–60*

ADIE, Richard fl 1837–60
(1) 58 Princes St Edinburgh 1835–42
(2) 50 Princes St Edinburgh 1843–60
*Opt.instr.; in partnership with his
father Alexander Adie 1835–58*

ADIE and Son fl 1835–60
(1) 58 Princes St Edinburgh 1835–42
(2) 50 Princes St Edinburgh 1843–60
*Opt.instr.; partnership of Alexander
Adie and his son Richard. The elder
man d. 1858. A large number of
barometers survive signed 'Adie and
Son' including SBs in narrow
mahogany cases with rounded or
triangular or square tops; also*
SB.m.urn.bow.g.

AGNEW, Thomas b. 1794—fl 1841
(1) 94 Market St Manchester 1810–26
(2) 10 Exchange St Manchester
1826–32
(3) 18 Exchange St Manchester 1834
(4) 14 Exchange St Manchester 1841
*Clo.bar., artists' materials, pictures,
china; born in Liverpool, app. to
Vittore Zanetti 1810 and became his
partner 1817 (Zanetti and Agnew). In
partnership with Zanetti's son 1825–34
(Agnew and Zanetti) but alone by
1835; founder of Thomas Agnew and
Sons Ltd.*

AGNEW and ZANETTI fl 1825–34
(1) 94 Market St Manchester 1826
(2) 10 Exchange St Manchester
1826–32
(3) 18 Exchange St Manchester 1834
Clo.bar., artists' materials, etc.;

*partnership of Thomas Agnew and
son of Vittore Zanetti, possibly
Joseph Zanetti who was later at
100 King St Manchester 1841*
SB(b).m.bp.g.thpl. WB-12.m.sp.
SB.m.sqp.urn.bow.g.

AIANO

SB(b).m.bp.g.hytop; WB-8.m.rt.pat.;
WB-10.m.rt.pat.painted dial

AIANO, Charles fl 1826–41
    (1) 9 Northgate, Canterbury 1826–8
    (2) Northgate Canterbury 1841
    (3) 90–1 Northgate Canterbury
    *Opt.bar.therm.clo. 'at the sign of
    the Providence'*
    SB(b).m.bp.g.thpl.(3) WB-8.m.bp.
    pat.(3) WB-8.m.sp.mi.(3)

ALBERTI, A.
    WB-8.m.bp.pat.
    Probably—

ALBERTI, Angelo fl 1822–5
    Fargate Sheffield
    Bar

ALBINO
   •   Cheltenham
    WB-8.m.sp.mi.

ALBINO, John fl 1839–60
    (1) 47 St John St West Smithfield
        London 1839–49
    (2) 63 Hatton Gdn London 1850–60
    Looking-glasses, bar.

ALFIERI
    Manchester
    WB-8.m.bp.pat.

ALFIERI, P.
    Halifax
    WB-8.m.rt.fg.

AMADIO, A.
    Ashby-de-la-Zouch
    AB in walnut case in style of
    Charles Orme, dated 1736; probably
    repaired and re-signed by Amadio

AMADIO, F.
    (1) 118 St John St Rd
    (2) 2 St John St Rd
    WB-8.m.rt.fg.inl.(1) WB-10.m.sp.
    sqb.(1 and 2) WB-10.m.sp.(2)
    WB-4.rw.sp.sb.(1)
    See Francis Amadio

AMADIO, F. fl 1840–60
    (1) 63 Moorgate London 1840–1
    (2) 35 Moorgate London 1842–51
    (3) 5 Cowpers Ct London 1852–60
    (4) 5 Birchin Lane London 1852–60

Opt.
WB-12.m.sp.fg.clo. (signed Cummins,
London) (1)

AMADIO, F. and Son
    118 St John St Rd
    WB-10.sw.sp.
    See Francis Amadio

AMADIO, Francis fl 1820–44
    (1) 10 St John St Rd London 1820–8
    (2) 118 St John St Rd London 1829–44
    *Artificial flowers., bar.phil.instr.;
    in partnership for some years at (2)
    with a son, possibly F. Amadio of
    63 Moorgate (Amadio & Son)*

AMADIO, J.
    17a Telegraph St Moorgate St London
    SB.m.sqp.g.ivpl.thca.
    *Possibly J. Amadio, opt.,
    (1) 6 Shorters Ct Throgmorton St
        London 1846–53
    (2) 7 Throgmorton St London 1854–60*

AMADIO and SON,
    118 St John St Rd
    WB-8.m.sp. WB-10.m.sp.sqb.inl.
    WB-10.m.sp.sqb.brass pillars—colln
    English, Scottish &
    Australian Bank Ltd.
    See Francis Amadio

AMBROSINI and MANZINI
    Portsea
    WB-8.m.bp.pat.

ANDERSON, F.
    Gravesend
    WB-10.m.sp.

ANDREWS
    Royston
    SB.m.
    *Baillie records a W. H. Andrews, clo.,
    'circa 1790'*

ANONE, Frs.
    Holborn London
    WB-8.m.rt.pat.
    See Francis Anone

ANONE, Francis fl 1802–8
    (1) 242 High Holborn London
    (2) 82 High Holborn London
    (3) 26 High Holborn London 1802–8
    *Prints, telescopes, bar.therm.; no trace
    in directories of (1) or (2) but
    Caesar Tagliabue was at (3) by 1809*
    WB-8.m.bp.pat.(1 and 2)

APRILE, J.
    WB-8.m.sp.mi. WB-10.m.sp. SB.m.rt.
    Possibly—

APRILE, Josh
Sudbury
WB-8.m.bp.pat. WB-10.m.sp.

ARNABOLDI
Lincoln
WB-8.m.sp.
See Lewis Arnaboldi

ARNABOLDI, Lewis   fl 1835
Steep Hill Lincoln
Bar.therm.

ARNOLDI, D.
Gloucester
WB-8.m.bp.pat.

ARZONI, G.
Canterbury
WB-8.rw.sp.mi. WB-6.m.sp.sqb.

ASH, M.
WB-8.rw.sp.
Probably—

ASH, Moses   fl 1856–60
(1) 36½ Tower St Birmingham 1856
(2) 75 Dale End Birmingham 1860
Bar.opt.

ATKIN
Alford Lincoln
WB-8.m.sp.mi.

ATKINS and Co
WB-8.m.sp.mi.

AUGUSTUS
Falmouth
WB-8.m.bp.pat.
Probably John Anthony Augustus,
math.instr., Church St Falmouth 1830

AYSCOUGH, J.
London
See James Ayscough

AYSCOUGH, James p 119

B

BAILEY, S.
Newcastle-upon-Tyne
SB.rw.rt.g.ivpl.

BAILEY, T.
Stanion
SB(b).m.bp.sqc.ppl. fluted pillars to
hood

BAKER
Shrewsbury
SB.m.rt.rc.g.thpl.

Probably William Baker, silversmith,
Market Sq Shrewsbury 1835

BAKER, Henry   fl 1848–58
90 Hatton Gdn London
Opt.phil.instr.bar.therm.

BALERNA, D.
WB-8.rw.sp.sqb.

BALERNA, L.
Halifax
WB-8.m.sp.mi. SB(b).m.bp.sqc.ppl.
plain pillars to hood
Probably Lewis Balerna, silversmith
(1) 8 Northgate St Halifax 1841
(2) 44 Northgate St Halifax 1842–7
(3) 71 Northgate St Halifax 1853

BALLARD
Cranbrook
WB-8.m.sp.sqb.mi.
Baillie records a Ballard, Cranbrook,
wa., 'early 19c.'

BALLARD
Lamberhurst
WB-8.m.sp.mi.
Probably Jas. Ballard, wa., Lamberhurst
1826–8

BALLARD, T.
SB(b).m.bp.g.thpl.
Possibly Thomas Ballard, 13 Charles St
Hatton Gdn London 1805

BALLARINI, P.
York
WB-8.m.sp.sqb.mi.
Probably Peter Ballarini, Kings Staith
York, b. 1801–d.1858: see
Cattaneo and Co

BANCE
Hungerford
WB-10. set in a late eighteenth-
century mahogany bookcase to the
left of the mirrored doors and
matched on the right by a clock
(signed by John Nethercott, Long
Compton): one pierced brass hand
with indicating arrows at each end,
the upper half of the engraved dial
giving summer indications and the
lower half winter. Colln J. McGarva,
sold Sotheby's 15 November 1963
Probably Matthew Bance, wa.,
Hungerford 1793–7

BANCKS, Robert   fl 1796–1834
(1) 440–1 Strand London
(2) 119 New Bond St London 1820–34
Opt. to the Prince of Wales, later

*George IV: in partnership with a son
from 1820 (Bancks and Son).
Barometers survive signed
'Banks 440–1 Strand'*

BANCKS and Son fl 1820–34
119 New Bond St London
'*Instrument makers and Opticians to
His Majesty*'.
Partnership of Robert Bancks and a son
WB-10.m.sp.sqb. WB-12.m.sp.sqb.

BANDOCK, C.
London
WB-8.m.sp.mi.

BANKS
440–1 Strand
SB.m.
See Robert Bancks

BARBON
21 Panton St Haymarket
SB(b).m.bp.g.

BARBON, S. and Co
Edinburgh
SB.m.sp.g.
*Taylor records a Peter Barbon,
opt.instr., at three addresses 1809–10
who may have been a predecessor*

BARELLA and Co
Newcastle
WB-8.m.sp.mi.

BARELLI, Jno, and Co
Bath
SB(b).m.bp.g.thpl. WB-8.m.bp.pat.

BARELLI, Josh, and Co
Reading
SB(b).m.bp.g.thpl.

BARINE, P.
York
SB(b).m.bp.g.thpl.

BARKER
Wigan
WB. set in door of long case
astronomical clock—*Connoisseur*
July 1911, A. J. Hawkes *Clockmakers
of Wigan* (1950) pp 45–51.
*Attributed to William Barker, clo.,
Wigan 1747–86 d.1786(?)*

BARNARDA, P. fl 1803–11
22 West St West Smithfield London
Bar., looking-glasses
WB-8.m.bp.pat.

BARNARDA, P. and Co
SB(b).m.bp.g.
Probably P. Barnarda

BARNASCHINA
Newcastle on Tyne
SB(b).m.bp.g.thpl.
Probably Francis Barnasconi

BARNASCHINA, Anthony
Gravesend
WB-8.m.bp.pat.
*Probably Anthony Barnaschina,
telescopes, cutlery etc.,
New Road Gravesend 1826–8*

BARNASCHONE
Devizes
WB-8.m.bp.fg.

BARNASCHONE, Chas.
Boston
WB-8.m.bp.pat.
*Possibly a relation of
Andrew Barnascone*

BARNASCHONI and MONTHI
WB-8.m.bp.pat.
See Bernaschoni and Monthi

BARNASCONE
Leeds
WB-8.m.bp.pat. WB-10.m.sp.
Possibly M. Barnascone

BARNASCONE, A.
WB-8.m.bp.pat.
Probably—

BARNASCONE, Andrew fl 1822
High St Boston
Bar.

BARNASCONE, G. B.
14 St Michaels Sq Southampton
SB.m.g.

BARNASCONE, J. and Co
London
WB-8.m.bp.pat.

BARNASCONE, M., *also spelt Bernasconi*
Leeds
WB-8.m.sp. WB-8.m.sp.mi.
WB-10.m.sp.mi. WB-10.m.sp.mop

BARNASCONI, F.
Newcastle
WB-8.m.rt.fg.
Probably—

BARNASCONI, Francis fl 1827–58
(1) 34 The Side Newcastle 1827–34
(2) 16 Groat Market Newcastle 1838
(3) 28 Groat Market Newcastle 1841
(4) 29 Groat Market Newcastle 1844
(5) 20 High Bridge Newcastle 1847–53
(6) 35 High Bridge Newcastle 1855–8

*Opt.bar.; also spelt Barnesconi in
directories, and named Barnesconi and
Son in 1841, 1844, 1853*

BARNASCONI, L.
Sheffield
WB-8.m.sp.sqb.mi WB-10.rw.sp.mi.
Probably Lewis Barnasconi, hardware
(1) 42 Burgess St Sheffield 1833–7
(2) 23 Waingate Sheffield 1834–41
(3) 19 Waingate Sheffield 1841

BARNASCONI and Son
See Francis Barnasconi

BARNETT, T.
SB.m.
Probably—

BARNETT, Thomas b. 1768 –d.1810
(1) 21 East St Lambeth 1789
(2) 61 Great Tower St London
*Opt.math.phil.instr.; instr.maker to
H.M. Boards of Customs and Excise;
trade card advertised 'Barometers for
indicating the approach of a storm at
sea, and other barometers, either
diagonal, wheel, standard, or portable'*
(Sc.Mus.London)

BASERGA, F. and Co
Ipswich
WB-8.m.bp.pat.

BASS
Northampton
WB-8.m.sp.mi.
*Probably George Bass, wa. and clo.,
Scarlet Well St Northampton 1841*

BASSNETT, James fl 1834–60
(1) 1 Roberts St Liverpool 1834–51
(2) 58 Roberts St Liverpool 1857
(3) 8 Roberts St Liverpool 1857–60
*Opt.wa. and clo. naut.instr.bar.therm.
charts etc.; in partnership with a son
1857–60 (Bassnett and Son)*

BASSNETT and Son
Liverpool
WB-8.rw.sp.mi.
See James Bassnett

BASTARD, William
WB.m. fretwork decoration, square
dial with chapter ring

BATCH, J.
Chichester
WB-8.m.sp.mi.

BATE
London
SB.m.sp.hytop. MB.-Sc.Mus.London

MB.-Mus.Hist.Sc.Oxford
*Probably Robert Brettell Bate,
opt.math.instr., fl 1807–49*
(1) 17 Poultry Cheapside London
(2) 20–1 Poultry Cheapside London

BATES
Kettering
WB-8.m.bp.pat. WB-8.m.sp.mi.
*Baillie records a John Bates, wa.,
Kettering, fl 1768–1800, possibly a
relation*

BATTISTESSA and Co
Edinburgh
WB-8.m.sp.mi.

BATTISTESSA and Co fl 1830–43
(1) 13 Baldwins Gdns London 1830–3
(2) 106 Hatton Gdn London 1840–3
*Looking-glasses, bar.therm.; in 1834
the firm was called Battistessa, Molteni
and Guanziroli and in 1835–6 Zerboni,
Battistessa, Molteni and Guanziroli
(see Anthony Zerboni): by 1845
G. and L. Guanziroli at (2)*

BATTISTESSA, MOLTENI and
GUANZIROLI fl 1834
13 Baldwins Gdns London
See Battistessa and Co

BEARETTI, Peter fl 1833
26 Great Bath St Clerkenwell
Bar.therm.

BEDWELL, Thomas fl 1825–49
*(1) Leman St Goodmans Field
London 1825*
(2) 53 Great Alie St London 1834–45
(3) 3–4 Little Alie St London 1846–9
Bar.therm.

della BELLA
Preston
WB-10.m.sp.mi. WB-12.rw.rt.mop.

BELLATTI, C.
Burton
WB-8.m.rt.pat.

BELLATTI, L.
Lincoln
WB-8.m.sp.mi.
*Probably Louis S. Bellatti, wa. and clo.,
34 Steep Hill Lincoln 1856: see also
L. Bellatti, Grantham, and Bellatti and
Son, Newark*

BELLATTI, L.
Grantham
WB-8.m.sp.sqb. WB-6.m.sp.sqb.
Probably Lewis Bellatti, opt.jeweller,

*High St Grantham 1822: possibly
identifiable with L. Bellatti, Lincoln*

BELLATTI and Son
Newark
WB.
*Possibly a relation of L. Bellatti,
Lincoln*

BELLONI, F.
WB-8.rw.sp.mi.

BELLOTTI and GUGERI
See Belotti and Gugeri

BELOTTI and GUGERI
15 Upper Union Ct Holborn
WB-10.m.sp.
See Belotti and Gugeri, Andrew

BELOTTI and GUGERI, Andrew fl 1829–36
(1) 15 Upper Union Ct Holborn
London 1829
(2) 16 Charles St Hatton Gdn
London 1830–6
*Looking-glasses, bar.therm.; became
Gugeri and Belotti by 1838 but the
names seem to have been
interchangeable before this date.
Belotti also spelt Bellotti. See also
Andrew Gugeri*

BENHAM, John
Collumpton
WB-10.m.sp.sb.
*Baillie records a John Benham, clo.,
Cullompton '18c.'*

BENNETT
Kettering
WB-8.m.sp.mi.
*Probably Anthony Bennett, clo.,
High St Kettering 1841*

BENNETT
London
Probably—

BENNETT, John p 121

BENTLEY, Thomas
Darlington
SB.m. the plates and cistern cover
each mounted on an oval frame,
the tube protected by a fluted column
*Baillie records a Bentley, clo. and wa.,
Darlington 1766*

BERGE
SB.m.sqp.urn.bow.g. ('late Ramsden'):
MB. ('late Ramsden')—Nat.Mar.Mus.
SB.m.rt.urn.g. SB.m.sqp.urn.bow.g.
thca. ('late Ramsden')
Probably Matthew Berge

BERGE
London
SB.m.urn.bow.g.
Probably Matthew Berge

BERGE, John b. c. 1742 –d.1808
(1) 59 St Paul's Churchyard London
1756
(2) Johnson Ct Fleet St London 1791
(3) 3 Crane Ct Fleet St London
1797–1803
(4) 26 Lower Eaton St Pimlico 1805–7
*Opt.math.phil.instr.; app. to
Peter Dollond 1756, Spectaclemakers'
Co. 1773. According to Taylor he was
Jesse Ramsden's chief workman and
successor: he was undoubtedly among
Ramsden's workmen in 1791 but
Ramsden was succeeded by
Matthew Berge*

BERGE, M.
London
SB.m.sqp.urn.bow.g.thca.
Probably—

BERGE, Matthew fl 1802 –d.1819
199 Piccadilly
*Opt.math.phil.instr.; succeeded
Jesse Ramsden (Berge 'late Ramsden').
His name appears in directories until
1830 but rate books of 1820 mention
his executors. See Berge and M. Berge,
London*

BERGNA, J. B. fl 1841
St Nicholas Churchyard Newcastle .
Bar.

BERI, G.
WB-10.m.sp.mi.

BERNASCHONI and MONTHI
Leicester
WB-8.m.bp.pat. SB(b).m.bp.
*Probably identifiable with
Barnaschoni and Monthi*

BERNASCONI, M.
Leeds
WB-8.rw.pt.mi.
See M. Barnasconi Leeds

BERRINGER
London
SB(b).m.bp.g.thpl.

BERRINGTON, J.
Leicester
WB-8.m.bp.pat.
*Probably John Berrington, furniture
brokers, High St Leicester 1822*

BERRY, D.
Huntingdon
WB-8.m.sp.sqb.

BERRY, J.
12 Little Chapple St Soho
WB-10.m.sp.

BERRY, J.
78 Wardover St Soho
WB-10.m.pt.

BERRY, John
Manchester
AB(b).w.case with moulded border
Probably—

BERRY, John fl 1738–d.1765
The Dial near the Cross Manchester
*Wa., jewellery, bar.; published and
printed the* Lancashire Journal
*1738–41 and a map of Manchester
and Salford 1741. Succeeded by his
widow and sons*

BESOZZI, B.
Weymouth
WB-8.m.bp.pat.

BETTALLY
London
SB(b).m.rt.rc.g.thpl.
Probably C. Bettally

BETTALLY, C.
London
WB. and companion th.1787
(Plates 42, 43)
Probably—

BETTALLY, C. fl 1787–8
(1) 1 Charlotte St Pimlico London
1787
(2) 292 Oxford St opposite Stratford
Place 1788
*Trade cards describe him as a
'Constructor of all sorts of barometers,
thermometers, hydrometers and all
sorts of phisical instruments of glass'
(Banks Colln, Brit.Mus.) (Plate 30):
also had a shop in Paris. Daumas
records a Betalli in Paris 1807. See
Plates 42, 43*

BEVAN, E.
MB.

BIANCHI
Ipswich
WB-8.m.bp.pat.
Probably George Bianchi

BIANCHI
Manchester

WB-8.m.bp.

BIANCHI, B.
Portsmouth
WB-8.m.bp.pat.

BIANCHI, B.
Tunbridge Wells
WB-8.m.sp.mi.

BIANCHI, G.
SB(b).m.bp.g. WB-8.m.bp.pat.
*Either G. Bianchi, Edinburgh, or
George Bianchi, Ipswich*

BIANCHI, G.
Edinburgh
SB(b).m.bp.g.

BIANCHI, G.
Ipswich
WB-8.m.bp.
Probably—

BIANCHI, George fl 1805–16
(1) St Clements St Ipswich 1805–8
(2) Westgate St Ipswich 1809–16
Bar.

BIANCHI, P.
Lane End
WB-8.m.sp.mi.

BIANCHI, V.
Dublin
WB-12.m.sp.clo.

BIOLO, B.
Norwich
WB-8.m.sp.

BIRD
London
Probably—

BIRD, John p 122

BIRD, Thomas fl 1856–60
39 Charles St Hatton Gdn London
*Bar.; succeeded Teodoro Franco.
William Hinton, frame-maker, also at
this address 1856–60*

BISHOP
Sherborne
WB-10.m.sp.mi.
*Probably John Bishop, silversmith, wa.
clo., Cheap St Sherborne 1816–30*

BITHRAY, S.
Royal Exchange
SB.m.sqp.urn.bow.g.thca.
*Probably Stephen Bithray, opt.,
North Gate 29 Royal Exchange, London
1827–60 who was noted for his
microscopes*

BLACKBOURN, Cuthbert fl 1847–8
    (1) 34 Hatton Gdn London 1847–8
    (2) 7 Alfred St City Rd London 1848
    Bar.therm.; in partnership with
    William Johnson 1847–8 (Johnson and
    Blackbourn)

BLUNT
    London
    See Thomas Blunt

BLUNT, Thomas p 123

BOGGAIA, D. fl 1839
    29½ Gt Warner St London
    Bar.therm.

BOLONGARO, Dominic fl 1817–60
    (1) 2 Old Millgate Manchester
        1817–30
    (2) 14 Market St Manchester 1832–3
    (3) 32 Market St Manchester 1834–54
    (4) 30–2 Market St Manchester
        1855–60
    Carver, gilder, printseller, 'ladies'
    repository for fancy painting' (1817),
    looking-glass and picture-frame maker
    (1819), bar. (1843): in partnership
    with his son Peter by 1848
    (Bolongaro and Son)
    WB-10.m.rt.(3)

BOLONGARO, Peter fl 1848–60
    See Bolongaro and Son

BOLONGARO and Son fl 1848–60
    (1) 32 Market St Manchester 1848–54
    (2) 30–2 Market St Manchester
        1855–60
    Carvers, gilders, bar.therm., artists'
    colourmen, picture restorers; described
    in 1855 as 'printsellers and publishers
    to the Queen'. Partnership of
    Dominic and Peter Bolongaro

BOMBELLI, Baldisaro fl 1828–34
    6 King St Whitehaven
    Bar.

BOND
    Okehampton
    WB-8.rw.sp.mi.

BOND, John
    WB-8.m.bp.pat.

BORBIDGE, Charles fl 1834
    1 King St Whitehaven
    WB-10.m.sp.

BORDER, G.
    Sleaford
    WB-8.m.sp.
    Probably George Border, wa. and clo.,

    (1) Sleaford 1816
    (2) Northgate Sleaford 1841

BORDESA, Peter fl 1834–60
    33 Bridge St Row Chester
    Jeweller, 'original bazaar, dealer in
    toys and fancy goods, manufacturer of
    weather glasses etc. . . . barometers
    and thermometers sold and repaired'
    (1846). See P. Bordessa

BORDESSA and EATON fl 1855–60
    (1) 54 Exmouth St Clerkenwell
        London 1855
    (2) 87 Hatton Gdn London 1856–60
    Bar.therm.; previously Novati,
    Bordessa and Eaton

BORDESSA, P.
    Chester
    WB-8.m.sp.sqb.mi.
    Probably Peter Bordesa

BORDOLI and CASSAROTI
    Stampford
    WB-8.m.bp.pat.

BORDOLI, P.
    22 Charles St Hatton Gdn
    WB-10.m.sp.mi. WB-6.m.sp.sqb.

BORELLI, Anthony fl 1852–60
    (1) 14 Leather Lane London 1852–4
    (2) 7 Gt Warner St London 1855–60
    Looking-glasses, bar.therm.

BORELLI, G.
    WB-10.rw.pt.mop.
    Possibly Gaetano Borelli, wa., Reading
    who worked after 1860

BORINI, P.
    WB-8.m.sp. WB-8.m.bp.pat.
    SB(b).m.bp.

BOSETTI, Francis fl 1851–8
    5 Wardrobe Place London
    Bar.therm. (1851), but later listed in
    directories as a boarding house

BOSSI, L.
    Hastings
    WB-8.m.sp.fg.

BOSSI, P.
    Rayleigh
    WB-10.m.sp.sqb.

BOUFFLER, Robert fl 1839
    7 Bell Ct Grays Inn Lane London
    Bar.therm.

BOURN, P. fl 1839
    40 Bull St Birmingham
    Bar.

BOVERI, Francis fl 1830–41
9 Eyre St Hill London
Bar.therm., looking-glasses, crown glass; also spelt Bouveri and Bouverie in directories
WB-8.m.bp.

BOWLEY
Salop
WB-8.m.bp.pat. WB.m.sp.with square dial at top of case (*cf.* Plate 48)
Probably—

BOWLEY, William fl 1809–16
Wyle Cop Shrewsbury
*Engraver; trade card describes him as 'Bowley, engraver, glass stainer, painter and printer, barometer and thermometer manufacturer' (Fitzwilliam Mus., Cambridge).
See Bowley, Salop*

BOYER, J. H.
WB-8.m.sp.mi.

BRABY
Tunbridge Wells
WB-8.rw.pt.mi.

BRACEGIRDLE
London
PB.m.g. on tripod feet

BRAENDLIN, Francis A. fl 1860
32 Newman St London
Phil.instr.bar.therm.

BRAGAZZI, A. and J.
Ashburn
WB-8.m.bp.pat.
Probably members of the Bregazzi family

BRAGONZI, P.
WB-8.m.sp.mi.

BRAHAM
Torquay
WB-6.m.sp.
Baillie records a James Braham, clo., Torquay 'early 19c.', 'clockmaker to the Duchess of Clarence'

BRAHAM, John fl 1830–56
(1) 42 College Green Bristol 1830
(2) 8 Pulteney Bridge Bath 1833
(3) 10 St Augustines Parade Bristol 1833–42
(4) 5 York Bldgs Bath 1837
(5) 17 St Augustines Parade Bristol 1856
Opt.math.instr.

SB(b).m.bp.g.(1) WB-8.m.sp.(1)

BREGAZZI
Derby
WB-8.m.rt.th. on dial
Probably S. Bregazzi & Co

BREGAZZI
Nottingham
WB-8.m.bp.pat. WB-8.m.sp.mi.

BREGAZZI, Innocent and Peter fl 1825–34
High Pavement Nottingham
Carvers, gilders, bar.; advertised SB and WB in 1825 directory (Plate 38). By 1840 Peter Bregazzi on his own at Bridlesmith Gate

BREGAZZI, J. P. and T.
High Pavement Nottingham
WB-10.m.sp.mi.
Probably Innocent and Peter Bregazzi

BREGAZZI, J.
Dursley
WB-10.m.sp.

BREGAZZI, P.
Nottingham
WB-8.m.sp. WB-8.m.sp.with clo. in square case above dial and th. in place of level
Probably—

BREGAZZI, Peter fl 1825–42
(1) High Pavement Nottingham 1825–34
(2) Bridlesmith Gate Nottingham 1840–2
Carver, gilder, bar., looking-glasses; in partnership with Innocent Bregazzi 1825–34 (Innocent and Peter Bregazzi)

BREGAZZI, S.
Derby
WB-8.m.bp.pat.
See S. Bregazzi & Co

BREGAZZI, S.
Darby
WB-10.m.bp.
See S. Bregazzi and Co

BREGAZZI, S. and Co
Derby
WB-10.m.sp.fg.
Probably—

BREGAZZI, S. and Co fl 1809
Willow Row Derby
Bar.

BROGGI
Chelmsford

SB(b).m.bp.g.
Probably Gillando Broggi

BROGGI, G.
Chelmsford
WB-8.m.bp.pat. WB-10.m.sp.
WB-10.m.sp.clo.
Probably—

BROGGI, Gillando fl 1826–8
Moulsham Chelmsford
*Math.instr.bar.; also spelt Browgi in
directories; see also Broggi, G. Broggi,
G. Broggio, G. Brogi*

BROGGIO, G.
Chelmsford
WB-10.m.sp.mi.
See Gillando Broggi

BROGI, G.
WB-10.m.sp.
Probably Gillando Broggi

BROSONI, M.
Brighton
WB-10.rw.sp.sqb.mop.

BROWGI, Gillando
Chelmsford
See Gillando Broggi

BROWN, John fl 1648–95
(1) Dukes Palace London
(2) Sphere and Sun Dyal, Minories
*A well-known math.instr.; noted for
barometers among many other
instruments (Taylor)*

BRUGGER, Lorenz and A. fl 1843–4
79 High Holborn London
*Bar.therm., looking-glasses; became
Brugger and Straub 1845*

BRUGGER and HOFFMEYER fl 1822
Norfolk St Lynn Regis
Clo.bar.

BRUGGER and STRAUB fl 1845–60
79 High Holborn London
*Bar.therm.; succeeded Lorenz and
A. Brugger; described in 1856 as
'German and French clock and
watchmakers, dealers in organs and
musical boxes'*

BRUNNER, I.
Birmingham
WB-8.m.sp.
Probably—

BRUNNER, Ignatius fl 1849–60
66 Edgbaston St Birmingham
Bar.

BRYSON
Edinburgh
WB-8.rw. ('Opt'.)
Probably-

BRYSON, James M. fl 1850–60
(1) 65 Princes St Edinburgh 1850–3
(2) 24 Princes St Edinburgh 1854
(3) 60 Princes St Edinburgh 1855–60
Opt.
SB.o.rt.rc.g.2v.(3)

BUCHAN, L.
*Taylor mentions a portable barometer
in the Edinburgh Royal Mus.*

BUCHANAN, A.
WB-8.m.sp.

BUDD
Banbury
WB-8.m.sp.mi.

BULL
Bedford
WB-8.m.sp.mi.
*Baillie records a John Bull, Bedford
'early 19c.'*

BULL, William
Stratford Essex
SB(b).m.bp.g.
*Baillie records a William Bull, clo.,
Stratford fl 1770–1804*

BULLA, A.
Exeter
WB-8.m.bp.pat.
Probably one of the partners of—

BULLA, GRASSI and FONTANA fl 1830
134 Fore St Exeter
*Bar.; two of the partners were probably
A. Bulla and B. Fontana; see also
Grasi and Fontana*

BULLOCK
WB-8.m.sp.

BURNETT
Durham
WB-10.rw.pt.

BURNS
Epsom
SB(b).m.rt.ivpl.

BURTON
London
SB.m.bp.rc.g.thca.hytop—Gloucester
Mus.
Possibly George Burton

BURTON, G.
> SB(b).m.rt.rc.
> *Probably—*

BURTON, George fl 1772–1815
> 136 High St Borough Southwark
> *Taylor records that Burton instruments were mentioned in several ships' lists and several, including two portable barometers, were used on Cook's second voyage 1772. On his S. American voyage 1792 William Gooch also carried a portable barometer by Burton. See G. Burton*

BURTON, Mark fl 1730–50
> Euclid's Head near the New Church Strand London
> *Math.phil.opt.instr.; his trade card also advertised 'all sorts of barometers and thermometers'—Westminster City Library Box 63 no. 2E (Gardner Colln). Taylor records that he worked for John Bird and suggests that Jesse Ramsden may have worked for him*

BUTTI
> Taunton
> WB-8.m.sp.mi.
> *Possibly Joseph Butti, hardware*
> (*1*) *East St Taunton 1830*
> (*2*) *Silver St Taunton 1840, reported insolvent 1842*

BUTTI, BARNASCHINA and Co
> Newcastle on Tyne
> WB-8.m.bp.
> *Francis Barnasconi worked at Newcastle*

BUTTI, L.
> Edinburgh
> WB-8.m sp.

BYRNE, Arthur Ethelbert fl 1853–60
> (1) 7½ Fountain Ct Strand London 1853–8
> (2) Savoy St 1859–60
> *Opt.bar.therm.*

BYWATER, John, DAWSON and Co
> fl 1819–35
> 20 Pool Lane Liverpool
> *Opt.math.naut.instr.; agents for Alexander Adie's sympiesometers*

C

CAGNI, I.
> WB-8.m.bp.pat.

CAIL, John
> SB.m.sqp.rc.2v.thca.
> *Probably John Cail, opt.*
> (*1*) *2 New Bridge St Newcastle 1825–37*
> (*2*) *44 Northumberland St Newcastle 1838–9*
> (*3*) *61 Pilgrim St Newcastle 1841–53*
> (*4*) *45 Quay St Newcastle 1841–53*
> (*5*) *21 Grey St Newcastle 1855–8:*
> *in partnership with S. A. Cail 1851–3*

CAIRNS
> 12 Waterloo Rd Liverpool
> WB-8.rw.mop.

CALDERARA, S.
> London
> WB-12.rw.sp.sqb.mop.clo.
> *Probably—*

CALDERARA, Serapheno fl 1831–60
> (*1*) *16 Kirby St London 1831–3*
> (*2*) *78 Leather Lane London 1834–51*
> (*3*) *42 Baldwins Gdns London 1852–60*
> (*4*) *2 Kings Terrace Bagnigge Wells Rd London 1854–5*
> *Bar.therm.*

CALLAGHAN
> SB.m.rt.ivpl.

CALLCOTT, John
> Cotton
> WB-10.m.sp.

CAMINADA, L.
> Manchester
> WB-8.m.sp. WB-8.m.sp.mi.

CAMINADA, P.
> WB-8.m.bp.pat.
> *Probably—*

CAMINADA, P.
> Taunton
> WB-8.m.bp.pat. WB-8.m.bp.pat. the dial engraved with religious symbols WB-10.rw.sp.mi.

CAMOTTA
> Halifax
> WB-8.m.sp.
> *Probably—*

CAMOTTA, Richard fl 1830–41
> (1) 14 Bull Close Halifax 1830
> (2) 12 Bull Green Halifax 1841
> *Opt., carver, gilder, bar.therm.: a Mrs Ann Camotta, probably his widow, at 14 Bull Green 1860. See Camotta*

CAMOZZI, C.
> Bicester

WB-8.m.bp.pat. WB-8.m.sp.
WB-8.m.sp.mi.
Probably Charles Camozzi, jeweller,
toy dealer, wa. and clo.
(1) Market End Bicester 1830
(2) Market Place Bicester 1832–50.
Succeeded by Eleanor Camozzi, his
widow, 1852

CAMPBELL, John
6 South Castle St Liverpool
WB-8.m.rt.scroll pattern
Possibly a later address of
John Campbell, jeweller, 17 Temple
Bldgs Dale St Liverpool 1834

CAMPI, John
Wolverhampton
WB-10.rw.sp.mi.

CAMPIONI and Co
Edinburgh
WB-8.m.sp.mi.

CAMPONOVO
Oxford
WB-8.rw.pt.mi.
Probably—

CAMPONOVO, Angelo fl 1846
St Thomas's Parish Oxford
Bar.

CANOVA, Peter
Halesworth
WB-8.m.sp.

CANTI, C. A.
Malling Kent
WB-8.m.bp.pat.

CANTI, C. A., Jnr.
59 Shoe Lane Holborn
WB-12.m.sp.clo.

CANTI, C. A. and Son
WB-8.m.sp.mi.
See C. A. Canti

CAPADURO
Deal
WB.
Possibly Copoduro, but no such name
recorded at Deal so far

CAPELLA, David fl 1854
46 Pershore St Birmingham
Bar.

CAPELLA, L.
WB-8.m.sp.

CAPELLA, M.
WB-10.m.sp.
Possibly—

CAPELLA, Michael fl 1854
53 Edgbaston St Birmingham
Bar.

CAPPI, William fl 1844–50
11 Bakers Row Clerkenwell London
Bar.therm., 'barometer frame maker'
(1850)

CAPRANI, L.
Leicester
WB-8.m.sp.mi.

CARACIA, C.
Edenbridge
WB-8.m.sp.mi.

CARACIA, Joseph
Edenbridge
WB-8.m.sp.mi.

CARINALLI, J.
Gloucester
WB-8.m.sp.

CARIOLI, A.
WB-8.m.bp.pat.

CARMAN
London
Standing barometer in carved
mahogany Corinthian column with
brass wheel dial and single hand; a
watch mounted on two cast dolphins
in centre of dial. A similar but
anonymous frame is in Gloucester
Mus.

CARNOVA, P.
Charlesworth
WB-8.m.bp.pat.

CARPENTER, Philip fl 1817–37
(1) Bath Row Birmingham 1817
(2) 111 New St Birmingham 1829
(3) 33 Navigation St Birmingham 1829
(4) 24 Regent St London 1830–7
Opt.math.phil.instr.; his business was
called Carpenter and Westley in
Birmingham by 1835 and in London by
1838

CARPENTER and WESTLEY fl 1835–60
(1) 111 New St Birmingham 1835
(2) 24 Regent St London 1838
Opt.math.phil.instr., globes; founded by
Philip Carpenter. Several barometers
survive

CARSARTELLY
WB-8.m.rt.pat.
Probably a variation of Casartelli

CARTA, George fl 1839–52
252 High St Exeter
Opt.,jeweller, bar

CARUGHI, Paul fl 1839–60
(1) 15 Brook St London 1839
(2) 128 Holborn London 1841–3
(3) 16 Charles St Hatton Gdn London 1844–5
(4) 38 Brook St London 1846–7
(5) 139 High Holborn London 1852–60
Bar.therm.,plate glass; in partnership with Andrew Gugeri 1844–5 (Gugeri and Carughi); succeeded at (1) by John Cetta

CARY
London
SB.m.sp.urn.bow. SB.m.bp.rc.g.thca. MB—Gloucester Mus.; two SB with overflow devices in cisterns—Mus.Hist.Sc.Oxford; SB.m.sqp.urn.bow.g.
Either William Cary or his nephews George and John

CARY
181 Strand
SB.m.sp.g. MB—Mus.Hist.Sc. Oxford
Probably—

CARY, George and John fl 1821–59
(1) 86 St James St London
(2) 181 Strand London 1825–56
Globes; sons of John Cary the cartographer and nephews of William Cary whose business they assumed 1825, retaining his name. See Cary, London and Cary, 181 Strand

CARY, William b. 1759–d.1825
(1) 272 Strand London 1786
(2) 182 Strand London 1794
(3) 181 Strand London 1794–1825
Opt.math.instr.; brother of the cartographer John Cary and a pupil of Jesse Ramsden; Taylor records that he supplied monthly meteorological observations to the Philosophical Magazine. *See Cary, London*

CASA, C.
WB-8.m.sp.mi.

CASARTELLI
SB(b).m.sqc.ppl. with carved crest and pendant festoons of fruits and flowers on each side of trunk
Possibly Lewis Casartelli, Liverpool; a very similar barometer is recorded by Charles Molliner

CASARTELLI
Liverpool
WB-10.m.sp.sqb.
Probably Lewis Casartelli

CASARTELLI, A.
WB-10.m.sp.
Possibly—

CASARTELLI, Anthony and Joseph fl 1845–57
20 Duke St Liverpool
Opt.; probably sons of Lewis Casartelli. Another L. Casartelli at this address 1860

CASARTELLI, L.
Liverpool
WB-8.m.bp.pat.
Probably Lewis Casartelli

CASARTELLI, Lewis
Market St Manchester
SB(b).m.bp.g.thpl.

CASARTELLI, Lewis fl 1820–43
(1) 37 King St Liverpool 1820–32
(2) 132 Duke St Liverpool 1834–43
(3) 133 Duke St Liverpool 1834
(4) 20 Duke St Liverpool 1835
Opt.math.instr.bar.; succeeded by Anthony and Joseph Casartelli

CASELLA and Co
London
WB-10.m.sp.
Probably Louis Casella and Co

CASELLA, L.
SB.m.
Probably Louis Casella and Co

CASELLA, L.
London, 'Maker to the Admiralty'
SB.m.rt.g.thca.
See Louis Casella

CASELLA, Louis fl 1838–60
23 Hatton Gdn London
Opt.phil.instr.bar.therm.; see Tagliabue and Casella, Casella and Tagliabue, Louis Casella and Co

CASELLA, Louis and Co fl 1848–60
23 Hatton Gdn London
Opt.phil.instr.bar.therm.; superseded Casella and Tagliabue 1848. Instrument makers to the Admiralty and Government of America (1856), East India Co and Board of Trade (1860). Many barometers survive

CASELLA and TAGLIABUE fl 1847
23 Hatton Gdn London
Bar.therm.; the firm was called

Tagliabue and Casella 1838–46 and
became Louis Casella and Co 1848

CASERTELLI
Liverpool
SB
See Casartelli

CASSINELLO, Geo. and Co fl 1856
23–4 West Smithfield London
Bar.

CASTELETI, John
Leicester
WB-8.m.bp.pat.
Probably—

CASTELLETTI, John fl 1841
High St Leicester
Bar.

CATELLI and Co
Hereford
WB-8.m.sp.

CATTANEO, Austin
Kings Staith York (before 1838)
Opt.wa.clo.bar, etc.; one of many
partners in a business which included
Henry and John Cattaneo,
Peter Ballarini and Joseph Fattorini

CATTANEO and Co
Reigate
WB-8.m.sp.mi.
Baillie records a P. Cattaneo, wa.,
Croydon and Reigate 'early 19c.'.
See P. Cattanio Croydon

CATTANEO and Co fl 1848
12 Castlegate York
Clo.wa., jewellery, cutlery, bar.;
partnership of Henry and
Philip Cattaneo and Joseph Fattorini

CATTANEO, H. and Co
York
WB-8.m.sp.mi.
Probably Cattaneo and Co,
12 Castlegate York

CATTANEO, Henry b. 1806–d.1860
(1) Kings Staith York
(2) 12 Castlegate York 1838–48
(3) 2 St Martins Lane York 1851
Opt., jeweller, bar.etc.; in partnership
with Austin and John Cattaneo,
Peter Ballarini and Joseph Fattorini
at (1), with Joseph Cattaneo at (2)
(Joseph and Henry Cattaneo) and with
Philip Cattaneo and Joseph Fattorini
at (2) (Cattaneo and Co)

CATTANEO, John
Kings Staith York (before 1838)
See Henry Cattaneo

CATTANEO, Joseph fl 1838–51
(1) 12 Castlegate York 1838
(2) Minster Gates York 1849
(3) 1 South Entrance York 1851
Opt.wa.; see Henry Cattaneo;
bankrupt 1849 but in business again
on his own 1851

CATTANEO, Philip fl 1848
12 Castlegate York
Clo.wa., jewellery, cutlery, bar.; see
Henry Cattaneo. Bankrupt 1848

CATTANIO, A.
Kidderminster
WB-8.m.sp.mi.
Probably Anthony Cattanio

CATTANIO, A.
Malton
WB-10.rw.sp.sqb.
Probably Anthony Cattanio, wa. and
clo., Market Place Malton 1841

CATTANIO, A. and L.
York
WB-8.m.bp.
Possibly Austin Cattaneo

CATTANIO, Anthony
Blackhall St Kidderminster
Bar.therm.

CATTANIO, C. and DOTTI
Braintree
WB-10.m.sp.

CATTANIO, P.
Croydon
WB-10.m.sp.sqb. WB-8.m.sp.
See Cattaneo and Co, Reigate

CATTANIO, V.
Worcester
WB-8.m.sp.mi.

CATTELY and Co
SB(b).m.bp.g. WB-8.m.bp.pat.

CATTELY and Co
81 Holborn London
SB(b).m.bp.g.
This was the address of several
makers—see James Lione, J. Cetti,
Josh Somalvico

CATTELY, G. and Co
SB(b).m.bp.g. WB-8.m.bp.pat.

CAVENS
Carlisle
WB-8.m.sp.

CAVERHILL and Co
Berwick-on-Tweed
WB-8.rw.sp.

CERI and PINI
Edinburgh
WB-8.rw.sp.mi.
Probably Ciceri and Pini

CETTA and Co
Stroud
WB-10.m.sp.
*Probably J. and J. Cetta, their
successors or antecedents*

CETTA, J. and Co
WB-6.maple.sp.sqb.

CETTA, J. and J.
Stroud
WB-8.m.sp.
See Cetta and Co

CETTA, John fl 1838–60
(1) 7 Union Ct Black Hill Holborn
London 1838
(2) 15 Brook St London 1839–44
(3) 14–15 Brook St London 1845–6
(4) 40 Hatton Gdn London 1847–60
*Looking-glasses, bar.therm.; succeeded
Paul Carughi at (2) and succeeded by
Wheelhouse and Bercini at (4)*

CETTI
Henley
WB-8.m.sp.

CETTI and Co
Redlion St Holborn London
WB-12.m.bp.clo.
Probably John or Joseph Cetti

CETTI and Co
25 Red Lion St Holborn
WB-8.m.bp.pat.
See Joseph Cetti

CETTI, E.
London
WB-8.m.sp. WB-8.m.sp.mi.
Probably Edward Cetti

CETTI, E. and Co
11 Brook St Holborn
SB.o.rt.ivpl.
See Edward Cetti

CETTI, Edward fl 1854–60
11 Brook St London
*Bar.therm.; the firm was called
Pastorelli and Cetti 1853*

CETTI, J.
81 High Holborn
SB(b).m.bp.g.thpl.
*Possibly Joseph Cetti but he is not
recorded at this address which was also
James Lione's*

CETTI, J. and Co
SB(b).m.bp.g.thpl.

CETTI, J. and Co
25 Red Lion St Holborn
WB-8.m.bp.pat. WB-8.m.sp.
*Probably Joseph Cetti who was at this
address 1816–39: later barometers
could however be attributed to—*

CETTI, John and Co fl 1840–8
25 Red Lion St London
*Looking-glasses, bar.; succeeded
Joseph Cetti*

CETTI, Jos
SB(b).m.bp.g.
Probably—

CETTI, Joseph and Co fl 1802–39
(1) 3 Long Lane Smithfield London
1802
(2) 54 Red Lion St London 1803–15
(3) 25 Red Lion St London 1816–39
*Looking-glasses, bar.therm., picture
frames, prints; succeeded by
John Cetti and Co*

CETTI, P.
WB-8.m.sp.mi.

CHADBURN Bros
Sheffield
SB.rt.g.2v.thca. (1851)
Identifiable with—

CHADBURN Bros fl 1837–60
26 Nursery St Sheffield
*The Chadburn family were important
makers and retailers of opt. and
math.instr.bar.etc. with a factory at
Sheffield and, later, a branch at
Liverpool (C. H. Chadburn). See
Chadburn Bros, Sheffield,
William Chadburn and
Chadburn and Co*

CHADBURN, Charles Henry fl 1845–57
71 Lord St Liverpool
*Bar.etc.; a wholesale and retail business
with a factory at Sheffield
(Chadburn Bros). Now Chadburns Ltd*

CHADBURN and Co fl 1830–33
(1) 40 Ladys Bridge Nursery St
Sheffield 1830

(2) 23 Nursery St Sheffield 1833
See William Chadburn and
Chadburn Bros, Chadburn and Wright

CHADBURN, William fl 1816–30
(1) 81 The Wicker Sheffield 1816–17
(2) Albion Works 27 Nursery St
Ladys Bridge Sheffield 1830
Opt.math.instr.bar, etc.; became
Chadburn and Co. See also
Chadburn and Wright

CHADBURN and WRIGHT fl 1830
(1) 40 Nursery St Sheffield
(2) The Wicker Sheffield
See Chadburn and Co

CHAMBERLAIN
SB.m.rt.g.
Possibly—

CHAMBERLAIN, James Bradley fl 1830–60
(1) 37 Broad St Bloomsbury London
1830–9
(2) 203 High Holborn London
1845–60
Opt.; in partnership with a son from
1852
SB.m.(2) WB-10.o.decorated with
carved gilt flowers and scrolls and
surmounted with a satyr head (1)

CHAMBERLAIN and Son fl 1852–60
203 High Holborn London
See J. B. Chamberlain

CHAMPIO, Anda
SB(b).m.rt.thpl.

CHAPMAN, Wm.
WB-8.m.sp.

CHARINETTI, D.
Gloucester
WB-8.m.sp.mi.

CHIPLEY, S. E.
SB(b).ppl.mounted on board

CHORLEY, T.
WB-8.m.bp.pat.

CICERI, P. and A.
WB-8.m.sp.

CICERI and PINI
8–9 Calton St Edinburgh
WB-8.m.sp. WB-8.rw.sp. WB-10.rw.pt.
WB-10.pt.painted and inlaid with
mop.
Ciceri and Pini, picture frames, are
recorded at 81 Leith St Edinburgh
1852–8. See Ceri and Pini

CLARE, Peter
Manchester
SB.m.
Baillie records two clo. and wa. of
this name at Manchester (1) 1764–1811
and (2) his son b. 1781 –d.1851

CLARK, Jno.
Chester
AB.m.

CLARK, Robert fl 1836–45
(1) 2 Whartons Place High Holborn
London 1836
(2) 27 Brook St Holborn Bars London
1838–45
Bar.therm.

CLARK, Thos. fl 1846–57
20 Kirby St London
Bar.therm.

CLEAVER
London
WB-8.rw.sp.sqb.
Probably—

CLEAVER, Samuel fl 1845–9
30 Theobalds Rd London
Bar.therm.

COGGS, John fl 1690–1740
Globe and Sun St Dunstans Fleet St
London
Math.phil.instr.; a trade card
advertised 'weather-glasses of all sorts'
(Heal Colln, Brit.Mus.).
Succeeded by a son of the same name

COHEN, D.
Newcastle-on-Tyne
WB-8.m.sp. WB-8.m.sp.mi.
Probably David Cohen, opt.
(1) 5 Collingwood St Newcastle
1821–37
(2) 1 Grey St Newcastle 1838–44
(3) 76 Grey St Newcastle 1847–51
(4) 30 Mosley St Newcastle 1853
(5) 9 Mosley St Newcastle 1855–8

COLE, Benjamin (1) b. 1695–d.1766
(1) Popping Ct Fleet St London
(2) Bull Alley Lombard St London
1744
(3) The Orrery 136 Fleet St London
1748–66
Opt.math.phil.instr.; succeeded
Thomas Wright and sponsored
Joseph Harris's Description and Use
of the Globes and Orrery. In
partnership with his son by 1751.
Among his apprentices was John Wright

and a bill survives, which is receipted by Wright, for 'cleaning and silvering ye plates of a barometer and new paper scale to ye thermometer' (Heal Colln, Brit.Mus.) (Plate 137). In 1751 and 1757 the Coles were advertising 'barometers of all sorts; thermometers, either the framed mercurial or spirit ones, nicely adjusted'

COLE, Benjamin (2) b. 1725–d.1813
136 Fleet St London
Opt.math.phil.instr.; son of Benjamin Cole (1) and app. to him 1739. In partnership 1751. His business absorbed by J. Troughton 1782 when he seems to have retired. See Benjamin Cole (1)

COLE, Benjamin and Son fl 1751–66
136 Fleet St London
See Benjamin Cole (1)

COLEMAN, Ann fl 1832–3
11 Vineyard Walk Clerkenwell London
Bar.therm.; succeeded Charles Coleman

COLEMAN, Charles fl 1823–9
(1) 7 Dorrington St Clerkenwell London 1823–8
(2) 11 Vineyard Walk Clerkenwell London 1829
Bar.therm.; succeeded by Ann Coleman presumably his widow

COLLIER, Benjamin
WB-8.m.rt.scroll pattern

COLLINGS, C. W. fl 1845–7
(1) 16 Mortimer St Cavendish Sq London 1845–6
(2) Royal Polytechnic Institute London 1847
Phil.instr.bar.

COLLIS, W. H.
Bury St Edmunds
WB-8.m.rt.

COLOMBA, A.
Salisbury
WB-8.m.sp.

COLOMBA, Andrew fl 1842–60
(1) 37 Charles St Hatton Gdn London 1842–59
(2) 89 Chancery Lane London 1846
(3) 16 Charles St Hatton Gdn London 1860
Bar.therm.; in partnership with Hare 1844–6 (Colomba and Hare).

Joseph Somalvico was at (1) until 1839 and Gugeri and Carughi at (3) 1844–5

COLOMBA and HARE
(1) 37 Charles St Hatton Gdn London 1844–6
(2) 89 Chancery Lane London 1846
Bar.therm.; see Andrew Colomba

COMBS, Oliver fl 1693–1747
(1) The Spectacles St Martin's Ct Leicester Fields London
(2) Second house from Essex St Temple Bar London 1747
Opt.; app. to Edward Scarlett; a trade card advertised barometers and thermometers (Heal Colln, Brit.Mus.; also Sc.Mus.London)

COMITTI, Jos
Banff
SB(b).m.g.

COMOLI, J. and Co
WB-8.m.bp.pat.
Possibly J. Comoli, Edinburgh

COMOLI, J.
Aberdeen
WB-8.m.bp.pat.
Possibly a branch of—

COMOLI, J. fl 1825–6
82 St Mary's Wynd Edinburgh
WB-8.m.bp.pat.
See Comoli and Nozzi

COMOLI and NOZZI
82 St Mary's Wynd Edinburgh
WB
See J. Comoli

COMOLI, P. and Co
High St Dudley
WB-8.m.bp.pat.
Probably—

COMOLI, Peter and Co fl 1817
High St Dudley
Bar.,hardware; spelt Curmoli in directory

COMOZZI, C.
Aylesbury
WB-8.m.bp.pat.

COMOZZI, C.
Buckingham
WB-8.m.sp.mi.

CONNELL
Cheapside
WB-10.rw.rt.mop.

COOK
London
WB-10.m.sp.hycen.

COOKE and Sons
York
WB-8.m.sp.
Probably Thomas Cooke, math.instr.,
b. 1807—d. 1868
(1) Micklegate York
(2) 50 Stonegate York 1837–8
(3) 12 Coney St York 1843–51
(4) 26 Coney St York 1860

COPINI, GATINI fl 1832–49
(1) 217 High St Shoreditch London
1832–41
(2) 280 High Holborn London
1839–41
(3) 37 Norton Folgate London
1842–9
Bar.therm., looking-glasses, carvers,
gilders

COPODURO, D.
Cirencester
WB-8.m.bp.pat. (the address spelt
'Cerincester')—Gloucester Mus.

CORBETTA, I.
11 Brook St Holborn
WB-10.m.sp.sqb.
This address was occupied by various
members of the Tagliabue family
1817–52, by Pastorelli and Cetti 1853
and by Edward Cetti 1854–60

CORNELL
Royston
WB-6.m.sp.sqb.
Baillie records a C. Cornell, wa.,
Royston 'early 19c.'

CORRALL
Lutterworth
WB-10.m.sp.
Probably William Corrall, wa.,
(1) Lutterworth 1822
(2) Church St Lutterworth 1835–41

CORTI
Exeter
WB-8.m.sp.mi.
Probably Paul Corti

CORTI, A.
7 Greville St London
WB-8.m.bp.pat. SB(b).m.sp.g.thpl.
Andrew Tarone & Co at this address
1802–19; Peter Primavesi also worked
there

CORTI, A.
Glasgow
WB-8.m.sp.
Probably—

CORTI, Antoni fl 1833–45
(1) 97 Nelson St Glasgow 1833–41
(2) 38 Candlerigg St Glasgow 1841–4
(3) 54 Glassford St Glasgow 1844–5
Bar, carver, gilder, looking-glasses;
possibly a relation of J. B. Corti

CORTI, F.
Newcastle
WB-8.m.bp.pat.

CORTI, J.
Colchester
WB-8.m.bp.pat.
Possibly the same as Jos Corti, Ipswich

CORTI, J.
London
SB(b).m.bp.g.thpl.
Probably John Corti

CORTI, J.
94 Holborn Hill
WB-8.m.bp.pat.
Possibly John Corti but he is not
recorded at this address which was
also occupied by Donegan and Co and
F. Saltery and Co

CORTI, J. B.
Glasgow
WB-10.m.pt. (Plate 50)
Possibly a relation of Antoni Corti

CORTI, Jno.
SB(b).m.sqc.ppl.plain pillars to hood
Probably—

CORTI, John fl 1815–34
(1) 27 Leather Lane London 1815–25
(2) 35 Eyre St Hatton Gdn London
1826–34
Bar.therm., wholesale, retail and 'for
exportation'. A. Grego occupied (1)
1827. Corti was probably an important
supplier of barometers to the trade

CORTI, Jos
Ipswich
WB-8.m.bp.pat.
See J. Corti, Colchester

CORTI, P.
Exeter
WB-8.m.sp. WB-8.rw.sp. WB-8.rw.
sp.sqb.
Probably—

CORTI, Paul fl 1850
    5 Market St Exeter
    Bar.; see Paul Courti, probably his son

CORTI, Peter fl 1845–50
    30 Eyre St Hill London
    Bar.therm.; John Corti had also
    worked in Eyre St

COULDREY
    WB-10.m.sp.
    Probably—

COULDREY, Jos fl 1819–51
    (1) Church Passage Tooley St London
        1819–29
    (2) 26 St Thomas St East Borough
        1838–51
    Math.instr.bar.therm.saccharometers

COURTI, Paul fl 1856–7
    (1) 38½ South St Exeter 1856
    (2) 7 High St Exeter 1856–7
    Bar.opt.wa. and clo., jewellery, etc.
    Probably son of Paul Corti whose
    name may also have been spelt Courti
    on occasions

COX, James
    London
    WB-8.m.bp.hycen.
    Probably James Cox, opt.
    (1) 5 Barbican Aldersgate St London
        1830–51
    (2) 85 Lombard St London 1839

COX, S. W.
    Market Harborough
    WB-10.m.sp.sqb.

COX, Wm.
    Plymouth Dock
    SB(b).m.g. MB.
    Probably—

COX, William Charles fl 1822–57
    (1) 86 Fore St Plymouth Dock
        1822–39
    (2) 89 Fore St Plymouth Dock
        1852–6
    (3) 24 Southside St Plymouth Dock
        1856
    (4) 83 Fore St Plymouth Dock
        1857
    Opt.math.phil.instr.bar.chronometers
    etc.

CREMONINI
    Bilston
    WB-10.rw.pt.mop.

CREMONINI, A.
    WB-8.m.bp.pat.

CREMONINI, F.
    WB-10.rw.rt.mop.

CRIGHTON, J.
    112 Leadenhall St
    MB
    Probably Joseph Crichton, opt.math.
    phil.instr., 112 Leadenhall St London
    1838–51

CROCE, A.
    Lewis
    WB-8.m.bp.pat.

CROCE, G.
    York
    WB-8.m.bp.pat. WB-8.m.sp.mi.
    Probably Joseph or Joshua Croce

CROCE, J.
    York
    SB(b).m.bp.g.ppl. SB(b)m.bp.
    WB-8.m.bp.pat. WB-8.m.sp.mi.
    Probably Joshua Croce but later
    examples may be attributable to—

CROCE, Joseph fl 1847
    York
    Bar.; possibly a son of

CROCE, Joshua fl 1823–d.1841
    15 Grape Lane York 1823–30
    Bar.,artificialflowers; see G. Croce,
    J. Croce

CROSTA and Co
    Nottingham
    WB-8.rw.sp.mi.
    Probably Crosta and Co., carvers,
    gilders, looking-glasses,
    Bridlesmith Gate Nottingham 1853–60

CROTCHIE, Chas.
    Inverness
    WB-8.m.sp.mi.

CROW, Francis fl 1780–1822
    (1) Faversham 1780–95
    (2) Gravesend
    (3) 37 Windsor Terrace City Rd
        London
    Math.phil.instr.wa.and clo.etc.
    WB(1)

CRUNDWELL
    High St Tunbridge Wells
    WB-8.m.sp.mi.
    Baillie records a Crundwell, wa.,
    Tunbridge 'early 19c.'

CUFF
    Probably—

CUFF, John p 124

CULPEPER, E.
　　London
　　Pillar B.w.
　　Probably Edmund Culpeper, opt.math.
　　instr., fl. 1686 –d.1737
　　(1) Cross Daggers Moorfields London
　　　　1706–31
　　(2) Black White Horse Moorfields
　　　　London
　　(3) Royal Exchange London 1725
　　an eminent maker known for his
　　microscopes (Daily Gazetteer
　　14 May 1737)

CUMMIN, J. fl 1851–60
　　(1) 7 Cobham Row Coldbath Sq
　　　　London 1851
　　(2) 1 Newcastle Place Clerkenwell
　　　　London 1852–7
　　(3) Phoenix Place Grays Inn Rd
　　　　London 1858–60
　　Phil.instr.opt.bar.therm.

CUMMING, Alexander b. *c.* 1732–d.1814
　　(1) 12 Clifford St Bond St London
　　　　1785
　　(2) 75 Fleet St London
　　Born Edinburgh, CC. 1781. One of the
　　leading clockmakers of his day;
　　published Elements of Clock and
　　and Watch Work *1766. Maker of*
　　two clock barographs—one for
　　George III (1765) now in Buckingham
　　Palace (Ambassadors' Staircase) (see
　　George IV's Pictorial Inventory *c. 1826,*
　　Vol. 2 Plate 9, H. C. Smith
　　Buckingham Palace *1931 and many*
　　other authors); the other, made in
　　1766, was bought after Cumming's
　　death by Luke Howard who used it for
　　the meteorological records published in
　　his Climate of London *1720*

CUMMINS, Alexander fl 1840
　　Leadenhall St London
　　Chronometers; patentee of 'certain
　　improvements in barometers and
　　sympiesometers'

CURMOLI
　　Dudley
　　See Peter Comoli

CUSHEE, E. fl 1729–68
　　(1) Globe and Sun between
　　　　St Dunstan's Church and
　　　　Chancery Lane Fleet St London
　　(2) The Orrery Water Lane Fleet St
　　　　London

Math.instr.,globes: son of
Richard Cushee and associated with
Thomas Wright. From 1757 associated
with Benjamin Cole

CUSHEE, Richard fl 1708–34
　　Globe and Sun between St Dunstan's
　　Church and Chancery Lane Fleet St
　　London
　　Math.instr.; associated with
　　Thomas Wright 1731–4 and succeeded
　　by his son E. Cushee

CUTTS, John P.
　　Division St
　　MB
　　Probably John P. Cutts, opt.math.phil.
　　instr. (1) 58 Norfolk St Sheffield 1825
　　(2) 43 Division St Sheffield 1828–60;
　　the firm was called J. P. Cutts Sons
　　and Sutton 1845–60

D

DALLAWAY
　　SB.m.bow.g.
　　Probably Joseph James Dallaway, opt.
　　(1) 4 George Lane Botolph Lane
　　　　London 1802
　　(2) 147 Tottenham Ct Rd London
　　　　1805–9

DANCER, John Benjamin fl 1838–60
　　13 Cross St Manchester
　　Opt.math.phil.instr.bar.therm.; in
　　partnership with Abraham until 1843
　　(Abraham and Dancer)

DANGELO and CADENAZZI
　　Winchester
　　WB.6.m.sp.sqb.

DAVENPORT, Stephen fl 1720–37
　　Against the Distillery High Holborn
　　near Drury Lane London
　　Math.instr.; also made air pumps,
　　cupping-glasses, marine and portable
　　barometers, thermometers, etc.

DAVIES
　　Liverpool
　　WB-8.m.rt.
　　Probably Edward Davies, opt.,
　　65 Bold St Liverpool 1835 or
　　James Davis, opt., 51 Paradise St
　　Liverpool 1835

DAVIES, Gabriel
　　Leeds
　　SB.m.sqp.
　　Probably Gabriel Davies (or Davis) opt.

(1) 20 Boar Lane Leeds 1822
(2) 34 Boar Lane Leeds 1826–53
in partnership with Edward Davies 1830
and succeeded by him

DAVIES, Owen
Llanidloes
SB.m.rt.g.thpl.
Probably Owen Davies, wa. and clo.,
Long Bridge Llanidloes 1835

DAVIS
London
SB(b).m.rt.
Possibly H. Davis, opt.math.instr.,
8 Macclesfield St Soho 1799–1817 or
his successor at the same address
David Davis 1825–7

DAVIS, D.
Glasgow
SB(b).m.bp.g.thpl.

DAVIS, G.
Leeds
WB
See Gabriel Davies

DAVIS, Gabriel
See Gabriel Davies

DAVIS, J.
Edinburgh
Sympiesometer
Probably J. Davis, math.phil.instr.opt.
(1) 64 Princes St Edinburgh 1837–40
(2) 78 Princes St Edinburgh 1841–2

DAVIS, Wm.
Shiffnall
WB. set in burr yew frame with
brass inlay. dial centre in octagonal
frame. th below. clo. on dial

DAWES
WB.m. incorporated in weight-driven
clock with mercurial pendulum

DAWSON, Nathan
SB.m.sp.

DEACON
SB.sabicu.inl. arched hood. enamelled
pl. and open cistern; another with
bulb cistern—Leicester Mus.
Several Deacons worked in or near
Leicester: see F., J., and S. Deacon

DEACON, F.
Leicester
SB(b).m.bp.rc.g.
Probably Frederick Deacon, wa. and
clo., Market Place Leicester 1822

DEACON, J.
Leicester
WB-8.m.rt.fg.—Leicester Mus.
Baillie records a J. Deacon, Leicester
'c. 1790': the Leicester Museum gives
his dates 'c. 1795–c. 1835'.

DEACON, S.
Barton
This signature appears on a finely
engraved brass plate used for printing
paper plates—Leicester Mus.; on
display as part of the workshop
equipment of Samuel Deacon, wa. clo.,
Barton-in-the-Beans, b. 1746–d.1816,
who worked at Barton from 1771

DEE, J.
Skipton
WB-10.m.sp.sqb.mi.

DELANDER
Probably—

DELANDER, Daniel p 126

DE LA TORRE
See Torre

DELLA BELLA
See Bella

DELLA TORRE
See Torre

DENNIS, J. C.
MB.—Sc.Mus.London
Probably—

DENNIS, John C. fl 1852–60
122 Bishopsgate Within London
Phil.instr.bar.therm.

DENTON, Joseph
Hull
SB
Baillie records a clockmaker of this
name but does not attempt to date

DIMMOCK, James
147 High St Ryde
WB-8.rw.sp.mi.

DIPPLE, C. and E. fl 1858–60
36 Gt Hampton Row Birmingham
Bar.

DIXEY, C. W.
3 New Bond St London
SB.m.sp.g. ('Opt. to the Queen')
WB-10.m. scroll pattern ('Opt. to the
Queen and HRH Prince Albert')
See Charles Wastell Dixey

DIXEY, Charles Wastell b. 1798–d.1880
(1) 335 Oxford St London 1821
(2) 78 New Bond St London 1822–3
(3) 3 New Bond St London 1825–60
Opt. to the Queen; in partnership with his twin brother 1821–38 (George and Charles Dixey) but on his own from 1839
SB.m.sqp.urn.bow.g.ivpl.thca.(3)
WB-8.m.sp.(3) WB.in French clock case—Buckingham Palace

DIXEY, G. and C.
3 New Bond St London
SB.m.sqp.rc.g.ivpl. SB.m.rt.g.thpl.
See George and Charles Dixey

DIXEY, George b.1798–d.1838
See George and Charles Dixey

DIXEY, George and Charles fl 1821–38
(1) 335 Oxford St London 1821
(2) 78 New Bond St London 1822–3
(3) 3 New Bond St London 1825–8
Opticians to the King; twin sons of Edward Dixey, opt., and succeeded to his business. Charles Wastell Dixey on his own from 1839. See G. and C. Dixey

DOBBIE, William fl 1821–45
Falkirk
Clo.wa.; Baillie records that he was clockmaker to the Queen. A contemporary account states that he made two barometers in 1845 in the style of John Russell (p 208)

DOBSON
SB.m.sp.bow.

DODD
Glasgow
WB-10.m.sp.
Probably Andrew Dodd, opt.math.phil. instr.
(1) 70 Hutcheson St Glasgow 1837–8
(2) 36 Glassford St Glasgow 1838–47
(3) 88 Glassford St Glasgow 1847–8

DOLLOND
London
See George Dollond, Peter Dollond

DOLLOND, George p 128

DOLLOND, John (1) b.1706–d.1761
Golden Spectacles and Sea Quadrant near Exeter Exchange Strand London
Opt.instr.; father of Peter Dollond and

originally a silk weaver but joined his son's optical business 1752

DOLLOND, John (2) b. *c*.1740 —d.1804
59 St Paul's Churchyard
Opt.math.instr.; Master Spectacle-makers Co 1790, 1792, in partnership with his elder brother Peter Dollond from 1766

DOLLOND, P. and J.
See Peter Dollond, John Dollond (2)

DOLLOND, Peter p 129

DONEGAN and Co
94 Holborn Hill
SB(b).m.bp.g.
This address also occupied by J. Corti and F. Saltery and Co. Possibly identifiable with P. Donegan and Co

DONEGAN, Joseph fl 1835
Lad Lane Newcastle-under-Lyme
WB-8.m.bp.pat.
Francis Donegan, carver and gilder, had been at this address 1822

DONEGAN, P. and Co
London
WB-8.m.bp.pat. SB(b).m.bp.
Possibly Peter Donegan, picture-frames, 7 Union Ct Holborn London 1805

DONEGANI
SB(b).m.bp.g.thpl.

DONEVAN, P.
London
WB-8.m.bp.pat.
Possibly a mis-spelling of Donegan

DORRINGTON
Truro
WB-10.rw.sp.sb.mi.

DOTTI, G.
Bath
WB

DOWLER, George fl 1858–60
90 Gt Charles St Birmingham
Bar.

DRING and FAGE
London
WB.m.fan-shaped pediment

DRING and FAGE fl 1798–1860
(1) 6 Tooley St Southwark London 1798
(2) 248 Tooley St Southwark London 1800
(3) 20 Tooley St Southwark London 1822–45

(4) 19–20 Tooley St Southwark
London 1846–60
*Bar.therm.; an important firm,
originally the partnership of John Dring
and William Fage*
SB.m.sp.g.thca.hycen (Plate 32)
WB.m.sp. with square dial at top of
case (Plate 48)

DUBINI, Peter fl 1832–60
(1) 11 Beauchamp St Leather Lane
London 1832–3
(2) 12 Beauchamp St Leather Lane
London 1836
(3) 47 Red Lion St London 1853–60
*Bar.; spelt Duhim (1832–3) and
Dulbini (1836) in directories.
John Spelzini at (1) by 1839*
WB-8.m.sp.mi.(1)

DUNN
Edinburgh
MB
*Probably John Dunn, opt.phil.instr.,
50 Hanover St Edinburgh 1825–42*

E

EAGLAND, Joseph fl 1856–9
3 Wellington Row Bethnal Green
London
Bar.

EDGECUMBE
Plymouth
WB-8.rw.sp.
*Baillie records various wa. and clo.
makers of this name at Bristol 1794–
1830*

EDKINS, Jas.
Kensington
WB-8.m.sp.
*Baillie records a J. Edkins, Kensington
London 'early 19c.'*

EDWARDS and HUNTER
Cornhill
MB—Gloucester Mus.

EDWARDS, John
Menai Bridge
WB-8.rw.sp.sqb.mi. painted simulation
of inl.

ELEY, H.
Boston
WB-10.m.sp.
*Probably Hodson Eley, wa. and clo.,
Wide Bargate Boston 1856–60*

ELLICOTT, John, p 131

ELLINETT
SB.w.ppl. indications in English and
Latin
*The clock of Plate 74 has an
Advertisement concerning the
Barometer by Thomas Ellinett
Charing Cross Norwich stuck inside
the door*

ELLIOT, John fl 1846–8
14 Stacey St Soho London
Phil.instr.bar.

ELLIOTT Bros fl 1854–60
(1) 56 Strand London 1854–8
(2) 5 Charing Cross London 1857–8
(3) 30 Strand London 1859–60
*Opt.; sons of William Elliott, opt.
The firm made or sold a large number
of barometers, most of them probably
after 1860. In 1857 it absorbed the
business of Watkins and Hill*

ELLISON
London
WB-8.m.sp.mi.

ELLISON
Norwich
WB-10.m.pt.

ELMER, W.
SB(b). black japanned frame. ppl.

EMANUEL, E.
Wisbech
WB-8.m.sp.mi.
*Probably Emmanuel Emmanuel,
jeweller, Upper Hill St Wisbech 1851*

EMANUEL, E.
Peterborough
WB-10.m.sp. WB-8.m.sp.mi.
*A Barnett Emanuel, jeweller, at
Narrow Bridge St Peterborough 1830*

EMANUEL, E. and B.
Portsmouth
MB
*Possibly Ezekiel and Emanuel Emanuel,
silversmiths, jewellers, 3 Common Hard
Portsmouth 1830*

ENDICOTT, John fl 1832–45
(1) 10 Norwich Ct Fetter Lane
London 1832–3
(2) 23 Little Saffron Hill London
1844–50
Bar.therm.

ESPLIN, E.
Wigan
WB-8.m.sp.mi.

EVE, George Frederick fl 1851–60
    (1) 4 Charles St Hatton Gdn London
      1851–3
    (2) 90½ Holborn Hill London 1854–60
    Phil.instr.bar.etc.

EZEKIEL
    Exeter
    SB.m.g. SB.m.bp.g.
    Probably either Abraham Ezekiel,
    silversmith, Fore St Exeter 1791 or
    Cath and America Ezekiel, goldsmiths,
    opt. (1) Fore St Exeter 1809–30
    (2) 179 Fore St Exeter 1828

F

FAGIOLI, D.
    Clerkenwell
    WB-10. with moulded gilt floral
    decoration; WB-10.m.sp. WB-10.rw.
    pt. WB-8.m.sp. WB-8.rw.pt.mop.
    Probably Dominic Fagioli

FAGIOLI, D. and Son fl 1840–54
    (1) 3 Gt Warner St Clerkenwell
      1836–51
    (2) 10 Gt Warner St Clerkenwell
      1851–4
    WB-12.rw.pt.(1) WB-10.m.sp.(1)
    WB-10.m.rt.(1) WB-8.m.sp.(2)
    WB-8.rw.pt.(1) WB-10.rw.pt.(1)
    MB(2)
    Partnership of Dominic Fagioli and a
    son, possibly J. Fagioli

FAGIOLI, Dominic fl 1836–54
    (1) 3 Gt Warner St Clerkenwell
      London 1836–51
    (2) 10 Gt Warner St Clerkenwell
      London 1851–4
    Bar.; in partnership with a son from
    1840 (D. Fagioli and Son)

FAGIOLI, J.
    London
    WB-8.rw.sp.mi. WB-8.rw.sp.mi.
    painted with simulation of inl.

FAGIOLI, J.
    5 Union Terrace
    WB-8.m.rt.pat.
    Possibly identifiable with—

FAGIOLI, J.
    30 Gt Warner St Clerkenwell London
    WB-10.sw.sp.sqb.mi.
    Possibly the son of D. Fagioli

FAGIOLI and Son
    3 Gt Warner St Clerkenwell London

WB-10.m.sp.sb.
See D. Fagioli and Son

FALCIOLA, B. and Co fl 1839–43
    53 Edgbaston St Birmingham
    Bar.

FALLOW, Joseph fl 1827–9
    127 Pilgrim St Newcastle upon Tyne
    Bar.

FARMER
    Christchurch
    WB-8.sw.sp.mi.

FASANA
    Bath
    SB(b).m.bp.g.

FASSANO, Jos
    WB-8.m.bp.pat.

FATORINI, A.
    WB-8.m.sp.

FATORINI, M.
    Chichester
    WB-8.m.bp.pat.

FATORINI, M.
    Chichester
    WB-8.m.bp.pat.

FATORINI, M.
    London
    WB-10.m.sp.

FATTORINI, Joseph fl 1838–48
    (1) King's Staith York (before 1838)
    (2) 12 Castlegate York 1848
    See Cattaneo and Co

FAVA, J.
    WB-8.m.bp.pat.

FAVERIO, F.
    WB-8.m.bp.pat.

FERARI, B.
    Ipswich
    WB-8.m.bp.pat.

FERRIER, W. T.
    Hull
    WB-8.m.sp.mi. WB-8.m.pt.
    Probably William Thornton Ferrier, wa.
    jeweller, silversmith, exchanger of
    foreign coins
    (1) 11 Queen St Hull 1826–42
    (2) 5 Nelson St Hull 1846–51
    or Thornton Ferrier, wa.clo., possibly
    his father
    (1) 34 Blackfriargate Hull 1817
    (2) Queen St Hull 1822–3

FESTE, L.
  WB-8.m.bp.pat.

FETTANI, T.
  WB-10.m.sp.

FIDLER, Robert fl 1811–2
  32 Wigmore St London
  *Opt.math.instr.; Daumas says that he
  made a barometer c. 1810*

FINNEY
  Liverpool
  AB with glass cistern set in mahogany
  case carved in classical style—Sc.Mus.
  London (Plate 25)
  *Baillie records three 18c. wa. and clo.
  makers of this name at Liverpool—
  Joseph 1734–61, John 1754, Joseph
  1770–96*

FIORA, J.
  Nottingham
  WB-8.m.bp.pat. WB-10.m.sp.
  *Probably J. Fiora, looking-glasses,
  Long Row Nottingham 1814–5*

FLOCKHART
  Covent Gdn
  SB(b).m.bp.
  *Probably Andrew Flockhart, clo. and
  wa., 5 King St Covent Gdn London
  1811–23*

FOLETTI, Michael fl 1844–60
  (1) 88 Curtain Rd London 1844–6
  (2) 4–5 Bateman's Row London
    1847–9
  (3) 64 Banner St London 1851–2
  (4) 89 Old St London 1853–60
  Looking-glasses, bar.therm.

FONTANA
  Wycombe
  WB-10. black lacquer.sp.mop.

FONTANA, B.
  Exeter
  WB-8.m.sp.mi.
  Probably—

FONTANA, B. fl 1856
  Cowick St St Thomas Exeter
  *Bar.; see Grasi and Fontana, and
  Bulla, Grassi and Fontana. Baillie
  records a Fontana, wa., Exeter 'early
  19c.'*

FONTANA, B. and J.
  Kettering
  WB-8.m.sp.

FONTANA, E.
  WB-8.m.sp.mi.

FONTANI, M.
  High Wycombe
  WB-8.m.bp.pat.

FORDHAM
  Bishops Stortford
  WB-8.m.bp.pat.
  *Baillie records a Thomas Fordham, clo.
  and wa., Bishops Stortford 1776*

FORREST
  SB.m.rt.
  *Baillie records several wa. and clo.
  makers of this name*

FORSTER, Clement fl 1670–94
  Mr. Davis's near Painter's Coffee
  House Salisbury Ct Fleet St London
  1694
  *Math.phil.instr., CC.1682; said in
  Houghton's Collection for the
  Improvement of Husbandry and
  Trade (Feb. 23rd 1694) to have made
  and sold 'excellent weather-glasses'
  priced from 12s. to 50s.*

FOSANELLI, Peter
  Bishops Castle
  WB-8.m.bp.pat.

FOX, E.
  Ely and Soham
  WB-8.m.pt.mi.
  *Probably Edmund Fox, wa., Broad St
  Ely 1851; Baillie records an E. Fox,
  wa., Ely 'early 19c.'*

FRANCO, Teodoro fl 1854–6
  (1) 2 Brookes Mkt Leather Lane
    London 1854
  (2) 39 Charles St Hatton Gdn London
    1855
  (3) 11 Cross St Hatton Gdn London
    1856
  Bar.

FRANKHAM, Richard and Henry fl 1829–55
  12 Wilson St Grays Inn Rd London
  *Bar.therm., engravers; became
  Frankham and Wilson 1856–60*
  MB—Gloucester Mus.

FRANKLIN
  WB-8.m.sp.mi.

FRANZONI, B. fl 1857–60
  36 Charles St Hatton Gdn London
  Bar.frames.

FRASER
  Bond St London
  SB.m.arch top. urn. bow. SB.m.arch
  top.urn. thpl.
  See Fraser London

FRASER
London
SB.m.sp.bow.g.thpl.hytop.
*Possibly William Fraser, opt. to the
King and Prince of Wales,
3 New Bond St London, b. c. 1720
d. 1815; in partnership with a son
from 1799 and succeeded by
Edward Dixey (see George and
Charles Dixey). See Fraser and Son*

FRASER and Son
Bond St London
SB.m.bp.hc.g.thpl.

FREEMAN
25 Gt Warner St Clerkenwell London
WB-8.rw.sp.mop. WB-8.m.sp.mi.

FRENCH
Royal Exchange
WB-6.m.sp. WB-12.m.rt.sqb.
SB.m.set. in carved Corinthian column
WB-12.rw.rt.clo.
*Probably Santiago James Moore French,
CC.1810*
(1) *14-15 Sweetings Alley Royal
Exchange London 1822–39*
(2) *80 Cornhill London 1840–4,
a notable clo. who advertised in
Spanish and sold clocks in New York*

FRIGERIO, J.
281 High Holborn London
WB-10.m.sp.pat.fg.

FROST, NOAKES and Co fl 1851–7
195 Brick Lane Spitalfields London
Bar.

FROWD
Hemel Hempstead
WB-8.m.sp.

G

GABALIO
3 Long Lane London
WB-8.m.bp.pat.

GABORY
123 Holborn London
SB.m.bp.hc.thpl.
Probably identifiable with—

GABORY
125 Holborn London
WB.m.sp.square dial at top of case.
thca.hycen. (*cf.* Plate 48)

GALE, Joseph fl 1828–41
46 King St Manchester
Looking-glasses, bar.

GALI, J.
Lincoln
WB-8.m.sp.

GALLETTI, A.
WB-8.m.bp.pat.

GALLY
Exeter
WB-8.m.bp.pat.
See John Gally

GALLY
Manchester
WB-10.m.sp.fg.

GALLY, C.
WB-8.m.bp.pat.
Possibly—

GALLY, Charles and Co fl 1852–4
68 Hatton Gdn London
*Looking-glasses, bar.therm.; this was
the address of Paul and Peter Gally
1849–60*

GALLY, G.
Glasgow
WB-8.m.bp.

GALLY, John
Exeter
SB(b).m.bp.thpl. SB(b).m.bp.g.

GALLY, P.
Cambridge
WB-8.m.bp.pat. SB(b).m.bp.rc.g.

GALLY, P.
Leeds
WB-8.m.sp.
*Probably Peter Galley, hardware, toys,
jeweller (1) 89 Kirkgate Leeds 1837–60
(2) 97 Kirkgate Leeds 1841*

GALLY, Paul and Peter fl 1809–60
(1) 8 Turnmill St Clerkenwell London
1809–11
(2) 9 Turnmill St Clerkenwell London
1815–25
(3) 50 Exmouth St Spitalfields London
1826–48
(4) 68 Hatton Gdn London 1849–60
(5) 3 Upper Nth Pl Grays Inn Rd
London 1852–4
*Picture-frames, looking-glasses, bar.
therm.; Charles Galley at (4) 1852–4*

GANDOLA, P.
12 Little Saffron Hill London
WB-8.m.bp.pat.

GANTHONY
London

WB-10.rw.sp.sb.
*Baillie records three London clo. of
this name (1) Richard, Lombard St,
   fl 1785–d.1845, CC. 1794,
   Master 1828, and his sons
(2) Richard Pinfold, Cheapside,
   fl 1821–d.1845 Master CC.1845
(3) Richard fl 1813–d. 1825, CC.1820*

GAPP, Cs.
   London
   SB(b).m.bp.g.

GARDENERS
   Glasgow
   SB.m.rt.bow.ivpl.
   See Gardners

GARDNER
   Glasgow
   SB.m.rt.sqc.ivpl. SB and companion
   th. in tortoiseshell and ormolu cases
   Probably—

GARDNER and Co fl 1837–60
   (1) 44 Glassford St Glasgow 1837–9
   (2) 21 Buchanan St Glasgow 1839–60
   (3) 53 Buchanan St Glasgow 1860
   *Opt.math.instr.; previously M. Gardner
   and Co*
   SB.m.bow.g.(3)

GARDNER, J. and J. fl 1799–1819
   43 Bell St Glasgow
   *Math.instr.; one of the partners was
   John Gardner; became Gardners
   Jamieson & Co 1820*
   SB(b).w.ivpl. with triangular top and
   patera inlay on cistern cover
   SB(b).sw.ivpl.2v. triangular top

GARDNER, John fl 1765–91
   Bell's Wynd Glasgow
   *Math.instr.; founder of a firm which
   during the nineteenth century became
   prolific barometer makers (J. and
   J. Gardner, Gardners Jamieson & Co,
   M. Gardner, etc.)*

GARDNER, M. and Co fl 1823–37
   (1) 43 Bell St Glasgow 1823–5
   (2) 92 Bell St Glasgow 1826–32
   (3) 44 Glassford St Glasgow 1832–7
   *Opt.math.phil.instr.; named
   M. Gardner and Sons 1824–33.
   Superseded Gardners and became
   Gardner & Co 1837. Several
   barometers survive which could be
   attributed to the firm during these years
   but definite attribution is difficult*

GARDNERS fl 1822
   43 Bell St Glasgow

*Opt.; the name appears for one year
only as a transition between
Gardners Jamieson and Co and
M. Gardner and Co*

GARDNERS, JAMIESON and Co fl 1820–1
   43 Bell St Glasgow
   *Opt.; superseded J. and J. Gardner
   and became Gardners 1822*

GARGORY, James
   Birmingham and Wolverhampton
   WB-6.rw.sp.sqb.thca. WB-4.rw.sp.sqb.
   *Probably James Gargory, opt., jeweller,
   goldsmith
   (1) 4 Bull St Birmingham 1835
   (2) 5 Bull St Birmingham 1850–6*

GATTI, Charles fl 1817–22
   89 Leather Lane Holborn London
   *Looking-glasses; spelt Gattie in
   directories*
   WB-8.m.bp.pat. WB-8.m.sp.

GATTI, T.
   53 Grays Inn Lane London
   WB-8.m.

GATTY, A.
   Fish Lane London
   WB-8.m.bp.pat.

GATTY, A.
   Reading
   SB(b).m.bp.rc.thpl.
   Probably—

GATTY, Antony
   Royal Oak Fisher Row Reading
   SB(b).m.bp.rc.g. WB-8.m.bp.pat.

GATTY, B.
   Reading
   WB-10.sw.sp.fg.

GATTY and Co
   WB-8.m.bp.pat.

GATTY, D.
   Lewis
   WB-12.m.sp.fg.

GATTY, D.
   Reading
   WB-10.sw.sp.
   see Dominico Gatty

GATTY, Domco
   London
   SB.m.rt.g.

GATTY, Dominico fl 1826
   111 Broad St Reading
   Bar.

GATTY, James p 137

GATTY, Jno.
Manchester
WB-12.m.sp.inl. mi.

GATTY, Josh
SB(b).m.bp.rc.g.thpl.hytop.

GATWARD, J.
Saffron Walden
WB-8.m.bp.fg.

GAY, Thomas fl 1668–1732
Sun Tavern Royal Exchange London
Opt.instr.; advertised weather-glasses

GERLETTI
Glasgow
WB-10.m.sp.sqb. WB-8.m.sp.
Probably—

GERLETTI, John fl 1853–8
(1) 95 Candlerigg St Glasgow 1853–4
(2) 55 St Enoch's Wynd Glasgow
1854–8
*Bar.; a Dominick Gerletti, opt., carver,
gilder, looking-glasses, picture frames,
fireworks, at (1) 10 Candlerigg St
Glasgow 1849–55
(2) 24 Glassford St Glasgow 1855–7
(3) 44 Trongate Glasgow 1857–8*

GERONIMO, P.
WB-10.m.sp.mi.

GESTRA, J., and SCHENA
Newport
WB-8.m.bp.pat.

GIANNA, L.
Salop
WB-8.m.bp.pat.clo. WB-10.m.sp.
*Probably L. Gianna, opt., Market Place
Shrewsbury 1816*

GIBBS, Thos
WB-10.m.sp.

GIERDELI, P.
7 Brooks Market
WB-8.m.bp.pat.

GILARDI
Bristol
WB-8.m.sp.mi.
Possibly a variant of—

GILARDONI, A.
Bristol
WB-10.m.sp. WB-10.rw.sp. WB-8.m.
sp.mi.

GILARDONI, B.
Exeter

WB-8.m.bp.pat. WB-10.m.sp.
*Probably B. Gilardoni, jeweller,
Fore St Exeter 1816*

GILBERT & GILKERSON fl 1792–1811
8 Postern Row Tower Hill London
*Math.instr.; one of the partners was
John Gilbert (2)*
SB(b).m.bp.g.thca.hycen.

GILBERT, John (1) fl 1726–63
The Mariner Postern Row Tower Hill
London
*Opt.math.phil.instr.; trade card
advertised all sorts of instruments
including barometers (Heal Colln,
Brit.Mus.) (Plate 18)*

GILBERT, John (2) fl 1767–94
8 Postern Row Tower Hill London
*Math.instr.; son of John Gilbert (1),
in partnership with Henry Gregory
from 1789 and with Gilkerson from
1792 (Gilbert and Gilkerson)*

GILLHAM
Eastbourne
WB-8.m.pt.mi.

GIOBBIO
Devizes and Trowbridge
WB-8.m.bp.pat.

GIOBBIO, B.
WB-10.m.sp.

GIOBBIO, G. B.
Burnley
WB-8.m.bp.pat.

GIREARO, J.
32 Ely
WB-8.sw.sp.

GIRLONI, D.
SB(b).m.bp.g.

GIRONIMO
London
WB-8.m.sp.
Possibly—

GIRONIMO, Laurence fl 1845
93 Leather Lane London
*Looking-glasses, bar.therm.;
Felix Gugeri at this address by 1854*

GISCARA, Jeremiah
WB-8.m.sp.

GITTINS, W.
113 Salop
SB(b).olivewood.bp.sqc. AB

GIUDICE, A. and Co
Stroud Water
WB-8.m.bp.pat. WB-8.m.sp.mi.

GIUSANI, P.
WB-8.m.bp.pat.
Possibly—

GIUSANI, P. and Sons
Wolverhampton and Bilston
WB-10.rw.sp.mop.
Probably P. Giusani, carver, gilder,
Cock St Wolverhampton 1835

GLADSTONE, J.
SB(b).m.bp.

GOBBI
Liverpool
SB.o. WB-8.rw.sp.

GOBBI, P.
WB-8.m.bp.pat.

GOBBI, P. and Son
Stroud
WB-8.rw.sp.mi.

GOGERTY, Robert fl 1848—d. 1856
72 Fleet St London
Opt.phil.instr.
MB

GONDOLA, P.
12 Little Saffron Hill London
WB-8.m.sp.mi.

GOOBBI, J. and Co
SB(b).m.bp.g.

GOODALL, Geo
WB-8.bp.pat.
Baillie records a George Goodall, wa.,
Tadcaster 'late 18c.'

GOODMAN
Pontypridd
WB-10.m.sp.mi.

GORLAND
London Wall
WB-10.rw.sp.sqb.mop.

GOUGH, Walter fl 1799–1810
21 Middle Row Holborn London
Opt.math.phil.instr.; trade card
advertised barometers

GOWLAND, C.
Sunderland
MB
Probably Clement Gowland, clo. and wa.,
High St Sunderland 1811–16

GRAFTON, Henry fl 1844–60
(1) 80 Chancery Lane London 1844–60

(2) 36 Holborn Hill London 1849–53
(3) 7–8 Rolls Bldgs London 1856–60
Phil.instr.bar.therm.

GRAHAM, George p 141

GRAHAM, Harriet fl 1832–3
25 Baldwins Gdns London
Bar.therm.

GRANT
SB.m.rt.

GRANT, John fl 1781 —d.1810
75 Fleet St London
Clo.; CC.1781; a notable clockmaker,
probably the maker of the regulator
clock in Guildhall Mus. with a
barometer and thermometer mounted
on either side of the glazed door

GRASI and FONTANA
Exeter
WB-8.m.bp.pat. WB-8.m.sp.
See Bulla, Grasi and Fontana

GRASSI, BERGNA and ORIGONI fl 1830–4
34 Dean St Newcastle
Bar.; John Origoni alone at this
address by 1837 and J. B. Bergna at
St Nicholas Churchyard 1841

GRAY, Stephen fl 1694–1701
(1) Canterbury
(2) Charter House London
F.R.S.; an amateur maker of
microscopes, sundials, etc.; the
Philosophical Transactions *Vol. 20*
p 176 contain his proposal for a
barometer (p 221 Note 1)

GRECHI, C. A.
Shaftesbury
WB-8.m.bp.pat.

GREEN
Grantham
WB-8.m.bp.pat.
Baillie records a William Green, wa.,
Grantham 'early 19c.'

GREGO, A. fl 1817
27 Leather Lane London
Looking-glasses; this was John Corti's
address 1815–25
WB-8.m.bp.pat.

GREGORY
Gloucester
WB-8.m.sp.mi.

GREGORY and Son
SB.m.rt.
Possibly—

GREGORY, Henry fl 1750–92
(1) Azimuth Compass near ye India House Leadenhall St London 1761
(2) 148 Leadenhall St near the East India House 1763
Opt.math.instr.; at some point took a son into partnership (Gregory and Son). By 1783 the firm was named Gregory and Wright and by 1789 Gregory, Gilbert and Wright; in 1792 it became Gilbert and Gilkerson

GREGORY and Son
148 near the India House London
WB. in elaborately carved gilt frame 'repaired by Gregory and Son'
See Henry Gregory

GRIGGI, J.
Liverpool
WB-8.m.rt.fg.

GRIMALDI, D.
WB-10.m.sp.mi.

GRIMALDI, Henry fl 1839–60
(1) 16 Brook St Hatton Gdn London 1839–42
(2) 4 Charles St Hatton Gdn London 1844
(3) 24 Greville St Hatton Gdn London 1845–7
(4) 31 Brook St Hatton Gdn London 1850–60
Opt.phil.instr.bar.therm.; sometimes spelt Grimoldi in directories. Dominick Lione at (1) 1821–36, G. F. Eve at (2) by 1851 and Anthony Tagliabue also at (4) 1850–4

GRIMSHAW
SB.m.
Baillie records a John Grimshaw, wa., Liverpool 1810–29

GRUNDY, John Clowes fl 1834–41
4 Exchange St Manchester
Bar., looking-glasses

GUANELLA, A.
Bristol
WB-8.m.sp.

GUANZIROLI, Giuseppe fl 1834–60
106 Hatton Gdn London
Looking-glasses, artificial flowers; one of the partners of Battistessa and Co until 1845 when with Luigi Guanziroli he succeeded to the business; on his own by 1853

GUANZIROLI, G. and L. fl 1845–52
106 Hatton Gdn London
Partnership of Giuseppe and Luigi Guanziroli

GUARNERIO, A.
St Ives
WB-8.m.sp.mi.

GUARNERIO, P.
Huntingdon
WB-10.m.sp.mi. WB-8.m.sp.mi.

GUDGEON, jnr
Abbey Gate St Bury
WB-8.m.sp.fg.
Probably George Gudgeon, wa. and clo., Abbey Gate St Bury St Edmunds 1830; Baillie records a Gudgeon junior, wa., Bury 'early 19c.'

GUGERI
WB-8.m.bp.pat.
Possibly Andrew or Dominic Gugeri

GUGERI, Andrew fl 1829–59
(1) 15 Upper Union Ct Holborn London 1829
(2) 16 Charles St Hatton Gdn London 1830–59
Looking-glasses, bar.therm.; in partnership with Belotti 1829–43 (Belotti and Gugeri, Gugeri and Belotti) and with Paul Carughi 1844–5 (Gugeri and Carughi)

GUGERI and BELLOTTI
15 Union Ct Holborn Hill London
WB-8.m.bp.pat. WB-12.m.sp.mi.
WB-14.m.sp.clo.—Gershom Partington Colln, Bury St Edmunds
See Gugeri and Belotti

GUGERI and BELOTTI fl 1838–43
16 Charles St Hatton Gdn London
Bar.therm., plate glass; previously styled Belotti and Gugeri but this combination seems to have been more commonly used on barometers (see Gugeri and Bellotti). See Andrew Gugeri. In 1844 the firm became—

GUGERI and CARUGHI fl 1844–5
16 Charles St Hatton Gdn London
Partnership of Andrew Gugeri and Paul Carughi; succeeded Gugeri and Belotti. By 1846 Gugeri on his own and Carughi at 38 Brook St London

GUGERI and Co
WB-10.m.sp.
Possibly Gugeri and Belotti

GUGERI, D.
    WB-10.m.bp.pat.
    Probably—

GUGERI, D.
    Boston
    WB-8.m. WB-8.m.sp.mi. WB-10.m.
    sp.mi.
    *Probably Dominic Gugeri, wa.clo.,
    silversmith, jeweller, Market Place
    Boston 1835–42. Baillie records him as
    'early 19c.'. See Domk Gugeri*

GUGERI, Domk
    Boston
    WB-8.m.bp.pat.
    See D. Gugeri Boston

GUGERI, Felix fl 1854–9
    93 Leather Lane London
    *Bar.; Laurence Gironimo at this
    address 1845*

GUGERI, J.
    Boston
    SB.m.sp.g.thca.

GUGGIARI, D. and ANZIANI fl 1832–60
    Pelham St Nottingham
    *Looking-glasses, carvers, gilders, bar.;
    Dominic Guggiari also appears on his
    own in directories 1835–41*

GUGGIARI, Charles fl 1858
    25 Digbeth Birmingham
    Bar.

GUGGIARI, Dominic fl 1835–41
    Pelham St Nottingham
    See D. Guggiari and Anzani

GUGIRE, D. and Co
    WB-8.m.bp.
    Probably a mis-spelling of D. Gugeri

H

HALLIFAX, George b.1725 —d.1811
    Doncaster
    *Clo.; fourth son of John Hallifax,
    became Mayor of Doncaster 1775 and
    1792*
    WB-w.(see p 149)

HALLIFAX, John p 145

HAMBLETON
    WB-8.m.sp.

HANSON
    Windsor
    WB-10.rw.sp.
    Probably William Hanson, clo.

(1) *Thames St Windsor 1816*
(2) *30 High St Windsor 1830: Baillie
records this maker as 'c. 1800'*

HARGRAVES
    Skipton
    SB(b).m.sp.oval c.g.inl.
    *Baillie records a Thomas Hargreaves
    or Hargraves, clo., Settle c. 1770–95*

HARRIMAN, John fl 1839–60
    (1) 58 Church St Birmingham 1839–49
    (2) 60 Church St Birmingham 1854
    (3) 100 Pritchett St Birmingham
        1858–60
    Bar.; spelt Harrison in 1847 directory
    WB-8.m.bp.mi.(1)

HARRIS, William and Co fl 1799–1848
    (1) 47 High Holborn London
        1799–1812
    (2) 50 High Holborn London 1813–48
    Opt.math.instr.; London and Hamburg
    SB.m.bow.ivpl.(2) SB.m.sp.rc.g.thca.
    (2)

HARRISON, John fl 1856–60
    29 Kirby St London
    Phil.instr.bar.

HARRISON, The Rev Robert
    WB-8.m.sp.pat.good inlays but
    pediment a replacement
    *Probably a case of the owner's name
    engraved on the dial*

HART
    London
    SB m.bp.hc.

HART, N.
    Woolwich
    WB-10.m.sp.mi.

HAUKSBEE, Francis (1) p 150

HAUKSBEE, Francis (2) p 151

HAWKINS
    Southampton
    WB-8.m.gothic case

HAYMAN
    Launceston
    WB-10.m.sp.mi.

HAYWARD
    Ashford
    WB-10.m.sp.sqb.

HEADLAM
    4 Silver St Stockton on Tees
    WB-8.m.pt.

HEALD
    Wisbeach
    WB-8.m.pt.pb.
    Probably—

HEALD, A.
    Wisbech
    WB-8.m.sp.mi.
    Probably Alfred Heald, wa.clo.opt.,
    silversmith, High St Wisbech 1851

HEATH
    Plymouth
    SB.m.rt.
    Probably William Heath, Devonport

HEATH, T.
    Probably—

HEATH, Thomas p 153

HEATH, William fl 1850–7
    (1) 46 Fore St Devonport 1850–2
    (2) 116 Fore St Devonport 1857
    Bar.opt.; with a Thomas Cornish 1850

HEATH and WING fl 1740–73
    Hercules and Globe Fountain Tavern
    Exeter Exchange Strand London
    Opt.math.phil.instr.; partnership of
    Thomas Heath and Tycho Wing,
    dissolved after Heath's death 1773
    when Wing retired. See trade
    card (Banks Colln, Brit.Mus.)
    (Plate 87). Succeeded by T. Newman
    SB.m.arched top.carved case (no
    address)

HEIGHWAY
    Cambridge
    SB.m.carved case.ivpl.

HEMINGWAY, Robert fl 1848–9
    18 Brook St London
    Bar.therm.

HEMSLEY
    140 Ratcliffe Highway
    MB
    Probably Henry Hemsley, opt.instr.
    (1) 135 Ratcliffe Highway London
    1828–45
    (2) 140 St George St London 1846–60

HENLEY, William Thomas fl 1844–8
    28 Haydon St Minories London
    Phil.instr.bar.therm.

HENSHAW
    London
    WB-8.m.sp.
    Baillie records an Isaac Henshaw, wa.,
    London 'early 19c.'

HEYWOOD
    WB-8.m.sp.mi.
    Baillie records a William Heywood, clo.,
    London 'early 19c.'

HICKS, George fl 1811
    43 Shoe Lane London
    Bar.

HICKS, Joseph fl 1814–22
    (1) 11 Brook St London 1814–6
    (2) 17 Lambeth Walk London 1817
    (3) 19 Kirby St London 1817–20
    (4) 117 Bishopsgate without London
        1820–2
    Bar.opt.instr., engraver

HIGGINS
    16 Saffron St London
    WB-8.m.rt.
    Probably John Higgins, cabinet-maker
    (1) 16 Saffron St Saffron Hill London
    1811–19
    (2) 3 Saffron St Saffron Hill London
    1822–3

HILL, M. fl 1860
    20½ Constitution Hill Birmingham
    Bar.

HILL, Nathaniel fl 1746–66
    Globe and Sun Chancery Lane
    London
    Math.instr.; trade card illustrates
    barometer similar to Desaguliers'
    barometer (Plate 17) (Sc.Mus.London)

HILLS, Jno
    Bury
    SB.m.bp.thpl.

HINTON, William fl 1856–60
    39 Charles St Hatton Gdn London
    Bar.frames; shared this address with
    Thomas Bird and probably made
    frames for him

HOLLAND, William fl 1849–60
    (1) 14 Greville St London 1849–51
    (2) 20 Greville St London 1852–9
    (3) 17 Greville St London 1860
    Bar.therm.; possibly one of the
    partners of—

HOLLAND and WITHERSPOON fl 1848
    24 Brook St London
    Bar.

HOLMES
    Derby
    WB-8.m.sp.mi.

HOLMES, John
    London

SB.m.rt.sqc.thpl.carved case
Possibly John Holmes, clo.wa.,
156 Strand London 1762–1815

HOPKINS
London
WB-8.m.sp.mi.
Baillie records several London
clockmakers of this name

HOPPE
London
SB.m.sp.g.thca.

HORNE, THORNTHWAITE and Co fl 1846–60
123 Newgate St London
Opt.phil.instr.bar.therm.; held
appointment to the Queen

HORROD, W.
WB-8.m.sp. WB-10.m.sp.mi.
WB-10.m.sp.sqb.
Probably either William or
William Thomas Horrod

HORROD, Wm. fl 1811
37 Laystall St Leather Lane London
Bar.; possibly identifiable with
W. T. Horrod
WB-12.m.sp.clo. signed 'Thorp.Bath'
(Plate 45); *Baillie records a Thorp,*
Bath, clo., 'early 19c.'

HORROD, William Thomas fl 1832–4
1 Bakers Row Clerkenwell London
Bar.therm., engraver; see
William Horrod

HORTON, Wm. fl 1842
12 Barbican London
Bar.therm.

HOUGHTON
Farnworth near Warrington
SB(b).m.sqc.ppl. in simple arched case,
tube enclosed by fluted column, plates
engraved 'Entwistle Sculp., Bolton'—
Gloucester Mus.

HOULISTON, James fl 1839–58
  (1) 3 St Albans Terrace Kennington
     Rd London 1839
  (2) 33 New Bond St London 1843–50
  (3) 85 New Bond St London 1851–8
Opt.bar.therm.; see Houlston

HOULSTON
New Bond St
WB-8.m.bp.
Probably James Houliston

HOWORTH, Charles
Halifax
SB(b).m.g.ppl.; several AB(b).m.rt.rc.

ppl. 2 tubes: two of these—Mus.Hist.
Sc.Oxford; another—Gabb Colln,
Nat.Mar.Mus., Catalogue No. O.4;
another—Bolling Hall Mus.Bradford,
Catalogue No. 17/32a. Of other
examples one had th. signed 'Lainton'
See Samuel Lainton, Halifax, who sold
identical barometers and—

HOWORTH, Charles
Pump Hill Shibden near Halifax
AB(b).m.—Bolling Hall Mus.
Bradford, Catalogue No. 62/283
See Charles Howorth, Halifax

HUDSON
Greenwich
WB-10.m.sp.mi.

HUDSON
London
WB-8.m.bp.pat.

HUDSON, John
Ottley
WB-8.rw.sp.mi.

HUDSON and Son
Greenwich
WB-14.m.sp.hycen.
See Hudson, Greenwich

HUNT, Harry b. 1635—d. 1713
Gresham House London
Robert Hooke's assistant to 1676, then
Operator to the Royal Society in
succession to Richard Shortgrave:
Librarian 1796. Made barometers of
various types; his barometers
recommended to Society members for
weather records by Dr. Woodward.
E. Halley in a letter to the Society
1697 wished for 'one of Mr. Hunt's
portable barometers' for use in
measuring height of Snowdon
(Philosophical Transactions Vol. 19
p 582). Made a WB for Hooke
(Hooke's Diary 11 April 1679) and
recommended by Halley for
manufacture of Hooke's MB
(Miscellanea Curiosa, ed. Halley,
1705–7, Vol. 1 p 255): he made one of
these for the Royal Society which was
presented to the meeting on
13 November 1695

HUNT, T.
Cork
MB
Probably Thomas Hunt, opt, Patrick St
Cork 1805–17

HUNT, Thos
WB-8.m.rt.pat.
*Possibly Thomas Hunt, Cork (see
T. Hunt)*

HUNTLEY
London
WB-10.m.sp.sqb. SB.ebony.g.ivpl.
2thpl.pewter inlay
*Probably Robert Huntley, opt. instr,
fl 1810–30
(1) Plummers Row City Rd London
(2) 53 High Holborn London
(3) 244 Regent St London
(4) 118 Oxford St London*

HURT, Joseph fl 1729–48
Archimedes and Three Golden
Spectacles Ludgate St London
*Opt.; trade card advertised 'curious
portable barometers with or without
thermometers' (Heal Colln, Brit.Mus.)*

HURTER fl 1787
London
*Math.instr.; Taylor records that a
barometer was used by H. B. de
Saussure on Mont Blanc*

HYDE, J.
Sleaford
WB-8.m.sp.mi.
*Probably John Hyde, wa.clo., jeweller,
engraver, Southgate Sleaford 1835–41;
his descendants are still in business in
Stamford*

HYNES, J.
Lynn
WB-8.m.sp.
*Probably John Hynes, opt., 98 High St
Lynn 1830*

I

ILLINGWORTH, Jonn
Halifax
SB.ppl.

INGRAM, L.
Lincoln
WB-8.m.sp.sqb.
*Probably Laceby Ingram, wa.clo.,
jeweller, 239 High St Lincoln 1838-41*

INTROFISI, P.
London
WB-8.m.bp.pat.

INTROSS, A.
Chatham

WB-8.m.sp.
See Intross and Co

INTROSS, A.
Rochester Bridge
WB-8.m.sp.sqb. WB-10.m.sp.sqb.
See Intross and Co

INTROSS, A. and Co
Strood
WB-8.m.pt.
See Intross and Co

INTROSS and Co fl 1858
5 Sims's Terrace Chatham
*Bar.; this maker, or his relations, had
branches elsewhere in the area
(A. Intross, Chatham, Rochester Bridge
etc.)*

INTROSS, P.
Chatham
WB-8.m.sp.mi.

INTROSS, P.
Rochester
WB-8.sw.

INTROSS, W.
Rochester Bridge
WB-8.m.sp. WB-8.m.sp.mi.

INTROVINI, G.
88 George Rd Manchester
WB-8.m.sp.mi.
Probably Gaspar Introvino

INTROVINO, G.
WB-10.m.bp.
Probably—

INTROVINO, Gaspar fl 1822–41
(1) 43 Thomas St Manchester 1822–6
(2) 88 St George St Manchester 1841
*Carver, gilder, bar.; sometimes spelt
Intronini in directories: see also
G. Introvini and G. Introvino*
WB-8.m.sp.mi.(2) WB-8.m.bp.pat.(1)

IRELAND
WB-8.m.bp.pat.

J

JACKSON
WB-8.rw.sp.sqb.mi.

JACOB, Isaac
33 Castle St Swansea
WB-10.m.pt.

JACOPI, C.
Salop
WB-10.m.sp.

JAMISON, George fl 1786–1810
    (1) 33 Charing Cross London 1800–5
    (2) High St Portsmouth
    Clo.wa.; chronometer maker to the
    Navy
    WB-10.m.sp.(1)

JENKINS, Alexander fl 1854–60
    (1) 15 Garnault Place Clerkenwell
        London 1854–6
    (2) 19 Remington St London 1857–60
    Bar.

JOHN, Peter
    Lynn
    WB-8.m.sp.sqb.

JOHN, Peter
    Wisbech
    WB-8.m.sp. WB-8.m.sp.mi.

JOHNSON and BLACKBOURN fl 1847–8
    34 Hatton Gdn London
    Partnership of William Johnson and
    Cuthbert Blackbourn

JOHNSON, S.
    London
    SB.m.arched top with 3 finials and
    brass pillars. hc.g.
    Probably—

JOHNSON, Samuel fl 1724–72
    Sir Isaac Newton and Two Pairs of
    Golden Spectacles 23 Ludgate St
    London
    Opt.; app. to James Mann and
    succeeded to his business. Trade card
    advertised barometers and thermometers
    (Sc.Mus.London)

JOHNSON, W.
    WB-8.rw.sp.mop.
    Possibly—

JOHNSON, Wm. fl 1830–60
    (1) 19 Cross St Hatton Gdn London
        1830
    (2) 20 Cross St Hatton Gdn London
        1831–3
    (3) 29 Kirby St London 1834–40
    (4) 34 Hatton Gdn London 1841–60
    Bar.therm.; in partnership with
    Cuthbert Blackbourn 1847–8
    (Johnson and Blackbourn)
    WB-12.m.sp.mi.(4)

JONES and Co
    London
    SB.m.g.

JONES, D.
    London
    SB

JONES, Henry fl 1654 —d.1695
    Inner Temple London
    App. 1654, CC. 1663 (Master 1691).
    A notable clockmaker and, according
    to Roger North, the first craftsman to
    offer barometers for sale: he did not
    apparently make barometers with much
    success (see p 15 et seq.)

JONES, J. and Son
    135 near Furnival's Inn Holborn
    London
    See Jones and Son

JONES, John b.1739 —d.1788(?)
    135 near Furnival's Inn Holborn
    London
    Opt.instr.; a well-known maker, father
    of William and Samuel Jones. In
    partnership with William 1784
    (Jones and Son)

JONES, Samuel
    See W. and S. Jones

JONES and Son fl 1784–8
    135 Holborn London
    Opt.instr.; partnership of John and
    William Jones; see W. and S. Jones

JONES, Thomas p 154

JONES, W. and S. p 156

JONES, William
    See W. and S. Jones

JUMP
    London
    WB in mahogany frame matching
    regulator clock by Vulliamy, London.
    Probably either (1) Richard Thomas
    Jump, clo., who according to Britten
    joined Benjamin Lewis Vulliamy 1812,
    or (2) his son Joseph Jump, clo., app.
    to B. L. Vulliamy 1827 and with him
    until 1854

K

KALABERGO, J.
    Banbury
    WB-8.m.bp.pat. WB-8.m.sp.
    WB-8.m.sp.sqb. WB-8.m.sp.mi.
    Probably—

KALABERGO, John b.1812 —d.1852
    (1) Market Place Banbury 1830–52
    (2) Bridge St North Banbury 1832–52

*Wa.clo, jeweller, bar.therm.; a prolific
barometer maker; see J. Kalabergo*

KARRATT, S.
Newcastle-under-Lyme
WB-8.m.sp.

KEEN and FRODSHAM
17 South Castle St Liverpool
MB
*Baillie records a Henry Frodsham, clo.
wa., Liverpool, app. 1823*

KETTERER
Queen St Portsea
WB-10.rw.sp.sqb.

KILLICK
WB-8.m.sp.mi.

KING, J. and Son
Bristol
WB-8.m.sp. WB-8.rw.sp.sb.
*Probably J. King, math.instr.opt.,
Clare St Bristol 1822, in partnership
with a son at 2 Clare St Bristol 1830*

KING, Peter
Southwark
WB-8.m.bp.pat.

KLEYSER and Co
Goswell St London
WB-8.m.sp. WB-8.rw.sp.sqb.
*Several German clo. and toy makers
of this name are recorded in directories
and by Baillie and Britten, but none of
them in Goswell St*

KNIE
Edinburgh
See Balthazar Knie

KNIE, Balthazar, p 158

KNIGHT
Braintree
WB-10.m.sp.
*Baillie records a Charles Knight, clo.
Dunmow 'c. 1800'*

KNIGHT
London
WB-8.m.bp.pat.

KNOWLES, Jeffery
SB(b).m.bp.enamel pl.

L

LADD, William fl 1851–7
29 Penton St Walworth Rd London
Phil.instr.bar.therm.

LAFFRANCHO, J.
Ludlow
WB-8.m.bp.pat. WB-8.m.sp.
WB-8.m.sp.mi. WB-8.m.sp.sqb. verre
églomisé panel beneath dial
Sometimes spelt—

LAFRANCHO, J.
Ludlow
See J. Laffrancho

LAINTON, Samuel
Halifax
AB(b).m.rt.rc.ppl. 2 tubes, th between
tubes—Whipple Mus.Cambridge
(identical to certain examples by
Charles Howorth, on one of whose
barometers the signature 'Lainton'
appears) AB(b).m.rt.rc.ppl.
*Probably Samuel Lainton, cabinet-
maker, 9 King Cross St Halifax 1860*

LAPPI and SOLCHA
Hull
WB-8.m.sp.mi.
*Lewis Solcha may have been one of
the partners*

LAWRENCE
WB-8.pt.painted

LAYBOURN
Royston
SB(b).m.bp.

LEACH
Salisbury
WB-8.m.
*Probably George Leach, wa.clo.,
Exeter St Salisbury 1830, fl to 1860*

LELLI, S.
Chichester
WB-10.m.sp.

LEONE
Exeter
WB-8.rw.sp.mi.

LEONE, John
Aylesbury
WB-8.m.sp.sqb. WB-8.m.sp.mi.
*Probably John Leone, jeweller,
Kingsbury Aylesbury 1830. See
J. Lione Aylesbury*

LEVI, Moses
Ipswich
WB-8.m.sp.mi.
*Probably Moses Levi or Levy, wa.clo.,
hardware, toys
(1) Carr St Ipswich 1839
(2) St Matthews St Ipswich 1844–6*

LEVIN
Penzance
WB-8.m.sp. MB

LEVIN, M. and E.
London
WB-8.m.sp. WB-8.m.sp.mi.

LEVY, J.
Gainsborough
WB-8.m.bp.pat.
Probably Isaiah Levi, wa.clo., jeweller,
dealer in pianofortes
(1) Lord St Gainsborough 1822–35
(2) Silver St Gainsborough 1841

LEVY, Moses
Ipswich
See Moses Levi

LILLY, S.
WB-8.m.sp.mi.

LINCOLN, C.
London
SB.m.bp.rc.thca.hytop.
Probably Charles Lincoln, opt.math.
instr., b. c.1744 —d.1807
(1) 11 Cornhill London 1763
(2) 62 Leadenhall St 1791–1801

LINGFORD, John
Nottingham
WB-8.m.bp.pat.mi.
Probably John Lingford, jeweller,
ironmonger
(1) Market Hill Nottingham 1793–1814
(2) Parliament St Nottingham 1835
(3) 5 Milton St Nottingham 1835

LINNELL, J.
Ludgate St London
AB.m.in plain case with rounded
end, fine engraving
See Joseph Linnell

LINNELL, Joseph b. c. 1740—fl 1764
Great Golden Spectacles and
Quadrant 33 Ludgate St London
Opt.math.phil.instr.; app. to
James Ayscough 1754 and succeeded
him 1763. Trade card advertised
'barometers, diagonal, standard, or
portable' (Heal Colln, Brit.Mus.)

LIONE and Co
81 Holborn London
WB-10.m.sp.
See James Lione

LIONE and Co fl 1820–36
(1) 14 Brook St London 1820
(2) 16 Brook St London 1821–36

Bar.; see Dominick Lione
WB-8.m.sp.(2)

LIONE, D.
Liverpool
WB-8.rw.sp.mi.

LIONE, D. and Co
81 High Holborn London
WB-8.m.bp.pat.
James Lione worked at this address,
also J. Cetti and Josh Somalvico.
Possibly Dominick Lione and
Joseph Somalvico shared a workshop
here before moving to 125 Holborn Hill
(see Lione Somalvico and Co)

LIONE, Dominick fl 1805–36
(1) 125 Holborn Hill London 1805–7
(2) 14 Brook St London 1811–20
(3) 16 Brook St London 1821–36
Bar.; in partnership with
Joseph Somalvico 1805–19
(Lione Somalvico and Co). See
Lione and Co. Henry Grimaldi at (3)
by 1839

LIONE and FARONI
WB-8.m.bp.pat.

LIONE, J.
London
WB-10.m.rt.th. and hy. mounted on
dial
Probably James Lione

LIONE, J.
Aylesbury
WB-8.m.sp.mi.
See John Leone, Aylesbury

LIONE, Jas
London
WB-14.m.sp.fg.mi. WB-8.m.bp.pat.
Probably—

LIONE, James
81 High Holborn London
WB-8.m.bp.pat. WB-10.m.dial at top
J. Cetti also worked at this address.
See Lione and Co, 81 Holborn, and
D. Lione and Co, 81 High Holborn

LIONE and SOMALVICO
125 Holborn Hill London
WB-12.m.bp.clo. WB-12.m.sp.sb.
WB-10.sw.sp.th.dial. no hy. or level

LIONE and SOMALVICO
16 Brook St Holborn
SB(b).m.bp.g.thpl.
The directories do not record the firm
at this address: but see Lione and Co.

It is not clear when the name Somalvico was dropped from the title

LIONE, SOMALVICO and Co fl 1805–19
(1) 125 Holborn Hill London 1805–7
(2) 14 Brook St London 1811–19
Opt.bar.; partnership of Dominick Lione and Joseph Somalvico. Lione on his own at (2) by 1820. Charles Stampa and Co at (1) 1802
A very large number of barometers survive including WB-10.m.rt.pat.hy. base (1) WB-10.m.sp.clo.(1) WB-10. sw.rt.pat.(1) WB-8.m.bp.pat.(1) WB-8.m.rt.pat.(1) WB-8.m.rt.fg. hycen.(1) WB-8.m.bp.pat.(2) WB-8.m.rt.hycen.(2) WB-10.m.sp.(2) WB-14.m.sp.(1) WB-12.sw.sp.clo.th. dial. no hy. or level (1)
See D. Lione and Co, 81 High Holborn, and Lione and Somalvico

LLOYD
Hereford
WB-8.rw.sp.mi.

LOCK
Oxford
SB.m.bp.hc.pat.thca.

LOMAS
SB(b).m.bp.thca.—Adlington Hall (National Trust)
Probably—

LOMAS, H.
Adlington
SB(b).m.bp.g. SB.m.classical pediment

LOMBARDINI
Bristol
WB-8.rw.sp.
Probably A. Lombardini, looking-glasses, 13 Lower Castle St Bristol 1856

LOMBARDINI and CASTELETTI
Salop
WB-8.m.bp.pat.

LOMBARDINI and Co
WB-8.m.bp.pat.

LOMBARDINI, F.
Totnes
WB-8.m.bp.pat.

LOMBARDINI, J.
WB-8.m.bp.pat. WB-10.m.

LONG, J.
Tiverton
WB-8.rw.pt.mi.

LONG, Jas
Royal Exchange London
SB.m.rt.g.thca.bayonet tube
See James Long

LONG, James fl 1769–1811
4 Back of Royal Exchange London
Opt., Master Spectaclemakers Co 1805, succeeded by James Smith by 1817
SB.m.sp SB.m.rt. WB-8.sw.sp.

LONG, Josh
20 Little Tower St London
WB-6.m.sp.thca.with dial at top
(*cf.* Plate 48)
See Joseph Long

LONG, Joseph fl 1820–60
(1) 43 Eastcheap London
(2) 20 Little Tower St London 1820–60
Bar.therm.math.phil.instr.opt.
SB.rt.(1)

LONGONI, F.
WB-8.m.bp.pat.

LOVI
SB(b).m.bp.pat.

LOVI
Edinburgh
WB-10.m.sp.

LUCIN, Francis fl 1839
142 Gt Saffron Hill London
Bar.therm.

LUCIONI, Giuseppe A. fl 1851–4
36 Ray St Clerkenwell London
Bar.therm.

LUVATE, D.
Preston
WB-10.m.sp.mi. WB-8.m.bp.pat. WB-8.m.sp.mi. WB-8.rw.sp.sqb.
Also spelt Luvatte; probably Dominic Luvate, looking-glasses, (1) 43 Friargate Preston 1828 (2) 27 Friargate Preston 1834

LUVATTE, D.
Preston
See D. Luvate

LYON
South Molton
WB-8.m.sp.mi.

LYON, C.
Bridlington
WB-8.m.sp.mi.
Probably Craven Lyon, wa.clo., High St Bridlington 1822–41

LYON, Jas
    London
    WB-8.m.sp.pat.fg.

M

McALLISTER
    London
    WB-8.m.bp.pat.

McHUGH, M.
    Staleybridge
    WB-8.m.sp.

McPHERSON, R.
    Dumfries
    SB-m.sp.bow.g. WB-8.m.bp.dial
    painted

MacRAE
    34 Aldgate London
    SB.m.sqp.sqc.g.thca.
    Probably Henry MacRae, opt.,
    34 Aldgate within London 1833–60

MacRAE
    29 Royal Exchange London
    WB-12.m.sp. WB-10.m.sp.

MAFFIA, A.
    WB-8.rw.sp.mop.

MAFFIA, C.
    WB-10.m.sp.

MAFFIA, P.
    Monmouth
    WB-8.m.sp. WB-8.rw.pt.

MAGGI
    SB(b).m.bp.g. WB.m.bp.pat.

MAGGI, M.
    Exeter
    WB-8.m.bp.fg.

MAGGI and ORTELLI
    WB-8.m.bp.pat.

MAIN, Peter
    Edinburgh
    SB(b).m.ivpl.carved frame with hood
    in Chinese style

MALACRIDA
    WB-8.m.bp.pat.

MALACRIDA
    237 Holborn London
    SB.m.rt.thpl.

MALLETT
    Woodbridge
    WB-10.m.sp.clo.

MALLUGANI, Mark fl 1830
    New St Dudley
    Bar., umbrellas

MALT, J.
    Wisbech
    WB-8.m.sp.mi.

MALT, James
    WB-8.rw.sp.mi.

MALTWOOD, Richard Austen fl 1829–59
    (1) 19 Charles St Hatton Gdn London
        1829–44
    (2) 3 Orange Row Kennington Row
        London 1842–5
    (3) 22 Charles St Hatton Gdn London
        1845
    (4) 129 Gt Saffron Hill London
        1846–8
    (5) 5 Cross St London 1854–9
    Bar.therm.; (2) was probably his home
    address
    WB-10.m.sp.mi.(1)

MANGACAVALI, Jno fl 1836
    5 Greville St London
    Bar.therm.; John Pensa also at this
    address 1836

MANN, James b. *c.* 1685—fl 1750
    Sir Isaac Newton and Two Pairs of
    Golden Spectacles 23 Ludgate St
    London
    Opt.; employer and later partner of
    James Ayscough. Succeeded by his
    apprentice Samuel Johnson. Trade card
    advertised barometers and
    thermometers (Sc.Mus.London)

MANSELL
    Fakenham
    WB

MANTEGANI, A.
    Wisbech
    WB-8.m.sp. WB-8.m.sp.sqb.
    Probably Antonio Mantegani, wa.clo.,
    High St Wisbech 1851–8

MANTICHA
    SB(b).m.bp.hc.g.thpl.masonic emblems
    engraved on pl.

MANTICHA
    London
    SB(b).m.sp.oval c.g.ppl. plain
    columns to hood. SB(b).m.sqc.ppl.
    columned hood. plates with masonic
    symbols (Plate 96)—Sc.Mus.London
    Probably Dominick Manticha

MANTICHA
    281 Holborn London

WB-9.m.rt.pat.fg.dial engraved with foliate swags and masonic symbols

MANTICHA, A.
SB(b).m.bp.g.

MANTICHA and Co
SB(b).m.sqc.ppl. (*cf.* Plate 96)
SB(b).m.bp.g.thpl. WB-8.m.rt.pat.
dial engraved with masonic symbols
Possibly Dominick Manticha

MANTICHA, D.
DB.m.ppl. (*cf.* Plate 41) dated 1781—
Sc.Mus.London
Probably—

MANTICHA, Dominick p 162

MANTICHA, P.
SB(b).m.bp.

MANTICHA, Peter
DB.m.boxwood pl. (*cf.* Plate 41)

MANTOVA, P.
Luton
WB-10.m.sp.mi.

MANZOCHI, G.
Hull
WB-10.m.sp.mop.
Probably Girolano Manzochi, looking-glasses, 22 Brook St Hull 1838

MARINONE, C.
Bedford
WB-8.m.bp pat.

MARKS, Solomon and Co
Cardiff
MB
*Probably Solomon Marks, wa.clo.,
Broad St Cardiff 1822–60*

MARKWICK, Jacobus
SB.w.hood with twisted pillars above pl.
Probably either
(1) *James Markwick, clo, Royal
Exchange London, fl 1656–98,
CC.1666 or*
(2) *his son James Markwick, clo.,
Royal Exchange London,
fl 1692—d. 1730, CC.1692,
Master 1720*

MARRATT
King William St London Bridge
SB.m.sqp.urn.bow.thca. SB.m.rt.hc.
ivpl.thpl.
*Probably John Marratt, opt.math.phil.
instr.*
(*1*) *54 Shoe Lane London 1833*

(*2*) *15 Gt Winchester St London
1841–4*
(*3*) *63 King William St London
1845–59; became Marratt and
Short 1860*

MARSH, B. fl 1858
83 Coleshill St Birmingham
Bar.

MARSHALL, John fl 1633–1725
(1) Archimedes and Two Golden
Spectacles Ludgate St London
1675
(2) Two Golden Prospects Ludgate St
London
*Opt.instr.; a well-known craftsman,
later opt. to George II. His shop was
not far from John Patrick's workshop
and he sold Patrick's range of
barometers. His neighbour was
John Yarwell*

MARSHALL, P.
WB-10.m.sp.mi.

MARTIN
London
See Benjamin Martin

MARTIN, B.
London
See Benjamin Martin

MARTIN, Benjamin p 164

MARTIN, Jno
Maidstone
WB-12.m.sp.clo.
Probably—

MARTIN, John
Maidstone
WB-8.m.
*Baillie records a Martin, wa.,
Maidstone 'early 19c.'*

MARTINELLI, Alfred fl 1839 —d.1851
(1) 43 Union St Borough 1839
(2) 96 Vauxhall St Lambeth 1843–4
(3) 18 Vauxhall St Lambeth 1845–51
*Bar.therm.; succeeded by his widow
Mrs. E. Martinelli*
WB.m.sp.mi.(3)

MARTINELLI, B.
WB-10.m.sp.

MARTINELLI, Mrs. E. fl 1852–3
18 Vauxhall St Lambeth
Bar.therm.; widow of Alfred Martinelli

MARTINELLI, Lewis fl 1803–11
82 Leather Lane London

Carver, gilder, printseller, bar.therm.;
succeeded P. L. D. Martinelli and Co
WB-12.m.sp.

MARTINELLI, Lewis fl 1834–46
62 King St Borough
Bar.therm.; in partnership with a son
1838–46 (Lewis Martinelli and Son)
WB-10.m.sp. WB-10.m.sp.mi.
WB-8.m.sp. WB-12.m.sp.clo.signed
'T. Combe, Camberwell'

MARTINELLI, Lewis and Son fl 1838–46
62 King St Borough
Looking-glasses, opt.bar.therm.; see
Lewis Martinelli

MARTINELLI, P.
Edinburgh
WB-8.m.bp.

MARTINELLI, P., RONCHETTI and Co
Coventry
SB(b).m.bp.g.thpl. WB-8.m.bp.pat.

MARTINELLI, P. L. D. and Co fl 1799
82 Leather Lane London
Bar.; Lewis Martinelli at this address
by 1803

MARTINELLI, W.
WB-10.sw.sp. WB-12.rw.sp.sqb.mi.
Possibly William Martinelli

MARTINELLI, W. and Sons
54 Snows Fields Borough
WB-8.rw.sp.mi.
Probably—

MARTINELLI, William fl 1840–59
(1) 21 Wells St Oxford St London
1840
(2) 5 Friars St Blackfriars London
1841
(3) 120 Snows Fields London 1853–9
Bar.

MASEFIELD, Robert fl 1767
Birmingham
SB.m.bp.enamel pl. Corinthian
columns to hood and carved eagle
finial (1767)

MASPOLI, A.
79 Lowgate Hull
WB-10.m.sp.sqb. WB-8.m.sp.mi.
WB-8.m.bp.pat. WB-8.m.sp.sqb.th.
beneath dial. rectangular mi. at base
See Augustus Maspoli

MASPOLI, A. and Co
Hull
WB-12.m.sp.fg.mi.
See Augustus Maspoli

MASPOLI, Augustus fl 1826–51
(1) 49 Salthouse Lane Hull 1826–31
(2) 79 Lowgate Hull 1835–51
Looking-glasses, bar.therm., telescopes,
spectacles, picture-frames, wa.clo.,
jewellery, musical boxes, etc.; wholesale
and retail; his forename also appears
in directories as Augustine and
Augustino. In partnership with
James Maspoli, possibly a son,
1831–5. See A. Maspoli

MASPOLI, Augustus and James fl 1831–5
(1) 49 Salthouse Lane Hull 1831
(2) 79 Lowgate Hull 1835
See Augustus Maspoli, James Maspoli

MASPOLI, G.
Hull
WB-8.m.sp.mi.
Probably James Maspoli

MASPOLI, J.
Hull
WB-8.m.sp.
Probably—

MASPOLI, James fl 1831–59
(1) 49 Salthouse Lane Hull 1831
(2) 79 Lowgate Hull 1835
(3) 17 Robinson Row Hull 1839–48
(4) 9 Robinson Row Hull 1851–9
Looking-glasses, bar., jewellery, wa.,
picture frames; in partnership with
Augustus Maspoli, possibly his father,
1831–5. The firm became Soldini and
Maspoli at (4) 1860. Anthony Soldini
is recorded at (3) 1848 and (4) 1851–5,
and Pasqual Soldini at (4) 1855. By
1855 Lewis Solcha at (3)

MASPOLI, MONTI and Co
Sandwich
Clo.bar.; Baillie records the firm as
'early 19c.'; P. Monti may have been
one of the partners
WB-8.m.bp.

MASPOLI, P. and V.
Canterbury
WB-10.m.sp.

MASTAGLIO, FORNELLI and MOLTENI
fl 1837
Grainger St Newcastle upon Tyne
Bar.; Fornelli had left the partnership
by 1841. See V. Mastaglio, C. Molteni
and Mastaglio and Molteni

MASTAGLIO and MOLTENI
Newcastle
WB-10.m.sp.mi.
Probably—

MASTAGLIO and MOLTENI fl 1841–7
24–5 Grainger St Newcastle-upon-Tyne
*Bar.; in 1837 the firm was called
Mastaglio, Fornelli and Molteni;
by 1851 V. Mastaglio is recorded on
his own at 24 Grainger St with
C. Molteni next door at 25 Grainger St
and in Collingwood St*

MASTAGLIO, V. fl 1851–60
(1) 24 Grainger St Newcastle-upon-Tyne 1851–3
(2) 45 Grainger St Newcastle-upon-Tyne 1855–60
(3) 4 Carliol Sq Newcastle-upon-Tyne 1857–60
*Bar.; probably one of the partners of
Mastaglio, Fornelli and Molteni, and
of Mastaglio and Molteni*

MATTHEWS, Alfred
Leighton
WB-8.m.sp.
*Baillie records a William Matthews,
clo., Leighton Buzzard 1785 and a
John Matthews, clo., Leighton Buzzard
'c. 1800'. Alfred may have belonged to
the same family*

MATTHEWS, W. and J.
Penrith and Kendal
WB-8.m.sp.mi.
*Probably William Matthews, wa.clo.,
gunsmith, silversmith, jeweller,
Burrowgate Penrith 1834*

MAUGHAM, J.
Beverley
WB-10.w.scroll pattern (Plate 49)

MAVER, J.
281 Holborn London
WB-8.m.bp.fg.hycen.
*Peter Ramos and Jno Poncione also at
this address. Possibly identifiable
with—*

MAVER, John fl 1832–3
46 Baldwins Gdns London
Bar.therm.

MAZZUCHI, B. and Co
Gloucester
WB-8.m.bp.pat.

MEARS, R.
Boston
WB-8.rw.sp.mi.

MEDCALF, S.
Steeple Bumstead
WB-8.m.sp.

MEDICI, Peter
Newcastle
WB-8.m.bp.pat.

MELLER, Joseph fl 1825–6
28 Princes St Birmingham
Bar.

MELLING, John fl 1672–1704
Abchurch Lane London
*Opt.instr.; Taylor suggests that he is
probably the maker referred to by
Robert Hooke in his Diary—
'Mr. Mellish about barometer'
(18 Nov. 1672): in the same diary
his name is also spelt Mellins, Mellin,
Malling*

MERCER, J. H.
Appleby
WB-10.m.sp.mi.

MERLINE, Paolo fl 1858
72 Hatton Gdn London
Bar.therm.

MERONE
98 Market St Lane Manchester
WB-14.m.sp.
See Joseph Merone

MERONE, Joseph fl 1816–41
(1) 98 Market St Manchester 1816–22
(2) 28 Market St Manchester 1822–41
Bar., looking-glasses

MEYER
Abingdon
WB-8.m.sp.sqb.

MILESIO, D.
Belfast
WB-8.m.bp.pat.

MILLER
Edinburgh
SB.m.rt.hc.thpl.hytop. SB(b).sycamore sp.
Probably John Miller

MILLER and ADIE fl 1804–25
(1) 94 Nicholson St Edinburgh 1804–7
(2) 96 Nicholson St Edinburgh 1807–9
(3) 8 Nicholson St Edinburgh 1810–11
(4) 15 Nicholson St Edinburgh 1811–12
*Partnership of John Miller and his
nephew Alexander Adie*

MILLER, J.
Edinburgh
Mountain B.—Sc.Mus.London
Probably—

MILLER, John fl 1774 —d.1825
    (1) Back of Fountain Well Edinburgh
      1774
    (2) Parliament Close Edinburgh
      1775–95
    (3) 38 South Bridge Edinburgh
      1795–1800
    (4) 86 South Bridge Edinburgh 1803–5
    (5) 94 Nicholson St Edinburgh 1804–7
    (6) 96 Nicholson St Edinburgh 1807–9
    (7) 8 Nicholson St Edinburgh 1810–11
    (8) 15 Nicholson St Edinburgh 1811–12
    Opt.math.instr.; uncle of
    Alexander Adie and his partner from
    1804

MINOLLA, G.
    39 Leather Lane
    SB(b).m.bp.g.thpl.

MODD
    Donnington
    WB-10.m.sp.

MOLESWORTH
    SB.m.

MOLINARI, A.
    Halesworth
    WB-8.m.bp.pat. WB-8.m.sp.
    Probably—

MOLINARI, Antonio fl 1830
    Halesworth
    Bar.therm.

MOLLINER, Charles
    SB(b).m.oval c. with carved crest and
    pendant festoons of fruits and flowers
    on each side of trunk
    A very similar barometer is recorded
    by Casartelli

MOLTENI, A. fl 1851–8
    (1) 185 Pilgrim St Newcastle-upon-
      Tyne 1851–3
    (2) 154 Pilgrim St Newcastle-upon-
      Tyne 1855
    (3) 152 Pilgrim St Newcastle-upon-
      Tyne 1857–8
    (4) 91 Clayton St Newcastle-upon-
      Tyne 1857–8
    Bar.; possibly a relation of C. Molteni

MOLTENI, A.
    Wigan
    WB-8.rw.sp.mi.

MOLTENI, Alex fl 1829
    13 Baldwins Gdns London
    Bar.therm.; one of the partners of

Battistessa, Molteni and Guanziroli
who were at this address 1833–6

MOLTENI, C. fl 1851–60
    (1) 25 Grainger St Newcastle-upon-
      Tyne 1851–3
    (2) Collingwood St Newcastle-upon-
      Tyne 1851–3
    (3) 47 Grainger St Newcastle-upon-
      Tyne 1855–60
    Bar.; probably one of the partners of
    Mastaglio and Molteni

MOLTON, F.
    St Lawrence Steps Norwich
    SB.m.sp.urn.bow.g.
    Probably—

MOLTON, Francis fl 1822–30
    (1) Dove Lane Norwich 1822–30
    (2) St Lawrence Steps Norwich
    SB(b).m.bp.g.(1) WB-8.m.rt.fg.(1)
    WB-8.m.bp.pat.(1) WB-8.m.sp.(2)
    WB-8.m.bp.pat.(2) WB-8.m.rt.fg.(2)
    George Rossi at (2) 1822–30

MONASTERI, L. and Co
    Darlington
    WB-8.m.sp.mi. WB-8.m.sp.sqb.mi.
    WB-8.rw.sp.sqb.mi.

MONTI, A.
    Canterbury
    WB-10.m.sp. WB-8.rw.rt. WB-8.rw.
    pt.mi. WB-8.rw.pt.mop.
    Probably Anthony Monti, wa.clo,
    Palace St Canterbury 1859–60

MONTI, J.
    Canterbury
    WB-8.m.sp.
    Probably either Joseph Monti, wa.clo,
    33 Northgate St Canterbury 1838 or
    John Monti, wa.clo., 82 Northgate St
    1847

MONTI, P.
    Sandwich
    WB-8.rw.pt.mi.
    Possibly one of the partners of
    Maspoli and Monti. Baillie records a
    P. Monti, wa., Sandwich 'early 19c.'

MOORE, John
    Worthing
    WB-8.m.sp.mi.

MORELEY and Sons
    Guildford
    SB.m.rt.ivpl.thpl.

MORELLI, F.
    London
    WB-8.sw.sp.

MORETTI, J. C.
Lynn
SB.m.rt.g.ivpl.

MORGANTI, B.
Brighton
WB-8.m.sp.mi. WB-12.m.sp.sqb.clo.
Possibly John Baptist Morganti, wa.,
jeweller, 31 George St Brighton 1823–8

MORISON
SB(b).m.sqc.

MORRELL
Whitby
WB-10.m.sp.

MORRIS, J.
Kendal
SB.m.sp.urn.bow.thca.

MUNRO
12 York Place Lambeth
WB-10.m.sp.clo.
A James Munro, opt., is recorded at
(1) 72 Oakley St Lambeth 1823–8
(2) 27 North St Lambeth 1826–8
(3) 4–5 North St Lambeth 1830–56

MYERS
Yarmouth
WB-6.m.sp.sqb.

MYERS, P.
Nottingham
WB-8.m.sp. WB-12.m.sp.sqb.mi.brass
columns
Probably Philip Myers, opt.math.instr.
(1) Smithy Row Nottingham 1825
(2) Pelham St Nottingham 1834–5

N

NAIRNE
See Edward Nairne

NAIRNE and BLUNT p 168

NAIRNE, Edward p 169

NAYLOR
Halifax
SB(b).m.oval c.g.ppl.fretwork hood

NEALE, J.
Leadenhall St London
SB.m.bp.thca. with boxwood scales.
tapered columns to hood
Probably John Neale, opt.instr.
Leadenhall St London 1743–59

NEEVES, Richard fl 1857–60
3 Regent Place Grays Inn Rd London
Phil.instr.bar.therm.

NEGRATTI, H. fl 1839
2 Dorrington St London
Bar.therm.; possibly Henry Negretti
but he is not otherwise recorded at
this address

NEGRETTI
36 Redcliffe St Bristol
WB-8.m.bp.pat.

NEGRETTI and Co
19 Leather Lane London
MB—Gloucester Mus.
Henry Negretti was at this address;
see Negretti and Zambra

NEGRETTI and Co
35 Pike St Plymouth
Bar.

NEGRETTI, E. A. L.
See Henry Negretti

NEGRETTI, Gaeton fl 1841
4 Thomas St Manchester
Bar.

NEGRETTI, Henry
One of the founders of—

NEGRETTI and Zambra p 171

NEGRINI, C.
Tenterden
WB-10.m.sp.clo. WB-8.m.bp.pat.

NEILL and Sons
Belfast
WB-8.m.sp.
Baillie records Robert Neill and Sons,
clo., Belfast 1818

NELSON
Dublin
MB
Probably either John Nelson, wa.clo.,
fl 1786–1817
(1) Dame Lane Dublin 1805
(2) 6 Dame Ct Dublin 1809
or William Nelson, opt., jeweller
(1) 21 Essex Quay Dublin 1830
(2) 20 Essex Quay Dublin 1832
(3) 24 Essex Quay Dublin 1834
(4) 37 Lower Ormond Quay Dublin
* 1834–44*
(5) 42 Lower Ormond Quay Dublin
* 1845–50*
(6) 66 Dame St Dublin 1852–8

NEWCOMBE, Frederick and Co fl 1859–60
8 Hatton Gdn London
Phil.instr.opt.bar.therm.

NEWMAN
Regent St London
See John Frederick Newman

NEWMAN, J.
122 Regent St London
SB.m.bp. SB.m.sqp.urn.bow.g.thca.
SB.m.sp.urn.bow.g.thca.WB-10.m.
scroll pattern
See John Frederick Newman

NEWMAN, James fl 1793—1827
Exeter Exchange Strand London
*Opt.math.instr.; app. to T. Newman,
possibly his father, 1793 and succeeded
him c. 1800. Made bar. and therm.
and aided Royal Society with
improvements to them. Probably
succeeded by John Newman*

NEWMAN, John Frederick fl 1816–60
(1) 7–8 Lisle St Leicester Sq London
1816–25
(2) 122 Regent St London 1827–60
*Opt.math.phil.instr.; one of the leading
barometer makers of the nineteenth
century. Made the Royal Society's
standard barometer 1822 and standard
and portable barometers for the Ross
Antarctic expedition. He devised a
portable iron cistern and his
meteorological station barometers
were installed throughout the British
Empire. See J. Newman*

NEWMAN, L.
MB—Sc.Mus.London

NEWMAN, T. fl 1758—1800
Exeter Exchange Strand London
*Math.phil.instr.; succeeded Heath and
Wing after Thomas Heath's death and
Tycho Wing's retirement 1773. Took
his son(?) James Newman into the
business 1793 and succeeded by him
c. 1800. His trade card is identical to
that of Heath and Wing (Plate 87)
(Heal Colln, Brit.Mus.)*

NICHO, P.
Liverpool
WB-8.m.sp.mi.

NICOLA, P.
Liverpool
WB-8.m.bp.fg.

NOAKES
Burwash
WB-10.m.sp.
*Baillie records a J. Noakes, wa.,
Burwash 'early 19c.'*

NODEN, Jno fl 1826–8
10 Charles St Hatton Gdn London
Bar.therm.

NOLLI, J. B. and Co
Perth
WB-10.sw.sp.

NORTHEN, Richard fl 1790–1841
(1) Lowgate Hull 1790–1
(2) 46 Lowgate Hull 1803–34
(3) 50 Lowgate Hull 1835–41
*Opt.wa.clo.bar.; a son was in
partnership at (2) (Richard Northen
and Son), presumably Edward Northen
who succeeded to the business 1842*

NORTHEN, Richard and Son
46 Lowgate Hull
WB-10.sw.3 finials. fg. (Plate 44)
See Richard Northen

NOVATI, BORDESSA and EATON fl 1853–4
54 Exmouth St London
*Bar.therm.; became Bordessa and
Eaton 1855*

O

OAKESHOTT, William fl 1844–5
29 St John St Clerkenwell London
Phil.instr.bar.therm.

OATES, John
Pump near Halifax
AB(b).m.rc.ppl.

OGILVIE, Robert A. fl 1845
19 Upper Wharton St London
Bar.therm.

ORIGONI
Newcastle
WB-10.rw.mop.
Probably—

ORIGONI, John fl 1830–47
34 Dean St Newcastle-upon-Tyne
*Bar.; one of the partners of Grassi,
Bergna and Origoni and alone by 1837.
Spelt Arigoni in an 1841 directory*

ORME, Charles p 173

ORREGGIO
Nottingham
WB-8.m.sp.mi.

ORTALLY, Josh
London
WB-8.m.bp.pat.
See Joseph Ortelli

ORTALY
WB-8.m.bp.pat.

ORTELLI
Marlborough
WB-10.m.sp.

ORTELLI, A.
WB-8.m.sp.mi.

ORTELLI, A.
Buckingham
WB-8.m.bp.fg. SB(b).m.bp.hc.g.thpl.

ORTELLI, A.
Oxford
WB-8.sw.bp.
*Probably A. Ortelli, clo.wa., High St
Oxford 1790–1846, succeeded by—*

ORTELLI, A. and D., and PRIMAVESI fl 1846
114 High St Oxford
*Opt, jewellers, wa.clo.bar.therm.,
looking-glasses. By 1848 Ortelli and
Primavesi at 49 Hatton Gdn London;
there may be a connection between the
two firms*

ORTELLI, A. M.
Godalming
SB(b).m.bp.g.thpl.—Gloucester Mus.

ORTELLI and Co
WB-8.m.bp.pat.

ORTELLI and Co
Macclesfield
WB-10.m.sp.
See P. Ortelli and Co

ORTELLI and Co
Oxford
WB-10.m.sp.mi.
See A. Ortelli

ORTELLI, Defendent fl 1852–60
49 Hatton Gdn London
*Looking-glasses, bar.therm.; succeeded
Peter Ortelli. One of the partners of—*

ORTELLI, Defendent and John fl 1854–60
49 Hatton Gdn London
Looking-glasses, bar.therm.

ORTELLI, Joseph and Co
London
WB-8.m.bp.pat. SB(b).m.bp.g.thpl.
Probably—

ORTELLI, Joseph and Co fl 1809–18
20 Cross St Hatton Gdn London
Bar.therm.

ORTELLI, N.
WB-8.m.bp.pat.

ORTELLI, N. and Co
WB-8.m.bp.pat.

ORTELLI, P. and Co fl 1805
Macclesfield
WB-8.m.bp.pat. (1805)
See Ortelli and Co, Macclesfield

ORTELLI, Peter fl 1835–56
(1) 3 Leather Lane London 1835–51
(2) 49 Hatton Gdn London 1848–51
(3) 15 Leather Lane London 1852–6
*Looking-glasses, bar.therm.; one of the
partners of Ortelli and Primavesi and
succeeded at (2) by Defendent Ortelli
1852. Also spelt Ortelle and Orrell in
directories*

ORTELLI and PRIMAVESI fl 1848–9
49 Hatton Gdn London
*Looking-glasses, bar.therm.; one of the
partners was Peter Ortelli. There seems
to have been a connection with A. and
D. Ortelli and Primavesi of Oxford*

OTTWAY, John fl 1826–51
(1) 87 St Johns Rd London 1826–33
(2) 5 York St Covent Gdn London
1830–9
(3) 10 King St Holborn London
1840–1
(4) 11 Devonshire St Queen Sq
London 1842–8
(5) 33 Upper King St London 1849–51
Opt.
WB-10.m.sp.sqb.(2)

P

PAGANI, A.
Gainsborough Nottingham
WB-8.m.bp.pat.

PAGANI, A.
Nottingham
WB-10.m.sp. WB-8.m.bp.pat.
WB-8.m.sp. WB-8.m.sp.mi.
*Probably Anthony Pagani, opt.,
Goose Gate Nottingham 1818–25*

PAGE, Thomas
Norwich
AB(b).m.rc.—Whipple Mus.
Cambridge
*Probably Thomas Page, clo.wa.,
Norwich fl 1750–d.1784*

PAIGE
Southboro Tunbridge Wells
WB.m.scroll pattern

PALMER   fl 1841–6
103 Newgate St London
Phil.instr.bar.therm.

PALRONI, B.
Exeter
WB-8.m.sp.mi.

PAPIN, —   fl 1672–92
near the Bell Inn Friday St London
*Phil.instr.; worked for
Hon. Robert Boyle 1687–91 and after
Boyle's death in 1691 set up on his own.
Taylor records that his barometers
were recommended by the editor of
Boyle's General Heads of a Natural
History of a Country (1692)*

PARACHINI, F.
WB-8.m.bp.pat.

PARKER
Theobalds St
WB-10.m.sp.sqb.

PARKER
London
SB.m.bow.hytop.
*Possibly James Parker, opt.,
53 Princes St Leicester Sq London 1817*

PARKER
Princes St Soho London
WB-10.m.rt.no ancillary instr.SB.m.bp.g.
See Parker, London

PARKER
Wisbech
WB-8.m.sp.mi.

PARRISH, H.   fl 1860
6½ Wood St Bath Row Birmingham
Bar.

PASINI, John
Dorchester
WB-8.m.sp.mi. WB-8.rw.sp.mi.

PASTORELLI
Bowling St Westminster
SB.m.bp.hc.g.thpl.

PASTORELLI, A.
WB-8.m.sp.mi.
Possibly Anthony Pastorelli

PASTORELLI, A. and F.   fl 1848–9
4 Cross St Hatton Gdn London
*Bar.therm.; partnership of
Anthony Pastorelli and his son Francis*

PASTORELLI, Anthony   fl 1829–49
4 Cross St Hatton Gdn London
*Bar.therm.,chronometers; succeeded
Fortunato Pastorelli; in partnership*

*1848–9 with a son (A. and F. Pastorelli)
who succeeded to the business 1850
(Francis Pastorelli)*

PASTORELLI and CETTI   fl 1853
11 Brook St London
*Bar.therm.; succeeded John Tagliabue;
Edward Cetti alone at this address by
1854*

PASTORELLI and Co
208 Piccadilly London
WB-10.m.sp.
See Francis Pastorelli and Co

PASTORELLI and Co
180 High Holborn London
WB-8.m.bp.
J. Pastorelli is recorded at this address

PASTORELLI, F.
London
WB-8.m.sp.fg.hycen.
Possibly Francis Pastorelli

PASTORELLI, F. and Co
London
WB-8.m.bp.pat.
Possibly Francis Pastorelli

PASTORELLI, F. and J.   fl 1817–8
4 Cross St Hatton Gdn London
Bar.therm.; one of the partners was—

PASTORELLI, Fortunato   fl 1805–30
(1) 252 High Holborn London 1805
(2) 156 High Holborn London 1811
(3) 4 Cross St Hatton Gdn London
    1815–30
*Bar., glassblower; in 1817–8 the firm
was styled F. and J. Pastorelli.
Succeeded by Anthony Pastorelli*

PASTORELLI, Francis   fl 1848–60
(1) 4 Cross St Hatton Gdn London
    1848–60
(2) 208 Piccadilly London 1856–60
*Opt.bar.therm.; son of
Anthony Pastorelli and in partnership
with him 1848–9 (A. and F. Pastorelli);
succeeded to the business 1850.
See Pastorelli and Co, under which
style the firm is recorded at (2)*

PASTORELLI, J.
180 High Holborn London
WB-8.m.bp.pat.
*This was J. M. Ronketti's address to
1797; Poncione Colomba and Co also
worked here. See Pastorelli and Co*

PASTORELLI, J.
Liverpool

WB-8.m.sp.
Probably—

PASTORELLI, John fl 1837–57
    (1) 28 Cable St Liverpool 1837
    (2) 55 Cable St Liverpool 1841–7
    (3) 61 Cable St Liverpool 1851
    (4) 10 South Castle St Liverpool 1857
    Opt.
    WB-10.m.sp.mi.(1)

PASTORELLI, Joseph fl 1820–7
    Leopards Ct Leather Lane London
    Bar.

PASTORELLI, Joseph fl 1852
    67 Hatton Gdn London
    Bar.

PATRICK, J.
    Old Baily London
    See John Patrick

PATRICK, John p 178

PAYNE
    Hadleigh
    WB-8.m.sp.
    Baillie records a William Payne, wa.,
    Hadleigh '1795–1900'

PEACOCK, W.
    Kimbolton
    WB-8.m.sp.
    Baillie records a William Peacock, clo.,
    Kimbolton 1778–90

PEARCE
    Cirencester
    WB-8.m.sp.sqb.
    Probably Thomas Pearce, wa.,
    silversmith, Cricklade St Cirencester
    1856

PEDLIO
    SB(b).m.sqc.ppl.columned hood

PEDRAGLIO
    Rochester
    WB-8.m.bp.pat.

PEDRETTI, C.
    Birmingham
    WB-10.m.sp.mi.

PEDRETTI, Peter fl 1834–51
    (1) Bath St Clerkenwell London
        1834–44
    (2) 13 Dorrington St London 1844–51
    Bar.therm., carver

PEDRONE Bros and Co
    Carlisle
    WB-8.m.sp.

One of the partners was possibly
L. Pedrone, opt, English St Carlisle
1834

PEDRONE, L.
    57 Lord St Liverpool
    WB-8.m.sp.mi.
    Probably Louis Pedrone, opt.math.instr.,
    57 Lord St Liverpool 1841–60

PEDUZZI
    Manchester
    WB-10.m.sp.
    Probably either Anthony or
    James Peduzzi

PEDUZZI, Anthony fl 1825–41
    (1) 23 Piccadilly Manchester 1834
    (2) 31 Oldham St Manchester 1841
    Bar.; James Peduzzi also in Oldham St

PEDUZZI, J.
    Manchester
    WB-10.rw.sp.sqb.mop. (Plate 51)
    Probably James Peduzzi

PEDUZZI, J.
    Newbury St Manchester
    WB-8.m.bp.pat.

PEDUZZI, James fl 1825–41
    (1) 49 Oldham St Manchester 1825–6
    (2) 97 Oldham St Manchester 1834–41
    Bar.; Anthony Peduzzi also in
    Oldham St

PEDUZZI, M.
    74 Leather Lane London
    WB-8.m.bp.pat.

PELEGRINO, Frans
    SB(b).m.bp.thpl. (Plate 36) WB-8.m.
    rt.pat.

PENSA, John fl 1830–9
    (1) 39 Charles St Hatton Gdn London
        1830–4
    (2) 5 Greville St London 1835–9
    Bar.therm.; described as Pensa and
    Son 1835. Margaret Pensa, probably
    his widow, at 25 Charles St 1840.
    John Mangacavali also at (2) 1836 and
    Andrew Tarone at (1) by 1842
    WB-8.m.bp.pat.(1)

PENSA, Margaret fl 1840–8
    25 Charles St Hatton Gdn London
    Bar.therm.; possibly John Pensa's
    widow

PENSA and Son fl 1835
    5 Greville St London
    See John Pensa

PENSOTTI, Joseph fl 1817
  High St Dudley
  Bar.

PEPPER
  Biggleswade
  WB-8.rw.pt.mi.
  *Probably Jno Pepper, wa.clo., gunsmith,
  Market Place Biggleswade 1830*

PETERS, Jas
  WB-10.m.sp.

PEVERELLE, John B. fl 1849–54
  16 Pershore St Birmingham
  Bar.

PHELPS, Thomas fl 1799–1823
  (1) Fetter Lane London 1799
  (2) 30 Red Lion St London 1802–5
  (3) 33 Monkwell St Cripplegate
      London 1817–8
  (4) 28 Holywell Lane Shoreditch
      London
  (5) 19 Jewin St Cripplegate London
      1819–22
  (6) 17 Jewin St Cripplegate London
      London 1822–3
  *Opt.; (4) was probably his home
  address*
  WB-12.m.sp.(2)

PIANTA and Co
  Birmingham
  WB-8.m.bp.pat.

PIFFARETTI
  48 Judd St Euston Rd London
  WB-6.m.sp.sqb.

PIGANDOLA
  WB-8.m.sp.mi.

PILLISCHER, Moritz fl 1853–60
  (1) 398 Oxford St London 1853
  (2) 88 New Bond St London 1854–60
  Opt.
  SB.m.rt.ivpl. (2)

PINI and Co
  WB-8.m.bp.pat.

PINI, J.
  13 Baldwins Gdns Holborn London
  WB-8.m.sp.
  *Battistessa and Co at this address
  1830–6*

PINI, J. and L. fl 1848–60
  23 Brook St Holborn London
  *Bar.therm, carvers, gilders; partnership
  of Joseph and Luigi Pini*

PINI, Joseph fl 1835–60
  (1) 1 Princes St Red Lion Sq London
      1835
  (2) 3 Princes St Red Lion Sq London
      1836
  (3) 23 Brook St London 1838–60
  *Bar.therm., carver, gilder; in partnership
  with Luigi Pini 1848–60 (J. and L. Pini).
  J. C. Zambra also at (3)*
  WB-8.rw.sp.(1) WB-8.m.sp.mi.(1)

PINI, Luigi
  See Joseph Pini, J. and L. Pini

PINNEY
  Stamford
  WB-8.m.sp.sb.

PINNI, Francis and Co
  Holborn
  SB.m.thpl.

PIOTI, James
  Boston
  WB-8.m.bp.pat.

PIOTTE
  Hull
  WB-8.m.bp.pat.
  *Probably James Piotte or Piotti, carver,
  gilder, picture-frames, opt. looking-
  glasses
  (1) Queen St Hull 1806–23
  (2) 2 Queen St Hull 1821–3.
  See also James Pioti, Boston, where he
  may have had a branch*

PIRELLI, D.
  WB-8.m.sp.mi.

PISTALLA, Charles fl 1805
  221 High Holborn London
  Bar

PIZZALA, A. fl 1840–53
  (1) 7 Charles St Hatton Gdn London
      1840–6
  (2) 19 Hatton Gdn London 1847–53
  *Opt.math.phil.instr.; succeeded
  F. A. Pizzala (1) and succeeded by
  F. A. Pizzala (2)*
  WB-10.m.sp.sqb.(2)

PIZZALA, Francis Augustus (1) fl 1838–9
  7 Charles St Hatton Gdn London
  *Opt.math.phil.instr.bar.etc.; succeeded
  by A. Pizzala. Henry Negretti
  apprenticed to him 1838–40.
  A barometer catalogued as 'Georgian'
  by F. A. Pizzala in a sale at Christies
  24.5.39 can probably be attributed to
  him*

PIZZALA, Francis Augustus (2) fl 1854–60
19 Hatton Gdn London
*Opt.math.phil.instr.bar.etc.; succeeded
A. Pizzala*

PIZZALLA, J.
84 Leather Lane Holborn London
WB-8.m.rt.fg.

PIZZI and CETTI
Buckingham
WB-10.m.sp. WB-8.m.sp.mi.
*Baillie records a firm of this name, wa.,
Buckingham 'early 19c.'*

PIZZI, Jane fl 1840–5(?)
19 Leather Lane London
*Widow of Valentine Pizzi and one of
the partners of—*

PIZZI and NEGRETTI fl 1840–5(?)
19 Leather Lane London
*Partnership of Jane Pizzi and
Henry Negretti*

PIZZI, Valentine fl 1835 —d.1840
27 Cross St Hatton Gdn London
*Bar.; after his death his widow Jane
continued the business with
Henry Negretti (Pizzi and Negretti)*

POCHAINE, John fl 1811
Dean St Newcastle-upon-Tyne
Bar.; probably a misprint for Pochine

POCHINE and Son
Newcastle
WB-8.m.bp.pat.
See John Pochaine

POLTI
Exon
AB. yew with mirror in centre and
ormolu mouldings at borders of case,
th. mounted on right of case, hy.
above mirror as finial in centre of bp.
SB.m.rt.thpl.

POLTI
from Italy
SB.m.rt.carved cover to tube

POLTI, J.
Leeds
WB-10.m.sp.mi. WB-8.m.bp.pat.
WB-10.m.sp.
Probably Joseph Polti

POLTI, J. and Co
WB-8.m.bp.pat.
Possibly—

POLTI, Joseph fl 1822–34
(1) 7 Kirkgate Leeds 1822

(2) 72 Kirkgate Leeds 1834
Bar., looking-glasses

POLTI, L.
Bristol
WB-8.m.sp.

PONCIA, A.
Norwich
SB(b).m.bp.thpl.

PONCIA, A.
Peterborough
WB-8.m.bp.pat.

PONCIA, A. and Co
Norwich
SB(b).m.bp.g.

PONCIA, J.
Hereford
WB-8.m.bp.pat.
*Probably J. Poncia, hardware,
Union St Hereford 1822*

PONCIONE COLOMBA and Co
180 High Holborn
WB-8.m.bp.pat.
*This was J. M. Ronketti's address to
1797; J. Pastorelli also worked here*

PONCIONE, Jno and Co
281 High Holborn
SB(b).m.bp.hc.thpl.
*J. Maver and P. Ramos also worked
at this address*

POND, Jas
Lynn
WB-10.m.sp.
*Probably James Pond, umbrella-maker
(1) High St Lynn 1822
(2) 35 Broad St Lynn 1830*

POOLE, John
Upper East Smithfield
MB

POOLE, Thomas fl 1817–8
Upper North Pl Grays Inn Gate
London
Opt.
WB-10.m.sp.sqb.

PORRE, VECCHIO and Co
17 Gt Queen St Lincolns Inn Fields
WB-8.m.bp.pat.
See Porri

PORRI
17 Gt Queen St London
SB.m.g.

PORRI, B.
    Skipton
    WB-8.m.sp.
    Probably—

PORRI, Benjamin fl 1834–41
    (1) Caroline Sq Skipton 1834
    (2) New Market Sq Skipton 1841
    Bar.

PORRI, Domenico
    London
    WB-10.m.sp.

PORRI, F.
    Dublin
    WB-8.m.sp.mi.

PORRI, G. B.
    Leicester
    WB-10.sw.sp.clo.

POTTS
    London
    WB-10.m.sp.
    Possibly Thomas Potts, opt.
    (1) 371 Strand London 1805
    (2) 18 St Martins Ct London 1807–14

POWELL, T.
    WB-10.rw.sp.mop.

POZOLY, A.
    SB.m.g.

POZZI, A.
    Wooton Bassett
    WB-8.rw.sp.

POZZI, C.
    WB-8.m.sp.sqb.

POZZI and Co.
    WB-8.m.bp.pat.

POZZI, J.
    WB-8.m.sp.

POZZI, Jos
    Rochdale
    WB-8.m.sp.

POZZI, Peter fl 1822–30
    Willow St Oswestry
    Bar.
    WB-8.m.sp.mi.

PRADA
    High Wycombe and Chesham
    WB-8.m.bp.

PRADA, C.
    High Wycombe
    WB-8.m.sp.

PRADA, F.
    Chester
    WB-8.m.bp.pat.

PRANDI, Francis fl 1825
    32 Church St Sheffield
    Bar.; see F. Prando and Co

PRANDO, F. and Co
    26 Church St Sheffield
    WB-10.m.bp.pat.
    Probably Francis Prandi

PREDARY
    Manchester
    WB-8.m.sp.
    Possibly Charles Predary, carver,
    gilder, 17 Oak St Thomas St
    Manchester 1841

PRIEST
    Newark
    WB-8.rw.sp.mi.
    Three watch and clockmakers of this
    name are recorded:
    (1) John and James, Middlegate
        Newark 1835
    (2) William, Boar Lane Newark 1835
    (3) James, Middlegate Newark 1841

PRIMAVESI Bros
    Poole and Wareham
    SB.mop.g.ivpl.—Gloucester Mus.

PRIMAVESI, F.
    WB-8.m.sp.mi.

PRIMAVESI, Peter
    7 Grevil St Holborn
    WB-8.m.bp.pat.
    Andrew Tarone at this address 1802–19;
    A. Corti also worked here

PULMAN, P.
    Axminster
    WB-10.rw.sp.sqb.
    Baillie records a Pulman, clo.,
    Axminster '18c.'

PULSFORD, G.
    WB-8.m.sp.
    Possibly—

PULSFORD, George fl 1848
    36 Charles St Hatton Gdn London
    Bar.therm.; B. Franzoni at this address
    by 1857

PURCHON, Geo
    Glass House
    SB.m.inl.painted pl. SB.sw.bp.oval c.
    inl.g.enamel pl.

PYEFINCH
London
Probably—

PYEFINCH, Henry p 184

Q

QUARE, D.
See Daniel Square

QUARE, Daniel p 186

QUINSEY, G.
Keighley
SB(b).m.th.—Bolling Hall Mus.Bradford

R

RABALIO
SB.m.bp.

RABONE, John fl 1829–60
(1) Ludgate Hill Birmingham 1829
(2) 61 St Pauls Sq Birmingham
1839–60
*Bar.; probably one of the partners of
Rabone and Mason, but on his own
1829 and 1839–60. Took a son into
partnership 1858*

RABONE and MASON fl 1834–7
61 St Pauls Sq Birmingham
Bar.; see John Rabone

RABONE, T.
London
SB.rw.ivpl.

RABONE, Thomas fl 1829–60
(1) 8 Court Water St Birmingham
1829
(2) 12 Court Broad St Birmingham
1835
(3) Hockley Hill Birmingham 1847
(4) 172 Hockley Hill Birmingham
1849–54
(5) 63 Gt Hampton St Birmingham
1858
(6) 61 Gt Hampton St Birmingham
1860
*Bar.math.instr.; possibly a relation of
John Rabone*

RADEMACHER
Beccles
SB.m.rt.rc.thpl.

RAMAGE
Aberdeen
WB-8.m.sp.with square dial at top of

case. thca. (*cf* Plate 48) SB.m.sqp.urn.
g.
*See Smith and Ramage; Baillie records
a James Ramage, clo., Edinburgh
'c. 1780–1820'*

RAMAS, P.
SB(b).m.bp.g.
Probably—

RAMOS, P.
281 Holborn London
WB-8.bp.pat.
*J. Maver and Jno Poncione also
worked at this address*

RAMPOLDI and Co
Huntingdon
WB-10.m.sp.mi.

RAMPOLDI, J. fl 1851–3
22 Grey St Newcastle-upon-Tyne
Bar.

RAMSDEN
London
See Jesse Ramsden

RAMSDEN, Jesse p.202

RAY
Battle
WB-8.m.bp.
*Baillie records Daniel Ray, wa., 'c. 1790'
and William Ray, wa., 'early 19c.',
both of Battle*

REALINI, C.
Preston
WB-10.m.sp.mi. WB-8.m.sp.mi.

REALINI, L.
Newcastle
WB-10.m.sp.sqb. WB-10.m.sp.mi.

REHE, S.
London
SB.m.rt.g. but case not panelled, cc. in
form of shallow urn, double scale
with English inches 27-31 on left
(Fair, Change, Rain) divided in
decimals and French inches 25-29 on
right (Beau Tems, Variable, Pluie)
divided in 12 lignes, double vernier
and ring pointer—Sir John Soane
Mus., London
*Probably Samuel Rehe, math.instr.,
Shoe Lane London 1770–92, a friend
of John Whitehurst (1)*

REID, Adam
Woolwich
SB(b).m.bp.g.

RENWICK, James fl 1844–7
    2 Booths Place Turnmill St London
    Bar.therm.

REYNOLDS, J.
    St Austell
    WB-10.m.pt.

REYNOLDSON, Thos
    7 Queen St Hull
    WB-10.rw.sp.sb.mop.

RHODES, M.
    Bradford
    WB-8.rw.sp.mop.
    Probably Manoah Rhodes, jeweller,
    138 Westgate Bradford 1841; Baillie
    records him as 'early 19c.'

RIBALDI, J.
    Limerick
    WB-8.m.bp.pat.

RIBRIGHT, T.
    WB-11.m.rt.fg. (Plate 16)
    Probably Thomas Ribright, opt.instr.,
    fl 1768—d. c. 1810, 40 Poultry London;
    app. to his father George Ribright
    1768, member of Spectaclemakers
    Co 1775 and in partnership with his
    father 1778–82 (Ribright and Sons):
    on his own in directories until 1795.
    In 1806 a report submitted to the
    Spectaclemakers Co said that he was
    in 'reduced circumstances'

RIMONDI, C.
    WB-10.m.sp. WB-8.rw.sp.
    Possibly Charles Rimondi, wa.clo.,
    jeweller, 8 Waterhouse St Halifax
    1841–53

RIVA
    Glasgow
    WB-8.m.bp.pat. WB-6.rw.sp.
    Several tradesmen of this name are
    recorded at Glasgow; see J. and
    M. Riva; also A. Riva

RIVA, A.
    Glasgow
    WB-8.m.bp.pat.

RIVA, A.
    Marlborough
    WB-8.m.sp.mi.

RIVA, C.
    Glasgow
    SB(b).m.bp.g.thpl.

RIVA, F.
    Reading
    WB-8.m.bp.pat.

RIVA, Ferdinando fl 1834
    7 Watson Walk Sheffield
    Opt.instr.bar.

RIVA, G. and Co
    WB-8.m.sp.

RIVA, J. and M.
    WB-8.m.sp.mi.
    Probably—

RIVA, J. and M. fl 1825–60
    (1) 70 High St Glasgow 1825
    (2) 143 High St Glasgow 1826–50
    (3) 147 High St Glasgow 1850–7
    (4) 63 John St Glasgow 1857–60
    Carvers, gilders, looking-glasses, bar.;
    see Riva, Glasgow. The directories also
    record A. Riva at (1) 1823,
    Michael Riva at (2) 1827 and
    Mrs. M. Riva at (2) 1828, all carvers,
    gilders

RIVA, M.
    Glasgow
    WB-8.m.sp.
    See J. and M. Riva

RIVA, P.
    Edinburgh
    WB-10.m.sp.mi.

RIVA, P. and Co
    Edinburgh
    WB-10.m.sp.sqb.

RIVERS, John fl 1822–35
    (1) Wind St Swansea 1822
    (2) Goat St Swansea 1830
    (3) High St Swansea 1835
    Bar.

RIVOLTA, A.
    WB-8.m.sp.mi. WB-8.m.bp.pat.
    WB-12.m.sp.sqb.clo.brass columns
    Possibly Anthony Rivolta

RIVOLTA, A.
    Chester
    WB-8.m.bp.pat. WB-8.m.sp.

RIVOLTA, Anthony fl 1822–51
    (1) 32 Brook St Holborn London
        1822–45
    (2) 21 Lower Calthorpe St London
        1846–51
    Bar.therm., looking-glasses; preceded at
    (1) by Alex Rivolta, looking-glasses,
    1819 who was at 11 Brook St Holborn
    London 1817–8 (see J. and J. Tagliabue).
    See A. Rivolta

RIVOLTA and Co
    WB-8.m.bp.pat.

RIVOLTA, D.
WB-8.m.bp.pat.

RIVOLTA, F.
Macclesfield
WB-8.m.bp.pat.

RIVOLTA, F.
Reading
SB(b).m.bp.g.

RIVOLTA, L.
WB-8.m.sp.

ROBB, William fl 1776—1816
Montrose
Clo.
Ab(b).m.; two AB(b).m.sqc.inl.thca.
very similar to Plate 93, one of them
also inscribed with the name
David Milne, Carnbegg

ROBELOU, Isaac fl 1719
London
SB(b). on chinoiserie frame (Plate 15)
—Sc.Mus.London

ROBERTS
Stonehouse
WB-10.w.scroll pattern

ROBINSON, Thomas Charles fl 1821–35
38 Devonshire St Portland Place
London
*Opt.math.phil.instr.; recorded by
Taylor as the maker of a mountain
barometer 1831*

ROE, J.
Ipswich
WB-8.m.sp.mi.
*Probably Joseph Adolphus Roe, wa.clo.,
Tacket St Ipswich 1855–60*

ROLANDS, J.
WB-8.m.bp.pat.

RONCHATE, Baptis
DB.m. (*cf.* Plate 41)—Mus.Hist.Sc.,
Oxford
See Bapt. Roncheti

RONCHETI, Bapt
SB(b).m.sqp.sqc.ppl.
*The name was also spelt Ronchate;
See Baptis Ronchate, Bapt Roncheti
and Co*

RONCHETI, Bapt and Co
AB(b).m.rc.g.—Gloucester Mus.
See Bapt Roncheti

RONCHETI and GATTY
WB-10.m.rt.pat.
Possibly a partnership between

*Bapt Roncheti or J. M. Ronketti and
James Gatty*

RONCHETI, T.
Bristol
SB(b).m.bp.sqc.g. (Plate 35)

RONCHETTI
Exeter
WB-8.m.bp.pat.
Possibly Thomas Ronchetti

RONCHETTI
Manchester
WB-10.m.sp.mi.
Probably Joshua Ronchetti

RONCHETTI, Edmund fl 1850
Waterbeer St Exeter
*Bar.; possibly a relation of
Thomas Ronchetti*

RONCHETTI, J.
Victoria St Manchester
WB-12.m.sp.
*Joshua Ronchetti is not recorded at
this address*

RONCHETTI and Son fl 1836–9
2 Hatton Gdn London
*Bar.therm.; succeeded at this address
by Joseph Somalvico and Co; possibly
identifiable with—*

RONCHETTI, John fl 1836–8
25 Hatton Gdn London
*Taylor records this maker, who is
mentioned in a paper submitted to the
Transactions of the Irish Academy
1836 by John Stevelley, entitled*
On a new self-registering Barometer

RONCHETTI, John B. and Joshua fl 1841
43 Market St Manchester
*Opt.phil.instr.bar.; one of the partners
was—*

RONCHETTI, Joshua fl 1828–41
(1) 29 Balloon St Manchester
(2) 43 Market St Manchester 1834–41
*Opt.phil.instr.bar.; in partnership with
John B. Ronchetti 1841 (John B. and
Joshua Ronchetti). See Ronchetti,
Manchester*

RONCHETTI, Thomas fl 1822–56
(1) New Bridge St Exeter 1822
(2) 4 Mount Pleasant Black Boy Rd
    Exeter 1830
(3) Black Boy Rd Exeter 1850–6
*Bar.opt.; Edmund Ronchetti also
also working in Exeter 1850*

RONCI
    London
    WB-8.m.mi.

RONCKETI, J. Merry
    SB(b).m.sqc.ppl.columned hood
    See John Merry Ronketti

RONKETTI and Co
    6 Peter St Bloomsbury
    WB-10.m.sp.
    See John Merry Ronketti

RONKETTI, J. G. H. fl 1845–6
    (1) 102 St Martins Lane London 1845
    (2) 116 Gt Russell St London 1845
    (3) 19 Leather Lane London 1846
    Phil.instr.bar.therm.

RONKETTI, J. M.
    180 Holborn
    See John Merry Ronketti

RONKETTI, J. M.
    6 Peter St Bloomsbury
    See John Merry Ronketti

RONKETTI, John fl 1823–44
    15 Museum St Bloomsbury London
    Bar.therm.; possibly identifiable with—

RONKETTI, John George fl 1820–1
    8 Back Hill Hatton Gdn London
    Math.phil.instr.bar.etc.; possibly
    identifiable with John Ronketti,
    15 Museum St Bloomsbury London
    1823–44 or with John Ronchetti,
    25 Hatton Gdn London 1836–8

RONKETTI, John Merry p 204

RONKETTI, Joseph fl 1854–60
    31 Northampton Rd London
    Bar.therm.

RONKITTE, J. M.
    6 Peter St Bloomsbury
    See John Merry Ronketti

ROOKE, J.
    Cirencester
    WB-8.m.sp.sqb. WB-8.rw.pt.mi.
    Probably John Rooke, wa.clo., Dyer St
    Cirencester 1856

ROSASPINI, P.
    Ticehurst
    WB-8.m.sp.mi.

ROSATI, F.
    SB(b).m.bp.g.

ROSATTE, J.
    Leeds
    Signature on ppl.

ROSS
    London
    WB-12.rw.rt.
    Possibly—

ROSS, Andrew fl 1830–56
    (1) 15 St Johns Sq Clerkenwell
        London 1830
    (2) 21 Featherstone Bldgs Clerkenwell
        London 1840–7
    (3) 2 Featherstone Bldgs Clerkenwell
        London 1848–56
    Opt.math.phil.instr.bar.etc.

ROSSI, G.
    Norwich
    WB-12.m.sp.clo. WB-12.m.sp.mi.
    WB-10.m.sp. WB-8.m.sp.mi.
    Probably George Rossi, looking-glasses,
    St Lawrence Norwich 1822–30;
    Francis Molton is also recorded at this
    address. Probably identifiable with—

ROSSI, G.
    Exchange St Norwich
    WB-12.m.sp.sqb.clo.
    See G. Rossi Norwich

ROSSI, P.
    SB(b).m.bp.g.

ROUTLEDGE
    Carlisle
    SB(b).m.rt.ppl.
    Probably Adam Routledge, wa.clo.opt.,
    32 English St Carlisle 1828–34,
    recorded by Baillie as 'early 19c.'

RUBERGALL
    London
    SB.m.sp.urn.bow.g.thpl. SB.m.sp.urn.
    bow.g. (Plate 33)
    See Thomas Rubergall

RUBERGALL
    24 Coventry St London
    SB.o.rt.ivpl. ('Opt. to the Queen')
    See Thomas Rubergall

RUBERGALL, Thomas fl 1802–54
    (1) Princes St Soho London 1802
    (2) 27 Coventry St London 1805–23
    (3) 24 Coventry St London 1826–54
    Opt.math.instr. to the Duke of
    Clarence, opt. to George III
    WB-8.m.bp.clo.(3) SB.m.rt.urn.g.ivpl.
    (2) SB.m.sp.urn.bow.(2) WB-12.m.sp.
    sb.clo.(3)

RUSSELL, John p 206

S

SALA, Dom
London
DB.m.ppl. (*cf.* Plate 41)—Gloucester
Mus.

SALA, Dominico
Londini
DB ('Great Double Barometer').
arched m.frame. the b.and th. scales
stamped on fruitwood: b. scale 0–100
extends over 28·5″

SALAMONI, M.
Oxford
WB-8.m.bp.pat.
Probably Mark Salmoni

SALDARINI, Joseph
Peterborough
WB-8.m.bp.pat.
Probably Joseph Saldarini, opt.,
Long Causeway Peterborough 1830–41

SALERI, F.
Nottingham
WB-8.m.bp.pat.

SALLA, Anthony fl 1832–9
(1) 65 Paradise Row Chelsea London
1832–3
(2) 66 Paradise Row Chelsea London
1836–9
Bar.therm.

SALMONI
Oxford
WB-8.m.sp.mi.
Probably—

SALMONI, Mark fl 1830–8
St Clements Oxford
Bar.; see M. Salamoni, Salmoni

SALMONI, P.
Bath
WB-14.sw.sp.fg. WB-10.rw.sp.sqb.
WB-10.m.sp.sqb.
Probably Peter Paul Salmoni, opt.,
fancy stationer, dealer in portable
desks etc.
(1) 4 Milson St Bath 1829–30
(2) 24 Union St Bath 1833–41

SALTERY, F., VECHIO and Co
94 Holborn Hill
SB(b).m.bp.g.thpl.
See Frans Saltery and Co

SALTERY, Frans and Co
94 Holborn Hill London
SB(b).m.bp.g. WB-8.m.bp.pat.

J. Corti and Donegan & Co also
recorded at this address. Possibly a
relation of Antonio Salteri, looking-
glass maker, Gt Queen St London
1805–28

SALVADE, P.
WB-8.m.bp.pat. WB-8.m.sp.mi.
Probably identifiable with—

SALVADE, P.
Liverpool
WB-8.m.sp. WB-8.rw.sp. WB-8.m.sp.
mi.—Brit.Mus.

SANGSTER
London
WB-8.m.sp.

SANKEY, J.
Coalbrookdale Salop
SB(b).m.bp.g.

SARGENT, T. C.
MB—Sc.Mus.London

SAUNDERS, Richard fl 1681–1715
(1) Ouston Leicestershire 1683–95
(2) Leesthorp Melton Mowbray
1696–1711
Taylor mentions that, besides publishing
an almanac, teaching surveying and
making dials, he made and repaired
weather-glasses

SAUNDERS, Thomas fl 1794–1819
(1) 7 Georges St Dublin 1794
(2) 35 College Green Dublin 1795–9
(3) 6 Church Lane Dublin 1800–18
(4) Eden Quay Dublin 1819
Math.instr.opt.
WB-12.sw.sp.

SCANTLEBURY, J. B.
Sheffield
WB-8.m.sp.
Probably—

SCANTLEBURY, John fl 1817
Campo Lane Sheffield
Bar.

SCARLETT, E.
Probably—

SCARLETT, Edward p 217

SCHALFINO
Taunton
WB-10.w.pt.scroll pattern WB-8.rw.mi.
Probably John Schalfino

SCHALFINO, John
Taunton
WB-8.m sp. WB-8.m sp.mi

WB-8.m.bp.pat.
Probably—

SCHALFINO, John fl 1840–3
East St Taunton
Bar.

SCHMALCALDER
SB(b).m.bp.thca. WB-6.m.sp.sqb.—
Mus.Hist.Sc.Oxford
Probably—

SCHMALCALDER
82 Strand London
SB.m.rt.hc.g.
See Charles Augustus Schmalcalder

SCHMALCALDER, Charles Augustus
fl 1806–38
(1) 82 Strand London
(2) 399 Strand London
*Opt.math.instr.bar.etc.; spelt
Schmalcalda in 1817 directory*

SCHULER
16 City Rd
WB-8.m.sp.mi.

SCHWERER and Co
Truro
WB-8.m.sp.mi.

SELVA, G.
Hull
WB-8.m.bp. WB-8.m.bp.pat.above
dial
See George Selvea

SELVA, John
Plymouth
WB-8.m.bp.pat.

SELVEA, George fl 1826
25 Grimsby Lane Hull
*Jeweller, hardware, bar.; succeeded by
John Selvea. See G. Selva*

SELVEA, John fl 1831
25 Grimsby Lane Hull
*Jeweller, hardware, bar.; succeeded
George Selvea*

SEMMONDS, H.
WB-8.m.sp.mi.
Possibly identifiable with—

SEMMONS
Truro
WB-8.m.sp.mi.

SEWILL, J.
Liverpool and London
SB with sympiesometer—Nat.Mus.
Hist.Sc.Leyden

SHAW, John fl 1672–1715
Holborn London
*Clo.; app. 1672, CC. 1682, Master
CC. 1712–5*
SB.w.marquetry inlay with arched
pediment and twisted pillars to hood
(p 26 Note 1)

SHEPHERD, C.
53 Leadenhall St London
WB-10.rw.pt.mop.fg.

SHORTGRAVE, Richard fl 1658—d. 1676
Gresham College
*Worked for Robert Hooke and became
Operator to the Royal Society;
succeeded by Harry Hunt. Hooke
wrote to Robert Boyle on 21 March
1666: 'I have given Mr. Shortgrave
directions for making of a wheel
baroscope for you by a new way,
which is much more facile than the
former, both in making, filling, and
rectifying'. (S. P. and S. J. Rigaud
Correspondence of Scientific Men of
the seventeenth century 1841)*

SHUTTLEWORTH
London
SB.m.
*Possibly Henry Shuttleworth, opt.,
fl 1746 –d.1812, 23 Ludgate St
London; app. to John Cuff 1746*

SILBERRAD
London
DB.m. (*cf.* Plate 41)—Mus.Hist.Sc.
Oxford
*Possibly Charles Silberrad, opt.,
34 Aldgate within London 1801–33*

SILVA, L.
WB-8.m.bp.pat.

SIMMS, William p 219

SIMONS, D.
Trowbridge
WB-8.m.sp.mi.

SIMONS, James fl 1773–91
(1) Sir Isaac Newton's Head corner of
Marylebone St and Golden Sq
London 1773–85
(2) 17 Marylebone St London 1791
*Opt.math.phil.instr.; trade card
illustrates a barometer (Heal Colln,
Brit.Mus.)*

SIMPSON
WB-10.rw.sp.sqb.mop.

SISSON, J.
    See Jeremiah and Jonathan Sisson

SISSON, Jeremiah p 220

SISSON, Jonathan p 222

SKIRROW, J.
    Wigan
    WB.m.sp.sb.—Adlington Hall
    (National Trust)
    *Baillie records a James Skirrow, clo.,
    Lancaster and Wigan 1783–1814*

SMART
    SB(b).m.bp.g.

SMITH
    Royal Exchange
    SB.m.sqp.urn.bow.g.thca.—Gloucester
    Mus. WB-10.m.sp.sqb. WB-8.m.bp.
    pat.
    See James Smith

SMITH, Addison p 224

SMITH, Egerton
    Liverpool
    WB-10.sw.sp.
    *Probably Egerton Smith, math.instr.,
    Newton's Head 17 Pool Lane Liverpool
    1766–1809; Taylor records that he was
    a stationer but employed instrument-
    makers*

SMITH, J.
    Royal Exchange London
    WB-10.m.sp.hycen. SB.m.sp.g.thca.
    See James Smith

SMITH, James fl 1817–28
    Royal Exchange London
    Opt.; succeeded James Long
    WB-12.m.sp.sqb.clo.brass pillars
    WB-10.m.sp.
    *See also Smith, Royal Exchange
    London*

SMITH, John p 225

SMITH and RAMAGE
    45 Regents Quay Aberdeen
    MB
    See Ramage

SMITH, W.
    Crowland
    WB-8.m.bp.pat.
    *Probably William Smith, wa., North St
    Crowland 1835–41*

SMYTH
    London
    WB-10.sw.sp.fg.

SNART, J.
    Tooley St
    WB-8.m.bp.pat.
    *Probably John Snart, opt.math.instr.,
    215 Tooley St London 1802–31
    succeeded by Neaziah Snart by 1833*

SNELLING, J.
    Alton
    SB(b).m.bp.g.
    *Probably James Snelling, wa.clo.,
    silversmith, High St Alton 1830;
    Baillie records a John Snelling, clo.wa.,
    Alton 1761–95*

SOLCA, A.
    Tunbridge Wells
    WB-8.m.sp. WB-8.rw.pt. WB-8.m.pt.
    pb.

SOLCA, Joseph
    Manchester
    WB-8.m.sp.mi.

SOLCHA
    Hull
    WB-8.m.sp.mi.
    Probably Lewis Solcha

SOLCHA, L.
    Hull
    WB-8.m.sp.mi. WB-6.sp.sqb.
    Probably—

SOLCHA, Lewis fl 1851–9
    (1) 1 Dagger Lane Hull 1851
    (2) 17 Robinson Row Hull 1855–9
    *Bar., looking-glasses, gilder; possibly
    one of the partners of Lappi and Solcha.
    James Maspoli at (2) until 1851. See
    L. Solcha*

SOLDINI, G.
    Wincanton
    WB-8.m.sp.mi.
    *Probably Giosue Soldini, jeweller,
    High St Wincanton 1830*

SOLDINI, P.
    Hull
    WB-8.m.sp. WB-8.rw.sp.
    *Probably Pasqual Soldini,
    9 Robinson Row Hull, described in
    1855 as a hawker; this was
    James Maspoli's address. The two
    makers probably partners of—*

SOLDINI, P. and MASPOLI fl 1860
    9 Robinson Row Hull
    *Bar.; both Pasqual Soldini and
    James Maspoli worked at this address*

SOLOMON, S.
　　　Lewes
　　　WB-8.m.sp.mi.
　　　Probably S. Solomon, wa., Lewes
　　　1815–30

SOMALVICO, C.
　　　London
　　　WB-8.m.bp.pat. WB-10.m.bp.
　　　Probably Charles Somalvico, brother of
　　　James Somalvico, and identifiable
　　　with—

SOMALVICO, C.
　　　11 Brook St
　　　WB-10.m.sp. WB-10.m.sp.octagonal
　　　frame to dial. brass inl. WB-10.m.sp.
　　　mi.
　　　See previous entry; this address was
　　　occupied by various Tagliabues
　　　1817–52, by Pastorelli and Cetti 1853
　　　and by Edward Cetti 1854–60

SOMALVICO, I.
　　　11 Brook St
　　　WB-12.m.sp.clo.
　　　This was C. Somalvico's address

SOMALVICO, J.
　　　67 Leather Lane Holborn
　　　WB-8.m.sp.mi. SB(b).m.bp.rc.g.thpl.
　　　No other trace of the Somalvico family
　　　at this address

SOMALVICO, J. and Co
　　　2 Hatton Gdn London
　　　SB.m.ogee crest. wide turned cistern
　　　cover
　　　See Joseph Somalvico (2)

SOMALVICO, J. and Son
　　　Hatton Gdn
　　　MB
　　　Probably identifiable with

SOMALVICO, J. and Son
　　　37 Charles St Hatton Gdn
　　　SB.m.rt.rc.g.thpl. SB.m.rt.rc.thca.
　　　hytop. WB-4.m.sp.sqb.
　　　Possibly a partnership between
　　　James Somalvico and his son Joseph,
　　　but James is not otherwise recorded at
　　　this address

SOMALVICO, James b. 1794(?)—fl 1820
　　　22 Kirby St Hatton Gdn London
　　　Bar.; son of Joseph Somalvico (1) and
　　　brother of Charles Somalvico (see
　　　C. Somalvico). Family records suggest
　　　that he also worked at 4 Leather Lane
　　　London and 91 Hatton Gdn London,
　　　but no dates are available

SOMALVICO, Joseph
　　　Charles St
　　　WB-10.rw.sp.sqb.mop.
　　　Probably Joseph Somalvico (2)

SOMALVICO, Joseph (1) b. 1759(?)—fl 1805–19
　　　(1) 125 Holborn Hill London 1805–7
　　　(2) 14 Brook St London 1811–19
　　　Bar.; in partnership with
　　　Dominick Lione 1805–19
　　　(Lione Somalvico and Co). Father of
　　　James Somalvico and Charles Somalvico

SOMALVICO, Joseph (2) fl 1833–60
　　　(1) 37 Charles St Hatton Gdn London
　　　　　1833–9
　　　(2) 2 Hatton Gdn London 1839–60
　　　Opt.bar.therm.phil.instr.,chronometers,
　　　etc.; son of James Somalvico and
　　　brother of Vincent Somalvico and
　　　another James. Under his direction the
　　　family firm achieved a prominent
　　　position. Succeeded at (1) by
　　　Andrew Colomba and succeeded
　　　Ronchetti and Son at (2). See
　　　Joseph Somalvico, Charles St;
　　　barometers signed thus cannot be firmly
　　　dated since the firm returned to
　　　16 Charles St Hatton Gdn London 1869
　　　SB.m.sqp.urn.bow.g.thca.(2)

SOMALVICO, Josh and Co
　　　81 Holborn London
　　　WB-8.m.bp.pat.
　　　J. Cetti and James Lione are recorded
　　　at 81 High Holborn London

SOMALVICO, Josh and Co
　　　256 Holborn
　　　WB-10.m.sp. SB(b).m.bp.g.
　　　No other trace of the family at this
　　　address

SOMALVICO, V. and Co
　　　London
　　　WB-8.m.bp.pat.
　　　Probably—

SOMALVICO, Vincent fl 1856–8
　　　14 Charles St Hatton Gdn London
　　　Phil.instr.bar.therm.; brother of
　　　Joseph Somalvico (2)

SORDELLI, G.
　　　23 Baldwins Gdns Holborn
　　　WB-8.m.sp.

SORDELLI, I.
　　　WB-8.m.sp.mi.

SORDELLI, J.
　　　London
　　　WB-10.m.sp. WB-8.m.sp. SB.m.rt.g.

SOWERBY, J.
  London
  WB-6.sw.sp.sqb.

SPEAR and Co
  College Green Dublin
  WB-8.m.sp.
  See Richard Spear and Co

SPEAR, R.
  College Green Dublin
  SB.m.sp.thpl.
  See Richard Spear and Co

SPEAR, Richard and Co   fl 1818–60
  (1) 27 College Green Dublin 1818–41
  (2) 28 College Green Dublin 1843–60
  Opt.math.instr., oil merchants,candle
  makers, etc.; Richard Spear is
  previously recorded at
  (1) 29 Capel St Dublin 1791–2
  (2) 23 Capel St Dublin 1793–1809
  (3) 35 College Green Dublin 1809–11
  (4) 27 College Green Dublin 1812–8.
  See Spear and Co

SPELZINI
  London
  WB-8.m.sp.mi.
  Possibly John Spelzini

SPELZINI
  Beauchamp St Leather Lane
  WB-8.m.sp.
  See John Spelzini

SPELZINI, G.
  WB-8.m.bp.pat.

SPELZINI, I.
  WB-8.m.bp.pat.—Gloucester Mus.
  Possibly John Spelzini

SPELZINI, J.
  11 Beauchamp St Holborn
  WB-10.rw.sp.
  See John Spelzini

SPELZINI, J.
  91 Leather Lane
  WB-12.m.sp.sqb. WB-10.m.sp.mi.
  WB-8.m.sp. WB-8.m.sp.mi.
  Possibly John Spelzini although he is
  not otherwise recorded at this address

SPELZINI, J.
  Manchester
  WB-8.m.bp.pat.

SPELZINI, J. and Son
  London
  WB-8.rw.sp.sqb.

SPELZINI, John   fl 1836–59
  (1) 8 Beauchamp St London 1836
  (2) 11 Beauchamp St London 1839–48
  (3) 74 Gt Saffron Hill London 1856–9
  Bar.therm.; he may have worked also
  at 91 Leather Lane London. See
  J. Spelzini, Beauchamp St and
  J. Spelzini, 91 Leather Lane

SPENCER, BROWNING and Co
  London
  MB. SB.m.bp.g.thpl.
  Probably an abbreviation of
  Spencer Browning and Rust, opt.math.
  instr.
  (1) 327 Wapping London 1783
  (2) 66 Wapping London 1801–38:
  they also appear in directories as
  Spencer and Co

SPENCER and Co
  London
  SB.m.sqp.rc.g.
  See Spencer, Browning and Co

SPENCER and Son
  Dublin
  SB.rw.rt.ivpl.
  Possibly John Spencer, opt.math.phil.
  instr.
  (1) 128 Summerhill Dublin 1838
  (2) 3 Aungier St Dublin 1845–50
  (3) 13 Aungier St Dublin 1852–8

SPRINGER, J.
  Bristol
  Probably—

SPRINGER, Joshua p 226

STAMPA and Co
  London
  SB.m.sp.rc.g.thpl.—Mus.Hist.Sc.
  Oxford
  Possibly Stampa and Son or
  Charles Stampa and Co, looking-
  glasses, carvers, gilders
  (1) 125 Holborn Hill London 1802
  (2) 25 Kirby St Hatton Gdn London
  1803–11. Lione Somalvico and
  Co at (1) by 1805

STAMPA, D.
  14 Leith St Edinburgh
  SB(b).m.bp.g.thpl. WB-8.m.bp.pat.

STAMPA and Son   fl 1802–18
  74 Leather Lane London
  Looking-glasses, bar.therm., printsellers

STANLEY
  Peterborough
  WB-6.rw.sp.sqb.

STARK
Torquay
WB-8.m.sp.

STEBBING
Portsmouth
MB. WB-8.m.sp.
Probably George Stebbing, math.instr.
(1) Broad St Portsmouth 1805–8
(2) Broad St Portsmouth 1810–45

STEBBING
Southampton
SB(b).m.g. MB—Gloucester Mus.
Probably J. R. Stebbing, opt.
(1) 47 High St Southampton 1845
(2) Dock Chambers Southampton 1857;
Stebbing and Wood at (1) 1851–3

STEBBING, Geo
66 High St Portsmouth
WB-10.m.sp.sb.
See Stebbing, Portsmouth

STEELE, J. and Son
Duke's Place Liverpool
WB-8.m.rt.

STEFFANI, D.
Eyre St Hill Hatton Gdn
WB-8.m.bp.fg.

de STEFFANI, William fl 1829–39
33 Exmouth St Spitalfields London
Bar.therm.

STERLING
London
SB(b).m.bp.g.

STEWARD
York
WB-8.m.sp.
Probably Henry Steward, clo., jeweller,
6 Low Ousegate 1823–60. Baillie
records a Henry Steward, who is
probably identifiable, 1816 d. 1870

STILES, William Mason fl 1853–60
70 Ossulston St London
Phil.instr.bar.therm.

STOCKTON, J.
London
WB-12.sw.sp.clo.

STOPANI, J.
SB(b).m.rt.ppl.

STOPANI, J.
Aberdeen
WB-8.m.sp.

STOPANI, N.
Sheffield

WB-8.m.bp.pat.
Probably Nicholas Stoppani

STOPPANI, N.
Sheffield
WB-8.m.bp.pat. WB-8.sw.sp.
Probably—

STOPPANI, Nicholas fl 1825
Orchard St Sheffield
Bar.

STORR, B.
Beverley
SB.m.frame carved with ribbons,
drapery, icicles etc.
See B. Storr, York

STORR, B.
York
SB.m.frame carved with ribbons,
drapery, icicles etc.
Probably Batty Storr, clo., b. 1710—
d. 1793 Minster Gates York. See
B. Storr, Beverley

STOTT
Dumfries
SB.m.sqp.urn.bow.g. (Plate 21)
SB.m.rt.g

STOTT, D.
Ashby-de-la-Zouch
WB-8.rw.pt.mi.

STRAIGHT, Thomas fl 1839
26 Bartlett Bldgs Strand London
Bar.therm.

STRAUB, C.
Norwich
WB-8.bp.case lacquered with Chinese
scenes on black ground

STRINGAL, F.
Carmarthen
WB-8.m.pat.

STRINGER, F.
Brecon
WB-8.m.bp.pat.

SULIVAN, Pat
London
SB.w.thca. (Royal Society scale).
carved gilt crest and base.
(R. W. Symonds *English Furniture*
from Charles II to George II fig. 250)
See P. Sullivan

SULLER, John
Edinburgh
SB.m.sp.g.

SULLIVAN, P.
Without Temple Barr London
SB(b).m.sqc.ppl.thca. (Royal Society
scale). plain pillars to hood—Nat.
Mar.Mus.,Gabb Colln Catalogue
No. O.27
*The same museum has a Royal Society
thermometer by P. Sullivan 'at ye
South back of St Clements Church
near Temple Bar London'. Probably
Patrick Sullivan or Sulivan,
Wickham Ct London 1738–43.
Wickham Ct used to be just to the
north of St Clements Church. See
P. Sulivan*

SUMERAU, Bartholemew fl 1840–60
27 Lisle St London
Looking-glasses, bar.therm.

SWAN
Carlisle
WB-8.m.sp.mi.

SWAN, A.
Edinburgh
WB-8.m.sp.

SWEET
London
WB-10.m.sp.clo. WB-8.m.bp.clo.

T

TABRAR, William fl 1832–6
38 Laystall St London
Bar.therm.

TACCHI, A.
Bedford
WB-8.m.bp.pat. WB-8.m.sp.

TAGLIABUE
294 High Holborn London
WB-8.m.bp.pat.
See C. Tagliabue

TAGLIABUE, A.
19 Leather Lane
WB-8.m.sp.
See Angelo Tagliabue

TAGLIABUE, A.
31 Brook St Holborn London
WB-10.rw.sp.sqb. (Plate 46)
See Anthony Tagliabue

TAGLIABUE, A. and A. fl 1829–31
11 Brook St Holborn London
*Bar.therm.; partnership of Angelo and
Anthony Tagliabue who was at
31 Brook St by 1832.
John Tagliabue also at this address*

TAGLIABUE, Angelo fl 1829–48
(1) 11 Brook St Holborn London
1829–33
(2) 19 Leather Lane London 1835–40
(3) 91 Leather Lane London 1841–4
(4) 3 Charles St Hatton Gdn London
1845–8
*Bar.therm.phil.instr.; in partnership
with Anthony Tagliabue 1829–31
(A. and A. Tagliabue). John Tagliabue
also at (1); Pizzi and Negretti at (2)
by 1841; and J. Spelzini is recorded
at (3). See A. Tagliabue,
19 Leather Lane*

TAGLIABUE, Anthony fl 1829–54
(1) 11 Brook St Holborn London
1829–31
(2) 31 Brook St Holborn London
1832–54
*Phil.instr.bar.therm.; with
Angelo Tagliabue at (1) 1829–31 and in
partnership with a Ciceri 1849
(Tagliabue and Ciceri). From 1850
Henry Grimaldi also at (2). See
A. Tagliabue, 31 Brook St, and
Tagliabue and Co, 31 Brook St*

TAGLIABUE, B., GAGGIA and Co
WB-10.sw.sp.

TAGLIABUE, C. fl 1820
68 Hatton Gdn London
*Bar.; no other trace of the family at
this address. Possibly Caesar Tagliabue*

TAGLIABUE, C. fl 1799
294 High Holborn London
*Opt.bar.; joined by a Torre by 1802
(Tagliabue, Torre and Co). Taylor
records that the first Tagliabue is
thought to have reached England 1769
but this is the first appearance of the
name in the directories. Possibly
Caesar Tagliabue. See Tagliabue,
294 High Holborn London*

TAGLIABUE, C. B. J. and Co
26 Holborn London
WB-10.m.sp. WB-12.sw.sp.fg.clo.
See Caesar Tagliabue

TAGLIABUE, Caesar fl 1807–46
(1) 26 High Holborn London 1807–14
(2) 28 Cross St Hatton Gdn London
1822–9
(3) 23 Hatton Gdn London 1829–46
*Opt.bar, etc.; possibly identifiable with
C. Tagliabue, 294 Holborn 1799,
and C. Tagliabue, 68 Hatton Gdn*

*1820. Recorded also as
Tagliabue and Co 1807–14; and see
C. B. J. Tagliabue and Co. From 1838
with Louis Casella at (3) and in 1846
the firm became Casella and Tagliabue.
Francis Anone also at (1) to 1808*
SB.m.sqp.urn.bow.thca.(3)

TAGLIABUE and CASELLA fl 1838–46
23 Hatton Gdn London
*Partnership of Caesar Tagliabue and
Louis Casella; became Casella and
Tagliabue 1846*

TAGLIABUE, Charles and Co fl 1835–6
11 Brook St Holborn London
*Bar.therm.; Angelo Tagliabue and
John Tagliabue also at this address*

TAGLIABUE and CICERI fl 1849
31 Brook St Holborn London
See Anthony Tagliabue

TAGLIABUE and Co
31 Brook St Holborn London
WB-8.m.sp.mi. WB-8.m.sp.
See Anthony Tagliabue

TAGLIABUE and Co fl 1807–14
26 High Holborn London
Opt.bar., etc.; see Caesar Tagliabue
SB.m.sp.mi.at base. WB-8.m.bp.fg.
WB-8.m.bp.pat.
See Caesar Tagliabue

TAGLIABUE, J. and J. fl 1817–9
11 Brook St Holborn London
*Opt.phil.instr.bar., etc.; one of the
partners was John Tagliabue.
Alex Rivolta also worked at this
address 1817–8*

TAGLIABUE, John (1) fl 1817–52
11 Brook St Holborn London
*Phil.instr.bar.,etc.; see J. and
J. Tagliabue. In partnership with a
Zambra by 1847 (Tagliabue and
Zambra). A. and A. Tagliabue also at
this address 1829–31, Angelo Tagliabue
1832–3, Charles Tagliabue 1835–6 and
by 1853 Pastorelli and Cetti*

TAGLIABUE, John (2) fl 1826–9
(1) 44 Leather Lane London 1826–8
(2) 23 Hatton Gdn London 1829
(3) 25 Eyre St Hill London 1834–8
*Bar.therm.; succeeded by
Catherine Tagliabue, possibly his
widow. Caesar Tagliabue at (2) by 1829*

TAGLIABUE, TORRE and Co fl 1802
294 High Holborn London
*Opt.; see C. Tagliabue who was here
1799*

SB(b).m.bp.g. SB.m.bp.g.thpl.
WB-8.m.bp.pat.

TAGLIABUE and ZAMBRA fl 1847–50
11 Brook St Holborn London
See John Tagliabue (1)

TANNER
Cirencester
WB-8.m.sp.
*Probably Joseph Tanner, wa., silver-
smith, Market Pl Cirencester 1856*

TARA, I.
Louth
WB.sw.sp. SB.m.rt.hc.g.thpl.

TARELLI, A.
WB-8.m.sp.mi. WB-6.rw.rt.mop.
Possibly Anthony Tarelli

TARELLI, A. and Son
Newcastle-on-Tyne
MB.rw.ivpl.carved case with
sympiesometer and th. fitted to trunk
Identifiable with—

TARELLI, A. and Son fl 1853–60
(1) 42 Dean St Newcastle-upon-Tyne
1853
(2) 65 Grey St Newcastle-upon-Tyne
1855–60
Opt.bar.; see Anthony Tarelli

TARELLI, Anthony fl 1827–60
(1) 41 Dean St Newcastle-upon-Tyne
1827–44
(2) 42 Dean St Newcastle-upon-Tyne
1847–53
(3) 65 Grey St Newcastle-upon-Tyne
1855–60
*Opt.bar.; a son in partnership from
1853 (A. Tarelli and Son)*

TARELLI, C.
WB-8.m.bp.pat. SB(b).m.bp.g.

TARELLI, C.
Northampton
WB-8.m.sp. WB-12.m.sp.clo.
See Charles Tarelli

TARELLI, Charles
Banbury
WB-8.m.bp.pat.

TARELLI, Charles
Northampton
WB-8.m.bp.pat. WB-10.m.sp.
*Probably Charles Tarelli, opt.,
Woodhill Northampton 1830*

TARELLY, Chas
WB-8.m.
See Tarelli

TARELY
WB-8.m.bp.pat.
Presumably another variation of Tarelli

TARONE, A.
SB(b).m.bp.g.
Possibly identifiable with—

TARONE, A. and Co
7 Grevil St Holborn London
WB-8.m.bp.pat.
*Andrew Tarone and Co, looking-glasses etc., is recorded at
(1) 7 Greville St London 1802–19
(2) 39 Charles St Hatton Gdn London 1842–4
(3) 4 Back Hill London 1845.
P. Primavesi and A. Corti also worked at (1)*

TARONE and Co
London
SB(b).m.bp.g.
See A. Tarone and Co

TARONE, Fra
SB(b).m.bp.

TARONE, J.
Holborn London
WB-8.m.bp.pat.

TARONE, John
Glasgow
WB-8.m.bp.pat.

TARONE, P.
Bristol
AB.m.
Probably—

TARONE, P. A.
Bristol
WB-12.sw.sp.fg.
Probably—

TARONE, P. A. fl 1809
Tucker St Bristol
Bar.therm.

TARONI, A. and G.
Hanley
WB-10.m.sp.

TARONI, George fl 1842–51
62 Whitefriargate Hull
Wa.clo.opt., looking-glasses, silversmith
WB-6.rw.sp.

TARONI and LOUAGHI fl 1829
9 City Rd London
Bar.therm.

TARONI, P.
Jersey
WB-10.rw.mop.

TASKER, William fl 1813–53
High St Banbury
Bar.therm., looking-glasses, jeweller
WB-8.m.bp.pat. WB-8.m.sp. WB-8.m.sp.mi.

TAYLOR, C. H. and Co fl 1860
12–13 Buckingham St Birmingham
Bar.

TAYLOR, J. B.
WB-12.rw.pt.

TAYLOR, T. L.
Pontefract
WB-8.m.sp.mi. SB.m.hc.hypl.
Probably Thomas Lee Taylor, wa.clo., Market Place Pontefract 1828–41

TELAMANZI
Colchester
SB(b).m.bp.g.

TERZZA, A.
WB-8.m.bp.fg.

TESTI
WB-8.m.bp.pat.
Possibly Joseph Testi

TESTI, J.
10 Leather Lane Holborn London
WB-10.m.sp. WB-8.m.bp.pat.
See Joseph Testi

TESTI, J.
15 Gt Saffron Hill London
WB-8.m.bp.pat.

TESTI, Joseph fl 1822
10 Leather Lane Holborn London
Looking-glasses, bar.; see J. Testi

THOMAS, D.
Carmarthen
WB-10.m.sp.sb.mi.

THOMAS, Daniel
London
SB.m.carved frame
Baillie records a Daniel Thomas, clo., fl 1675–1711 Minories London, app. 1675, CC. 1682

THOMAS, J. B.
Southampton
WB-10.rw.pt.mi.

THOMPSON
WB-8.m.sp.mi.

THOMS, William fl 1848
289 Strand London
Phil. instr. bar. etc.

TOBIAS
31 Minories London
MB
*Probably Morris Tobias, clo., in
partnership with a Levitt at
31 Minories London 1816–42*

TOD, S.
Edinburgh
SB(b).m.thpl.hypl.carved frame with a
gilt sea-serpent twisting round the
fluted trunk. (R. W. Symonds *English
Furniture from Charles II to George II*,
Fig. 214, now Private Colln)

TOGNIONI and Co
Bristol
WB-8.m.bp.pat.

TOGNOLA, James
Ipswich
WB-10.m.bp.pat.

TOMLINSON, Jno
Horncastle
WB-10.rw.sp.sqb.
*Probably John Tomlinson, wa.clo.,
silversmith, Bull Ring Horncastle
1835–41*

TOMPION
London
See Thomas Tompion

TOMPION, Thomas p 229

TORRE
DB.m.boxwood pl. (*cf.* Plate 41)—
Mus.Hist.Sc.Oxford

TORRE, Anthony fl 1767–88
(1) 44 Market Lane Pall Mall London
1767–86
(2) 132 Pall Mall London 1786–8
*Son of G. B. Torre, whose London
branch he managed; barometers were
probably among the stock. After his
father's death he took a Ciceri into
partnership in Paris but this was
dissolved 1782. In 1784 he employed
Paul Colnaghi to sell prints in Paris
and Colnaghi joined the London
business 1785; this was the origin of
P. and D. Colnaghi, fine art dealers.
Torre may have been one of the
partners of Tagliabue, Torre and Co
and is possibly identifiable with or at
least a relation of Anthony de la Torre*

de la TORRE, Anthony fl 1805–23
(1) 12 Leigh St Red Lion Sq London
1805–11
(2) 4 Leigh St Red Lion Sq London
1815–23
*Opt.bar., etc.; see Anthony Torre and
Torre and Co. Became della Torre and
Barelli by 1826*

della TORRE and BARELLI fl 1826–33
9 Lamb's Conduit St London
*Looking-glasses, bar.therm.,prints;
succeeded Anthony de la Torre.
Joseph della Torre and Co, merchants,
at this address 1834–51*
WB-10.m.sp.sqb.

TORRE & Co
London
SB(b).m.bp.g.thpl.
Possibly Anthony de la Torre

TORRE & Co
12 Holborn London
SB(b).m.sqp.g.

TORRE and Co fl 1805
12 Leigh St Red Lion Sq London
Opt.; see Anthony de la Torre
WB-8.m.bp.pat. SB(b).m.bp.g.
SB.m.rt.g.

TORRE, Giovanni Battista fl 1753 —d.1780
44 Market Lane Pall Mall London
1767–80. .
*Prints, etc.; well known as a
pyrotechnist, he opened a shop in
Paris 1760 for manufacture and sale of
instruments and barometers. The
London branch was opened 1767 under
the management of his son
Anthony Torre*

della TORRE, J.
Perth
WB-10.m.sp.mi. WB-8.m.sp.
WB-8.m.sp.mi. WB-6.rw.sp.sqb.brass
inl.

TORRI and POZZI
Wotton Bassett
WB-8.m.sp.mi.

TOULMIN, Saml
AB.m.hc.
*Probably Samuel Toulmin, wa., Strand
fl c. 1757–83*

TREMLETT, Richard fl 1852–8
9 Albemarle St Clerkenwell London
Phil.instr.bar.therm.

TRESOLDI, G.
WB-8.m.sp.mi.

TRESOLDI, J.
 6 Union Bldgs Leather Lane London
 WB-10.rw.sp.sqb. WB-8.m.sp.

TROMBETTA
 Norwich
 WB-8.m.bp.pat.

TROMBETTA, Charles
 WB-8.m.bp.pat. WB-8.m.rt.pat.

TROUGHTON, Edward p 240

TROUGHTON, J. and E. p 240

TROUGHTON, J. and J.
 See John Troughton

TROUGHTON, John p 240

TROUGHTON and SIMMS p 241

TRUSCOTT
 St Austle
 WB-10.rw.pt.mi.

TRUSCOTT
 St Columb
 WB-10.rw.sp.mi.

TUCKER, R.
 Taunton
 WB-10.m.sp. WB-8.m.sp.mi.
 Probably Robert Tucker, jeweller,
 41 North St Taunton 1859

TULLEY, H.
 Bath
 WB-10.m.sp.sqb.
 Probably Henry Tulley, opt.
 (1) Kingston Bldgs Bath 1822
 (2) 3 Pulteney Bridge Bath 1830

TURCHETTI, Peter
 Dorchester
 WB-8.m.sp.mi.

TURNBULL, Thos
 SB(b).m.bp.g.
 Baillie records a Thomas Turnbull, clo.,
 Whitby 1818–40

TUTHER
 London
 SB.m.sp.thca.
 Probably John Tuther, opt.
 (1) 64 Upper King St Bloomsbury
 London 1817
 (2) 221 High Holborn London 1819–25

TUTTELL, Thomas p 244

TYLER, Mrs F. fl 1857–60
 (1) 21 Charles St Hatton Gdn London
 1857–8

(2) 23 Charles St Hatton Gdn London
 1859–60
 Bar.; probably James Tyler's widow

TYLER, James fl 1844–56
 (1) 5 Charles St Hatton Gdn London
 1844–55
 (2) 21 Charles St Hatton Gdn London
 1856
 Bar.therm.; succeeded by Mrs F. Tyler.
 George Woodward also at (1) 1851–60

TYLER, John fl 1829–36
 (1) 15 Great New St Fetter Lane
 London 1829–33
 (2) 22½ Kirby St London 1836
 Bar.therm.

U

UNDERHILL, T.
 4 Old Mill Gate Manchester
 WB-12.m.sp.
 Possibly identifiable with
 Thomas Underhill, math.instr.,
 70 Bridge St Deansgate Manchester
 1841

V

VAGO, F.
 Leeds
 WB-8.m.bp.pat. WB-8.m.sp.mi.

VAGO, P.
 WB-8.rw.pt.

VANINI and MONTINI
 Peterborough
 WB-8.m.bp.pat.

VANNINI, A.
 25 Spring St Sheffield
 WB

VANNINI, Anthony
 7 Orange St West St Sheffield
 Bar.therm., looking-glasses
 WB-8.m.sp.sqb.

VANNINI, J.
 Sheffield
 WB-8.m.sp.mi.

VASSALLI
 Scarborough
 WB. in gilt gesso case depicting game
 See J. Vassalli

VASSALLI, G.
 WB-10.m.sp.
 Possibly—

VASSALLI, J.
Scarborough
WB-8.m.bp.pat. WB-10.m.sp.
WB-8.m.sp.mi.
Probably Jerome Vassalli, jeweller
49 Merchants Row Scarborough 1841

VEALE, J.
Exmouth
WB-8.rw.pt.

VECCHI
Nottingham
SB.m.rt.g.thpl.

VECCHIO
Nottingham
WB-8.m.bp.pat.

VECCHIO
Shaftesbury
WB-8.m.bp.pat.

VECCHIO and Co
22 Union Passage Bath
WB-8.m.bp.pat.

del VECCHIO and DOTTI
WB-10.m.sp.

del VECCHIO and DOTTI
Shrewsbury
WB-8.m.bp.pat.

VECCHIO, J.
SB(b).m.bp.g.

VENTOM
London
WB-8.m.bp.pat.

VERGA, J.
Bath
WB-8.m.sp.mi.

VERGA, J.
Chester
WB-8.m.sp.

VERGA, J.
London
WB-8.m.bp.pat.

VERGA, J. L.
WB-10.m.sp.

VERGA, J. M.
Macclesfield
WB-10.m.sp.
Probably John Marie Verga, carver,
gilder, tea dealer
(1) Market St Macclesfield 1828
(2) Mill St Macclesfield 1834

VERGA, P.
Huntingdon
WB-8.m.bp.pat.

VISMARA, G. B.
Bury
WB-8.m.bp.pat.

VOLANTERIO, G.
WB-10.m.sp.
Probably—

VOLANTERIO, G.
Doncaster
WB-8.m.bp.pat.
Probably—

VOLANTERIO, Joshua fl 1822–41
(1) Frenchgate Doncaster 1822
(2) High St Doncaster 1834
(3) Baxter Gate Doncaster 1841
Bar.

VOLONTE, C.
Crown Inn Devizes
SB(b).m.bp.g.thpl. WB-10.m.sp

VULLIAMY
London
Clock and b. each set in a design of
ormolu and porcelain figures on a
painted satinwood stand, the b. in
form of an armillary sphere, the clo.
dated 1787—Victoria and Albert
Mus., Catalogue Nos. W15, 16—1958
Probably Benjamin Vulliamy, clo. to
George III, fl 1775–1820, who carried
on the business and reputation of his
father Justin

VULLIAMY, Justin fl 1730—*c.* 1790
Pall Mall London
This well-known clockmaker made some
very fine barometers in conjunction
with leading cabinet-makers. I will be
discussing some of his work, including
the wheel barometer at Nostell Priory
(p 54 n. 6) in the Journal *of the*
Furniture History Society 1966

W

WADHAM, C.
Bath
WB-8.m.rt.

WALDEN, J.
Jersey
WB-12.m.sp.sqb.clo.

WALFORD
Banbury
WB-8.m.sp.
Baillie records a John George Walford,
clo., Banbury 1790–1832

WARD, John fl 1843–51
79 Bishopsgate within London
Bar.

WARLTIRE
SB.m.carved frame.thpl.
*Possibly belonged to the eighteenth-
century itinerant lecturer John Warltire
and used to illustrate his lectures on
pneumatics*

WARNER, John fl 1684–1722
Kings Arms and Globe Lincoln's Inn
Fields Portugal Row London
*Math.instr.; Taylor records that at first
he specialised in barometers and that
in 1684 he helped a Col. Windham
with barometric experiments on the
spire of Salisbury Cathedral*

WATKINS
London
*See Francis Watkins, J. and
W. Watkins*

WATKINS, Francis (1) p 245

WATKINS, Francis (2)
See Watkins and Hill

WATKINS and HILL p 251

WATKINS, J. and W. p 252

WATKINS and SMITH p 253

WATKINS, W.
St James's St London
See William Watkins

WATKINS, W.
70 St James's St London
See William Watkins

WATKINS, William p 256

WATT, James
Glasgow
B.pl.—Sc.Mus.London
*From the workshop of James Watt, the
engineer, b.1736 —d.1819, who having
been apprenticed to John Morgan,
math.instr., Cornhill London, returned to
Glasgow 1756 and was appointed Math.
Instr. Maker to the College of Glasgow
1757. He was a friend of John
Whitehurst and both were members of
the Lunar Society*

WATTLEWORTH
Whitehaven
WB-10.rw.pt.

WATTS, W.
WB-8.m.bp.pat.

WAUTHIER, Jules fl 1853–5
45 Wilmington Sq London
Bar.

WEATHERSTON
Newcastle
SB(b).m.bp.g.
*Probably John Weatherston, clo.wa.,
Woolmarket Newcastle-upon-Tyne
1787–1801*

WEBB
London
SB.m.rt.g. WB-6.m.sp.sb.
Possibly—

WEBB, John b.1760 —d.1846
(1) 408 Oxford St London
(2) 192 Tottenham Ct Rd London
1817
(3) 28 Francis St London
*Opt.math.phil.instr.; a trade card issued
from (2) advertised barometers
(Sc.Mus.London)*

WEBBER
Woolwich
WB-8.m.sp.sqb.
*Baillie records a John Webber, clo.,
Woolwich 'c. 1800'*

WEBSTER
London
SB.m.sp.urn.bow.g.thca.
Possibly—

WEBSTER, Henry fl 1843–60
(1) 3 Vineyard Walk Clerkenwell
London 1843–6
(2) 37 Coppice Row London 1847–60
Looking-glasses, bar.therm.

WELLS, John fl 1748
Birmingham
AB.m.—Nat.Mar.Mus. Gabb Colln
Catalogue No. O.2
*Probably John Wells, glass toy maker,
d. 1756, Moor St Birmingham 1749–55*

WEST
London
SB.m. in elaborately carved case—
Christie's 16 Nov. 1955
*Possibly C. West, opt.math.instr.,
83 St James St Pall Mall London
1817–25, or—*

WEST
83 Fleet St London
WB-10.m.sp.
See Francis West

WEST, Francis fl 1821–59
    (1) 17 Rupert Ct Drury Lane London
    (2) 83 Fleet St London 1830–48
    (3) 41 Strand London 1844–56
    (4) 92–3 Fleet St London 1849–59
    Opt.instr., also bar.; see West, London

WHEELHOUSE and BERCINI fl 1860
    40 Hatton Gdn London
    Looking-glasses, bar.therm.; succeeded John Cetta

WHIPP
    Rochdale
    WB-12.rw.pt.fg.mop.
    Probably Thomas Whipp, wa.clo., Yorkshire St Rochdale 1834

WHITEHURST
    Derby
    See John Whitehurst (1), (2) and (3)

WHITEHURST, John (1) p 257

WHITEHURST, John (2) p 261

WHITEHURST, John (3) p 263

WHITEHURST and Son
    See John Whitehurst (2) and (3)

WHITFORD, Samuel fl 1750–72
    Archimedes and Three Spectacles
    27 Ludgate St London
    Opt.math.phil.instr.; a trade card advertised 'Barometers £1 11s. 6d., ditto, best sort £2 2s. 0d., ditto, with thermometers £2 12s. 6d., ditto, ditto, with hygrometers £3 3s. 0d.' (Heal Colln, Brit.Mus.); another card advertised 'barometers, diagonal, standard, or portable' (Sc.Mus. London)

WILKINS, John fl 1851–2
    1 Cropley St Hoxton
    Phil.instr.bar.therm.

WILLATS
    WB-8.m.sp.mi.

WILLATS, Benjamin fl 1849
    55 Bartholemew Close London
    Phil.instr.bar.therm.; possibly a relation of—

WILLATS, Richard fl 1850–60
    (1) 98 Cheapside London 1850
    (2) 28 Ironmonger Lane London
        1851–6
    (3) 2 Church Lane Homerton 1857–60
    Opt.phil.instr.bar.therm.; in partnership with Thomas Willats 1850–3 (Thomas and Richard Willats)

WILLATS, T.
    SB.m.

WILLATS, Thomas and Richard fl 1850–3
    (1) 98 Cheapside London 1850
    (2) 28 Ironmonger Lane London
        1851–3
    Opt.math.phil.instr.bar.therm., etc.; see Richard Willats

WILLIAMS
    WB-8.pt.mi.painted

WILLIAMS and HAYDON
    WB-8.m.bp.pat.

WILLIAMS, Rice
    Somerset House by the New Church Strand London
    Trade card advertised 'barometers or weather-glasses of all sorts, as wheel, diagonal, portable, or marine' (Heal Colln, Brit.Mus.)
    WB.w. illustrated in R. W. Symonds *Masterpieces of English Furniture and Clocks*, fig. 130

WILLIAMS, W.
    Devonport
    WB-10.rw.sp.

WILMOT, George fl 1844–6
    (1) 46 Gee St London 1844
    (2) 14 Willow Row Gee St London
        1845–6
    Bar.

WILSON
    WB-8.rw.sp.mi.

WILSON
    Stamford
    WB-5.rw.sp.sb.
    See J. Wilson, Stamford

WILSON, J.
    Folkestone
    WB-8.m.sp.sb.mi.

WILSON, J.
    Stamford
    WB-8.rw.sp.sb.
    Baillie records a J. T. Wilson, wa., Stamford 'early 19c.'

WILSON, Jno
    Peterborough
    WB-10.m.sp.
    Probably John Wilson, wa., jeweller, Peterborough 1816 Narrow Bridge St Peterborough 1830–41

WING, Tycho fl 1731 —d.1776
    See Heath and Wing

WINTERHALDER, J.
Bishopsgate without London
WB-8.rw.sp.

WISE
SB(b).m.bp.

WISKER
York
SB.m. WB-10.m.sp.

WISKER, Elizabeth fl 1822–7
Spurriergate York
*Opt.bar.; widow of John Wisker and
succeeded to his business with her son
Matthias*

WISKER, Jno
York
SB.m.rt.hc.
Probably—

WISKER, John fl 1804 —d.1822
Spurriergate York
*Opt.bar.; succeeded his father
Matthew Wisker and was succeeded by
his widow Elizabeth and son Matthias*

WISKER, M.
York
SB
Probably—

WISKER, Matthew fl 1777–1804
Spurriergate York
*Opt.,glass-grinder, bar.,etc.; succeeded
an optician named Berry. See
John Wisker*

WISKER, Matthias fl 1822–51
(1) Spurriergate York 1822–9
(2) 13 Spurriergate York 1830–51
*Opt.instr.bar.,etc.; with his mother
Elizabeth succeeded his father John,
but on his own by 1827. By 1860
J. T. R. Wisker at (2)*

WOLF, Ezekiel fl 1854
206 Sherlock St Birmingham
Bar.

WOLLER, Charles fl 1839–58
63 Edgbaston St Birmingham
Bar.; also spelt Waller and Wooler

WOLLER, Matthew fl 1809–17
51 Edgbaston St Birmingham
Clo.bar.
SB(b).m.sp.g.thpl.

WOOD
Liverpool
WB-8.m.pt.
Probably Benjamin Wood, math.instr.
(1) 51 Wapping Liverpool 1816

(2) 50 Wapping Liverpool 1822
(3) 21 Bath St Liverpool 1834

WOOD, Chas and Co
WB-10.m.sp.

WOOD, John
SB(b).rt.

WOODHEAD, Joseph fl 1856–60
10 Little Warner St London
Bar.

WOODRUFF
Margate
SB.m.
*Baillie records a Woodruff, wa.,
Margate 'early 19c.'*

WOODS, H.
Warrington
SB.m.rt.rc.g.ivpl.thca.carved case

WOODS, Robert Carr
47 Hatton Gdn London
WB-8.m.rt.
*Middleton records that he was one of
the original members of the
Meteorological Society and suggests
that he fl 'c. 1830'*

WOODWARD, George fl 1851–60
5 Charles St Hatton Gdn London
*Bar.therm.,globes; James Tyler also at
this address until 1855*

WOODWARD, J.
8 Clements Inn Passage St Clements
Inn
WB-5.m.sp.sb.
*Probably John Thomas Woodward, opt.
instr.*
(1) 1 Clements Inn Passage London
1823–8
(2) 8 Clements Inn Passage London
1830–56

WOOLF
MB

WORBOYS
Ashwell Baldock
WB-8.rw.pt.painted simulation of inl.

WORTHINGTON
London
WB-8.m.sp.

WORTHINGTON and ALLAN
London
SB.m.sqp.urn.bow.thca.
*Probably Nathaniel Worthington and
Allan, math.instr., 196 Piccadilly
London 1821–46, successors probably
to Matthew Berge*

WRIGHT, John fl 1753–6
Sphere and Hadleys Quadrant near
St Stephens Church Bristol 1756
*Opt.math.phil.instr.; app. to
Benjamin Cole (1) but moved to Bristol.
His signature appears on a bill in
Cole's name 1753 (Plate 137).
Advertised 'barometers, either standard,
diagonal, or portable, with or without
thermometers' (Felix Farley's Bristol
Journal 13–20 March 1756).
Succeeded by Joshua Springer. He may
have been a relation of—*

WRIGHT, Thomas p 263

WYNNE, Henry p 264

Y

YARWELL, John b.1648 —d.1712
(1) Archimedes and Spectacles St Pauls
Churchyard London, later
Archimedes and Three Golden
Prospects
(2) Ludgate St London
*Opt.instr.; Spectaclemakers' Co 1669.
A trade card advertised 'all sorts of
weather-glasses' (Brit.Mus.). Taylor
suggests that like his neighbour and
rival John Marshall he sold barometers
made by John Patrick*

YEATES
Dublin
SB(b).m.bp. WB-12.rw.sp.mop.
*Possibly Samuel Yeates, opt.
(1) 4 Upper Ormond Quay Dublin
1790–4
(2) 29 Capel St Dublin 1795–1810
(3) 89 Dame St Dublin 1811–26
(4) 2 Grafton St Dublin 1827–31.
See Yeates and Son*

YEATES and Son
Dublin
WB.in carved giltwood frame
*Probably Samuel Yeates and Son, opt.,
2 Grafton St Dublin 1832–45*

YOULE, William fl 1822–60
(1) 22 Fieldgate St Whitechapel
London 1822–33
(2) 79 Leadenhall St London 1844
(3) 83 Leadenhall St London 1845–60
Opt.math.phil.instr.
WB-8.m.sp.sqb.(2)

Z

ZAMBRA
London
WB-10.rw.pt. WB-8.m.sp. WB-8.rw.
sp.mi.
Possibly J. C. Zambra

ZAMBRA, G.
51 Spear St Manchester
WB-10.m.sp.

ZAMBRA, J. C.
23 Brook St Holborn
WB-10.m.sp. WB-8.m.sp.mi.
Joseph Pini at this address 1838–60

ZAMBRA, Joseph Warren
See Negretti and Zambra

ZANDRA, G.
WB-12.m.sp.

ZANETTI and AGNEW fl 1817–25
94 Market St Manchester
*Clo.bar.,artists' materials, etc.;
partnership of Vittore Zanetti and
his former apprentice Thomas Agnew.
Succeeded by Agnew and Zanetti.*
SB.m.sp.g.thca.

ZANETTI, J.
King St Manchester
SB.m.rt.hc.g.thpl.
*Probably Joseph Zanetti, clo.,
100 King St Manchester 1841*

ZANETTI, Jos
WB-10.m.rt.
See J. Zanetti

ZANETTI, Vincent fl 1822–6
5 Wrights Ct Market St Manchester
WB-12.m.sp.hycen. WB-10.m.sp.mi.
WB-8.m.bp.pat.

ZANETTI, Vitto
87 Market St Lane Manchester
WB-10.sw.sp.fg.
Probably—

ZANETTI, Vittore fl 1810–25
94 Market St Manchester
*Clo.bar.,etc.; took his apprentice
Thomas Agnew into partnership 1817
(Zanetti and Agnew). He may have
worked at 87 Market St Manchester
before 1810*

ZANFRINI and GUGERI
Blandford
WB-8.m.sp.mi.

ZAPPA, C.
      WB-8.m.bp.pat.

ZERBONI, Anthony fl 1833–6
      (1) 24 Cross St Hatton Gdn London
      (2) 13 Baldwins Gdns London
      (3) 106 Hatton Gdn London
      Artificial flowers, bar.,etc.; one of the
      partners of—

ZERBONI, BATTISTESSA, MOLTENI and GUANZIROLI fl 1835–6
      (1) 24 Cross St Hatton Gdn London 1835
      (2) 13 Baldwins Gdns London 1835
      (3) 106 Hatton Gdn London 1836
      Looking-glasses, bar.therm.;
      Anthony Zerboni had worked at (1)
      and Battistessa and Co, or Battistessa
      Molteni and Guanziroli, at (2). By

1840 the name was again Battistessa and Co

ZIPFEL, G.
      11 Cockey Lane Norwich
      WB-8.m.bp.pat.
      Probably George Zipfel, Little Cockey
      Lane Norwich 1822

ZUCCANI, Emilio
      London
      WB-10.m.sp.
      Probably Emilio Zuccani, looking-
      glasses
      (1) 41 Brick Lane London 1841–5
      (2) 32–3 Mansell St London 1849
      (3) 17 Mansell St London 1851–60

ZURAGHI, Felix fl 1832–3
      9 City Road London
      Bar.therm.,looking-glasses

BIBLIOGRAPHY

THE FOLLOWING LIST of primary sources does not include any of the makers'
broadsheets or catalogues, local or commercial directories, contemporary news-
sheets or the membership registers of Guild Companies. Reference to these
important sources, where they are specifically relevant, will be found either in the
text or the footnotes. References to modern catalogues of private and public
collections and articles and illustrations in modern books and journals will also be
found in the notes or the text where they are of interest.

PRIMARY SOURCES

*A Short Dissertation on the Barometer, Thermometer
and other Meteorological Instruments*
London 1790 — ADAMS, GEORGE

Lectures on Natural and Experimental Philosophy
London 1794 — ADAMS, GEORGE

*Traittez des Baromètres, Thermomètres et Notiomètres
ou Hygromètres* (par Mr Dxxx)
Amsterdam 1688 — d'ALENCÉ, JOACHIM

*Remarques et expériences phisiques sur la Construction
d'une nouvelle Clepsidre, sur les Baromètres,
Thermomètres et Hygromètres*
Paris 1695 — AMONTONS, GUILLAUME

A Manual of the Barometer
London 1849 — BELVILLE, J. H.

Lettres Astronomiques
Berlin 1771 — BERNOULLI, JEAN

*Cyclopaedia: or an Universal Dictionary
of Arts and Sciences*
London 1728 — CHAMBERS, EPHRAIM

Journal Books — CLOCKMAKERS' COMPANY

Meteorological Observations and Essays
London 1793 — DALTON, JOHN

Meteorological Essays
London 1823 — DANIELL, J. F.

A Course of Experimental Philosophy
London 1744 — DESAGULIERS, J. T.

Lexicon Technicum
London 1704–10 — HARRIS, JOHN (ED.)

Physico-Mechanical Experiments on Various Subjects
London 1709 — HAUKSBEE, F.

Micrographia
London 1665 — HOOKE, ROBERT

Diary (1672–80)
Ed. H. W. Robinson and W. Adams
London 1935 — HOOKE, ROBERT

Mathematical and Philosophical Dictionary
London 1795 — HUTTON, CHARLES

Oeuvres Complètes
Ed. Societé Hollandaise des Sciences
La Haye 1888–1950
HUYGENS, CHRISTIAN

Recherches sur les Modifications de l'Atmosphere
Geneva 1772
de LUC, JEAN ANDRÉ

Description et Usages des Nouvaux Baromètres
London 1779
de MAGELLAN, JEAN HYACINTH

*Baroscopologia, or a Discourse of the Baroscope
or Quicksilver Weather Glass*
London 1708
NEVE, RICHARD

*The Life of the Right Honourable Francis North,
Baron of Guilford*
London 1742
NORTH, HON. ROGER

*Abridgements of Specifications
Relating to Optical Mathematical
and other Philosophers Instruments 1636–1866*
London 1875
PATENT OFFICE

London in 1710
London 1934
QUARRELL, W. H.
& MARE, M.

Cyclopaedia
(a revision of Chambers')
London 1788
REES, ABRAHAM

Journal Books
ROYAL SOCIETY

Philosophical Transactions
ROYAL SOCIETY

*An Historical and Philosophical Account
of the Barometer*
London 1735
SAUL, EDWARD

*The Hydrostatics . . .
Together with a Short History of Coal*
Edinburgh 1672
SINCLAIR, GEORGE

The Principles of Astronomy and Navigation
Edinburgh 1688
SINCLAIR, GEORGE

*Natural Philosophy . . .
touching the Mercurial Weather-Glass, Hygroscope, etc.*
London 1683
SINCLAIR, GEORGE

*A Compleat Discourse of the Nature, Use, and
Right Managing of that Wonderful Instrument,
the Baroscope or Quick-Silver Weather-Glass*
London 1688
SMITH, JOHN

*Horological Disquisitions concerning the Nature of
Time . . . To which is added Rules for the Use of the
Quick-Silver or Spirit Weather-Glass*
London 1694
SMITH, JOHN

The History of the Royal Society
4th edn. London 1734
SPRAT, THOMAS

*Construction d'un Nouveau Baromètre,
avec la manière d'en pouvoir construire
de telle grandeur qu'on voudra*
Paris 1723
de VIRVILLE, A. FORTIER

*A Course of Mechanical, Optical, Hydrostatical
and Pneumatical Experiments*
London 1713
WHISTON, WILLIAM

SECONDARY SOURCES

Some Account of the Worshipful Company of the Clockmakers of the City of London
London 1881
ATKINS, S. E. & OVERALL, W. H.

Watchmakers and Clockmakers of the World
3rd edn. London 1951
BAILLIE, G. H.

Old Clocks and Watches and their Makers
3rd edn. London 1911
BRITTEN, F. J.

The History of the Microscope
London 1932
CLAY, R. S. & COURT, T. H.

Les Instruments Scientifiques aux XVIIe et XVIIIe Siècles
Paris 1953
DAUMAS, MAURICE

Early Science in Oxford
Oxford 1923–25
GUNTHER, R. T.

Early Science in Cambridge
Oxford 1937
GUNTHER, R. T.

London Tradesmen's Cards of the 18th Century
London 1925
HEAL, AMBROSE

The Signboards of Old London Shops
London 1947
HEAL, SIR AMBROSE

The House of Lyme from its foundation to the end of the 18th Century
London 1917
LEGH, EVELYN, BARONESS NEWTON

The History of the Barometer
Baltimore 1964
MIDDLETON, W. E. K.

Antiquities in Leicestershire
(Bibliotheca Topographica Britannica Vol. 8)
London 1790
NICHOLS, JOHN

Buckingham Palace Its Furniture, Decoration and History
London 1931
SMITH, H. C.

Old Scottish Clockmakers
Edinburgh 1921
SMITH, JOHN

Thomas Tompion: his Life and Work
London 1951
SYMONDS, R. W.

The Mathematical Practitioners of Tudor and Stuart England
Cambridge 1954
TAYLOR, E. G. R.

The Mathematical Practitioners of Hanoverian England
(Manuscript)
TAYLOR, E. G. R.

At the Sign of the Orrery
1958
TAYLOR, E. W., & WILSON, J. S. & MAXWELL, P. D. S.

L'Expérience Barométrique ses antécédents et ses explications
Thouards 1936
de WAARD, CORNELIS

Worthies, Families and Celebrities of Barnsley and District
York 1880
WILKINSON, JOSEPH

A History of Science, Technology and Philosophy in the 16th and 17th Centuries
London 1950
WOLF, A.

INDEX

NOTE: The main references to primary makers are in bold type